FAMILIAR FRESHWATER FISHES OF AMERICA

HARPER & ROW, PUBLISHERS

New York, Evanston, and London

FAMILIAR

FRESHWATER

FISHES

OF AMERICA

HOWARD T. WALDEN *2d*

Drawings by Carl Burger

TO JO

CONTENTS

Acknowledgments

The author is grateful to the following individuals and organizations for their assistance in the gathering of material for this book: Alaska Department of Fish and Game, Juneau; Evelyn Angell, Palisades, N.Y.; Loran Baker, Area Chief, Canada Department of Fisheries, Halifax, N.S.; Mike Ball, Fishing Contest Editor, *Field & Stream*, New York; John E. Bardach, School of Natural Resources, University of Michigan, Ann Arbor; Gerard Beaulieu, Ministere de la Chasse et des Pécheries, Quebec; E. Kliess Brown, State of Idaho Department of Fish and Game, Boise; California Department of Fish and Game, Sacramento; Canned Salmon Institute, Seattle; Lyle M. Christenson, Chief Fishery Biologist, Wisconsin Conservation Department, Madison; A. B. Cook, Chief, Fish Division, Michigan Department of Conservation, Lansing; Bernard W. Corson, Chief of Fisheries Division, New Hampshire Fish and Game Department, Concord; E. J. Crossman, The Royal Ontario Museum, University of Toronto, Toronto; George W. Davis, Commissioner, State of Vermont Fish and Game Department, Montpelier; Millard Demarest, Hackensack, N.J.; Kenji Ego, Chief, Fisheries Branch, Hawaii Division of Fish and Game, Honolulu; W. Harry Everhart, Editor, American Fisheries Society, University of Maine, Orono; Allister M. Fleming, Assistant Director, Fisheries Research Board of Canada, St. John's, Newfoundland; Florida Game and Fresh Water Fish Commission, Tallahassee; E. H. Grainger, Fisheries Research Board of Canada, Montreal; Vernon A. Hacker, Wisconsin Conservation Department, Oshkosh; Joe L. Herring, Louisiana Wildlife and Fisheries Commission, Baton Rouge; Institute for Fisheries Research, Ann Arbor, Mich.; Iowa State Conservation Commission, Des Moines; James C. MacCampbell, University of Maine Library, Orono; Neil MacEachern, Canada Department of Fisheries, Halifax, N.S.; John Macrae, Harper & Row, Publishers; Maine Department of Inland Fisheries and Game, Augusta; Minnesota Conservation

Department, St. Paul; Montana Department of Fish and Game, Helena; New York State Conservation Department, Albany; Hudson M. Nichols, Tennessee Game and Fish Commission, Nashville; Oregon State Game Commission, Portland; Mark Phillips, Blauvelt, N.Y.; G. Power, University of Waterloo, Waterloo, Ont.; Clarence E. Pratt, State of Washington Department of Game, Olympia; Charles A. Purkett, Jr., Assistant Superintendent of Fisheries, Missouri Conservation Department, Jefferson City; Hortense A. Quimby, Averill, Vt.; Mildred Rippey, Palisades Free Library, Palisades, N.Y.; Andrew L. Ruskanen, State of Wyoming Game and Fish Commission, Cheyenne; Richard Salmon, Grandview, N.Y.; Harry E. Schafer, Supervisor, Fisheries Section, Louisiana Wildlife and Fisheries Commission, New Orleans; Walter Taradash, Blauvelt, N.Y.; V. R. Taylor, Canada Department of Fisheries, St. John's, Newfoundland; T. H. Turner, Canada Department of Fisheries, Ottawa; U. S. Fish and Wildlife Service, Department of the Interior, Washington; E. B. Walden, New York.

H. T. W.

Palisades, New York
January 27, 1964

INTRODUCTION

A note on the description of fishes and on certain other elements of this book may be helpful to the reader. Since a single species of freshwater fish may be known by a dozen local and erroneous aliases, scientific names are not only convenient but necessary for identification. The taxonomy or classification of fishes and the scientific nomenclature it entails may appear formidable though it has undergone a drastic narrowing in recent years. Many fishes, once considered separate and distinct species, are now classified as subspecies or varieties, and grouped under single specific heads. For example, the Kamloops trout of the West, formerly with the scientific name *Salmo kamloops*, is now classified as a variety of the rainbow trout, *Salmo gairdneri*, and takes that name. At least six chars formerly regarded as distinct species are now held to be varieties of the Arctic char, with the specific name *Salvelinus alpinus* applying to all. The same narrowing is to be noted in families other than the Salmonidae. Hence many scientific names have been expunged from the once numerous clutter. Doubtless further simplification will occur.

In this volume the listings of the American Fisheries Society are largely followed, and that body's procedure in attributing authority for scientific names is used. Accordingly, the author's name(s) follows the specific name directly and without punctuation if the species, when originally described, was assigned to the same genus in which it is now known; if the species was described in another genus, the author's name(s) appears in parentheses. For example, the brook trout was originally named *Salmo fontinalis* by Mitchill; it is now known as *Salvelinus fontinalis* (Mitchill). The scientific name of the smallmouth bass appears as *Micropterus dolomieui* Lacépède (without parentheses) since, when this fish was originally described, it was assigned to the same genus, *Micropterus*.

Descriptions of the various fishes in this book are necessarily limited to the usual or typical appearance and colors of the species in most of their habitats. Since many fishes vary in color throughout their range it is not possible in each case to describe the fish as it may appear to all who behold it. The drawing of the bass pictured below names the fins and other major parts, but no single drawing can depict all external features of all fishes.

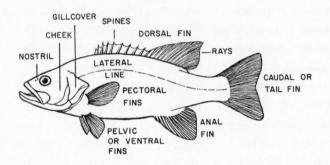

Record freshwater fishes taken on sporting tackle, as cited herein, are those listed by *Field & Stream,* New York, unless otherwise noted, and the author gratefully acknowledges that magazine's assistance in supplying these data.

This book, however, is but incidentally concerned with scientific names, descriptions, and the recounting of record fish. Being a book about fishes it is necessarily a book about water too, for a fish is interesting chiefly as related to its habitat and to the other fishes and other life forms which share its waterbound world. Out of water, a trout or bass is only a morsel of food, a trophy for the admiration of anglers, or a specimen for ichthyological research. In the water, as it feeds, undertakes its migrations, and reproduces its kind, the fish is an element of a complex but beautiful and logical design.

This fluid world is a strange one to man if only because it is so far removed from his firm and familiar milieu. Nothing here has the rectilinear precision of man's accustomed perspectives. Intensities of light and pressure vary from the sunshot shoal to the abyssal darkness 500 feet down, and in the upper levels the bright water may in an instant become suffused with dusk as a cloud obscures the sun or a sudden shower stipples the surface. The "gravity-free" state, that modern concern of space travel, has always been, to a degree, the condition of the fish. In its relative equilibrium the fish courses with little effort depths of a few inches to several hundred feet.

Under the calm surface of a lake or a river pool there is desperate and unceasing competition, with the stakes nothing less than survival. All animal forms under water, beginning with plankton and continuing upward through insect larvae, tiny crustaceans and mollusks, and the young and adult stages of all fishes, are hunting and hunted. This immemorial sequence of predation, of the great upon the small, and sometimes vice versa, constitutes what man calls the "food chain." In the end the larger fish which do not die after spawning succumb to man or to natural predators, to drought or flood, perhaps to overwhelming numbers of smaller fishes, or even to microscopic parasites.

From the human viewpoint this world of the fish may seem one of utter violence and anarchy, but to the fish it is the condition of life. Conceivably it holds its fishy satisfactions, its moments of calm and intervals of truce, as any casual observation of fishes in nature seems to disclose.

Certainly man has been the greatest predator upon the fish. Where man and his works multiply, the fixtures of nature diminish, and in this inevitable context man is not wholly to blame. He can be charged, however, with a callous and wanton lack of restraint in a thousand instances of overfishing and pollution, and with other sins against his heritage. Roadbuilding has changed the natural channels of rivers into sterile ditches, smothering by siltation the aquatic insects and other stream-bed organisms which are the food of fishes. Indiscriminate spraying of toxic chemicals has accomplished similar destruction. Dams have impeded spawning migrations and flooded tributaries where salmon and other fishes once found ideal spawning shoals. Deforestation and the overgrazing of cattle have caused erosion and a lowering of water tables.

Partly because of such aspects of man's so-called industrial and agricultural progress no less than 68 species of freshwater fish were classified, in 1964 by University of Michigan zoologist Robert Rush Miller, as "rare, restricted, and/or threatened." Many other species, not yet so drastically reduced, have suffered steep declines in their once abundant populations.

Conservationists, however, are stemming further depletion of the fisheries resource in many waters and even increasing game-fish numbers in some areas. Conservation measures include tighter regulation of commercial and sport fishing and industrial pollution; artificial propagation of game species; selective breeding for greater size and earlier maturity; control of overpopulations of trash fish; the building of fish ladders and lifts at dams; the construction of artificial spawning grounds in lakes where the natural facilities are scanty or lacking. The campaign against the sea lamprey in the Great Lakes (see Chapter 21) has averted the possible extinction of the lake trout in those waters.

Such works of course conserve a food resource and promote the sport of angling. But they do far more than that. For the mere *presence* of wild fish in our fresh waters—aside from their potential for food or sport—is an asset of incalculable worth. It becomes the value of water itself, for where there are fish populations the water is alive, organic, and to a great extent self-purifying. Where the fish have been exterminated or greatly depleted, the water is dead. Pollution, exhausting the oxygen in water and producing the toxins of anaerobic bacteria, has changed many a fertile river into a lifeless ditch. The fish resource is in essence the water resource; if we conserve the one we help to conserve the other.

One of our rare treasures today is a wilderness stream or lake, forest-hemmed, flowing in its native purity and full of its native animal and plant life, far from the sound and smell of traffic and untainted by the discarded beer can or other refuse of men. There are still a few such lakes in the woods of northern Maine and in the remote high country of the far West. Among the streams only segments remain inviolate—the upper tributaries which flow for a brief space through wilderness before their march to the sea meets man and his inevitable contaminations. Such virgin waters as are left must be preserved at all cost; those only partially defiled must be defended against further invasion if what remains of this country's bounteous heritage is to be held intact for posterity.

Chapter 1

BROOK AND BROWN TROUT

BROOK TROUT
Salvelinus fontinalis (Mitchill)

This gem of the cold northeastern rills is a char, not a trout, but to generations of anglers who have accorded the brook trout a unique and almost reverential regard it is and always was a trout. It is of the family Salmonidae, a coldwater clan native only to the Northern

NOTE: Illustration is of caddis fly; caddis larvae in cases are of four separate species.

Hemisphere and including the chars, trouts, salmons, whitefishes, and graylings.

In New York, New Jersey, Pennsylvania, and most of New England this member is known as brook trout, brookie, and native trout. In Maine it is the squaretail, in Canada the speckled trout. "Native trout" has served to distinguish this char from two trouts—the brown and rainbow—which were introduced into eastern streams in the late 1800's.

The chars differ from the trouts in their smaller, almost microscopic scales, a general absence of black spots on the body, and in the character of the vomer, a bone on the roof of the mouth. In chars this bone has few teeth, situated at the front end. In trouts the vomer is longer and its entire length is studded with teeth.

The brook trout has acquired a sparkling reputation and a kind or romantic aura in the centuries since the first colonists saw it flash in its native streams. For boys who edged their angling wits against the brookie its presence lent enchantment to countless little waters of the Northeast. Wherever it swam and lurked and fed on caddis larvae from the stream-bed rocks, people knew the water was pure, for this fish cannot tolerate pollution.

Today, grown to adult size in the state hatcheries, the brook trout is stocked in western waters and others far from its former native range. Geographically, this range had the form of an inverted letter L. From its angle in Labrador the westward extension ran across Quebec and Ontario; the southward arm, east of the Appalachians, reached as far as northern Georgia.

A widely credited theory is that the Salmonidae originated in the Arctic Ocean, as migratory or anadromous fishes. In Pleistocene glacial periods they were forced south by the advancing ice. When the ice receded they were left landlocked in lakes and streams and thus became widely distributed away from their original common home. Over the centuries the separated populations each acquired its own markings and other characteristics through varying influences of environment and food.

Though the wild brook trout persists in Canada with little diminution, it becomes progressively more rare as civilization usurps its ancient haunts. The populous areas of the Northeast have virtually lost it. Occasionally one strays down from the remote upper waters into the big angling stretches of such classic eastern trout rivers as the Beaverkill and Willowemoc, now heavily stocked with brown trout. Anglers, fly-fishing for browns on these rivers and taking the surprise brookie, regard it as the jewel of their creels.

The angler's high esteem for the brook trout has an anomalous aspect. In a nation traditionally worshipful of size, this fish is a smallish reward. Though the species reaches five pounds or more in some wilderness waters, the trout of the angling millions are little ones, seven to ten inches long. Today a one-pound brookie is a prize in any eastern stream. A three-pounder will make even a veteran fisherman think of the taxidermist. The all-time angling record belongs to a specimen taken long ago, in July 1916, on the Nipigon River, Ontario, by Dr. W. J. Cook. This giant *fontinalis* weighed 14½ pounds and was 31½ inches long.

The brook trout has attributes other than size, however. Its coloration and clean continuity of line are perhaps without parallel in the world of fishes. Typically, the back is a deep bronze-green covered with lighter vermiculations which extend over the top of the head and into the dorsal fin. The dark color of the back fades lower to an iridescent bluish along the lateral line, then to yellowish on the lower sides and pale pinkish on the belly. The sides are sprinkled profusely with yellow spots interspersed with a few of brilliant red. The lower fins are orange to carmine, margined with a narrow black band next to a white stripe on the forward edge. Spawning males have a heightened brilliance, acquiring a bright red along the belly and upon the lower fins, and many of their red spots are ringed with blue.

The color of the fish and its flesh can vary greatly from one area to another. In the sunlit meadow streams of a half century ago the wild native trout were very bright and their meat sometimes as pink as a salmon's. Yet in the same or adjoining counties there were semi-wilderness areas where the brooks were amber-colored and deep-shadowed under hemlocks or where, in specific regions, the soil contained iron deposits. Here the trout were very dark, their red spots gleaming like rubies against the dusky setting, and their meat was yellowish rather than pink.

No less game than beautiful, the brook trout fairly hooked on a fly is incredibly strong and active. A ten-incher on a light rod will amaze the uninitiated by the speed and power of its rushes. Though it never resorts to the spectacular surface play of the rainbow it is a hard, deep-boring fighter, quick to utilize any asset—the sunken snag, the sharp undercut rock, the maze of roots, or the inch-deep shoal—to cut the leader or to shake the fly.

The meat of the wild brookie has a firmness and delicacy of flavor to delight the most sensitive fancier of food. "Brook trout" listed on restaurant menus are hatchery-fattened, for conservation laws everywhere prohibit the commercial taking of *fontinalis* from lakes and streams.

The brook trout begins its life in the cold crystalline upper rills. In the autumn, from October to early December, the mature males and females migrate to the shallow upper reaches of the brook to spawn. The female clears out pebbles and detritus, by strong and active fanning of her tail, on an oval space of a foot or more of gravel bottom. Meanwhile the males, whose lower jaws at spawning time become elongated and hooked, compete belligerently for the favor of a female, fighting each other and occasionally locking jaws.

After the nest has been prepared, the female and her attending male simultaneously extrude eggs and milt. They then proceed upstream a few feet; the female clears another space, and the gravel from this one washes downstream to cover the eggs in the lower nest. The spawning act occurs again; with a large female it may be repeated several times, perhaps with assists by more than one male, before the eggs are completely shed. After spawning the spent fish descend downstream to deeper water.

Brook trout inhabiting lakes usually go up a tributary stream to spawn, but sometimes move only into shoal water along the lake shore.

Small female trout may deposit 200 to 500 eggs in the spawning; large individuals may shed as many as 5000. The eggs are large and non-adhesive, orange-colored in wild trout, pale or colorless in hatchery-reared fish. In the wild, the incubation period varies widely, averaging perhaps forty days but lasting as long as 140 days if the water temperature is very low.

The newly hatched sac fry remain in the nest for a time, subsisting

Brook Trout
Salvelinus fontinalis

on the contents of the yolk sac. As this food supply is absorbed, the young brook trout begin to take on the character of fish and eventually emerge from the nest as free-swimming fry.

Though autumn spawning is common to the chars, an angler may suppose the brook trout to be a spring spawner because he finds roe inside a female caught in April or May. The clue to spawning time, however, is not the presence of eggs but their diameter. Canadian fisheries scientist Vadim D. Vladykov points out that each female brook trout, from fry to adult, carries eggs in her two ovaries *at all times*. In spring and early summer the eggs are very small—from $\frac{1}{15}$ to $\frac{1}{12}$ inch in diameter—but by spawning time their size is about that of a small green pea, and they now occupy the entire body cavity of the female.[1]

Some rivers of Maine and the eastern provinces of Canada harbor brook trout with a seagoing urge. After spawning they descend to the tidal estuary and thence to sea, as the salmon does. Called sea trout or "salters," they remain in the sea for two years. The return to fresh water usually occurs in June or July; the upstream migration follows, and the spawning act is repeated in the fall.

The sea trout coming in from the ocean is dark-backed and silvery-sided, with sparse reddish spots. After a week or two in fresh water, however, it recovers the original brook trout markings and color.

Little is known of the homing faculty of the sea-run brook trout, but certain experiments with tagged fish indicate that this sense of the native river, seemingly so acute in the salmon, is poorly developed in the sea trout.

Sea-run brook trout in salmon rivers prey upon small parrs upstream. Unlike the spent salmon, spawned-out sea trout returning to salt water are in excellent condition, and in the estuaries they feed heavily upon salmon smolts going to sea for the first time. Some observers rank the sea trout as the worst of all salmon predators.

Mature brook trout of the *same age* may vary greatly in size, depending on environment. Big fish not only are present in big water but may sometimes occur, even at non-spawning times, in very small streams accessible from big water. A meadow brook four feet wide

[1] "Trout," *Fishes of Quebec*, Album No. 1, Department of Fisheries, Quebec.

can hold a two-pounder if that brook has a deep hole here and there, undercut banks, and no dam or high falls in its course to the larger stream it feeds. In ranging for food, large trout frequently move into such tributaries. Conversely, in the small rock-hemmed pools of those steep brooks that pitch down our eastern mountainsides, the mature trout are seldom more than eight inches long though their age may be equal to that of the two-pounder in the lower levels. They may descend to larger waters and grow big. But if they remain upstream, as many do, their food is restricted to the aquatic life of the little pool and what may drift through it from above.

Look for the brookie where any obstruction turns the free flow of the stream. A bankside tangle of roots, a windfall, a collapsed bridge, a broken dam or other barrier which creates its own extraordinary eddies and backwaters is ideally the lair of *fontinalis*.

A voracious feeder, with a powerful digestive system and very short intestinal tract, the brook trout can be rid of food fifteen or twenty minutes after its intake. The normal food supply includes the caddis worm (and its casing of gravel and sticks), nymphs, flies, minnows, chub, stone cats and smaller trout, shrimp and crayfish, and any land-derived form of life—earthworms, grubs, various insects, even mice and shrews—that happens to be adrift in the stream. Fish almost half the trout's length are fair game. An angler casting an oversize streamer in the hope of a big trout may be astounded at the assault of a ten-inch brookie upon this lure.

The brook trout, however, is not inclined to feed at night. Also, strong sunlight and high water temperatures depress feeding on or near the surface. The fact that trout rise for insects and artificial flies mostly during early-morning and evening periods of low light intensity may be attributable, however, merely to greater insect activity at such hours. Feeding can occur at high noon on a bright day if a hatch of flies takes place.

Enemies of the brook trout are almost as numerous as its normal prey. Chief among them are the mink, otter, watersnake, snapping turtle, and larger trout. Bass and pickerel in a trout stream may in time clean out the entire trout population. The kingfisher hunts constantly for small trout; the osprey is capable of bearing off a one-pounder. Finally, the trout has that common and most formidable foe of all fishes: man.

In his angling tactics man cunningly utilizes his knowledge of trout food: the various nymphs and the flies into which the nymphs are metamorphosed. All stages of the stream insect are closely matched in the angler's artificial nymphs, wet flies, and dry (or floating) flies. Trout of three pounds or more are occasionally taken on flies no larger than your fingernail. Most of the large trout coming to angler's nets, however, are captured on gobs of nightcrawlers, live minnows, or such artificial minnow-simulators as the big streamer and bucktail flies and the metal spinners.

In the northeastern United States millions of hatchery brook trout are stocked annually in the put-and-take game of modern fishing. But one is inclined to use the past tense in writing of the wild brook trout. Constitutionally incompatible with the advance of civilization, this exquisite fish is dying. Where man has dried up his springs by deforestation, polluted his waterways, straightened streams into ditches and denuded them of their natural cover, the wild brook trout has vanished. And with it has gone an essence of that early America which somehow it symbolized: rural peace, unmachined enterprise, and nature left to herself.

BROWN TROUT
Salmo trutta Linnaeus

When Izaak Walton wrote "The last fish I caught was with a worm," the fish of his mildly ambiguous reference was a brown trout. Sir Isaak never knew the brook trout, nor did his famous predecessor in angling literature, Dame Juliana Barnes.

The brown trout was originally an inhabitant only of Europe, the British Isles, and possibly a few Asian waters on the Urals' eastern slopes. It is a trout, not a char, with the characteristic larger scales and larger adipose fin, and a vomer containing teeth on its entire length.

An ancient fish in angling annals though biologically recent, the brown is celebrated in many a classical text. Tennyson was probably unaware that in

> Here and there a lusty trout,
> And here and there a grayling

his trout was a brown—and even had he known it, the specific reference would have ruined the meter of his line. The brown trout has been useful as a poetic allusion to others than Tennyson, who were not writing for dry-fly purists anyway.

Despite its aristocratic backgrounds in Europe, the brown trout was once held to be something of a vulgar upstart in America. It was first brought to our shores and planted in our freshwater streams in 1883. For this import, which was destined to revolutionize fly-fishing in the United States, American anglers could thank (or blame, as many did) a fellow American named Fred Mather, and a German named Von Behr. Mather, a New York State conservationist and fisherman, had cast his flies upon Old World streams. He knew and admired the brown trout. Von Behr could get eggs for export. This happy alliance culminated in action: presently a German liner arrived in New York with a strange item of cargo—some 80,000 brown-trout eggs consigned to the New York State hatchery at Cold Spring Harbor. Other shipments followed.

Mather was doubtless amazed at the ensuing storm of criticism and protest. The imported brown, though welcomed by some anglers, was deemed by many to be a coarse fish from both the sporting and the gustatory standpoint, a defiler of our native-trout waters, and a cannibal to boot. (The last charge was certainly just, as it would have been if levied against the brookie itself, or any of the other trouts or chars.)

Salmo trutta, however, proceeded to thrive and multiply. It was soon apparent to fish culturists and sportsmen that the brown prospered in waters much too warm for the brook trout, and tolerated mild degrees of pollution that would be insufferable to the brookie. Fishermen who at first had deplored this invasion of our streams came reluctantly to admit that the brown trout had positive virtues. It grew to a larger size than the brook trout, was a ready taker of flies and, when hooked, fought with *élan* and dash, occasionally resorting to aerial leaps such as the brook trout never essayed.

For years this new fish was called the German brown trout, English brown trout, European trout, Von Behr trout, and Loch Leven trout. Early in World War I a few chauvinists attempted to designate the German brown as the "liberty trout," but happily this name, like "liberty cabbage" for sauerkraut, proved as ephemeral as a Mayfly.

The Loch Leven, a subspecies of the brown trout, was brought from Scotland and stocked in western United States waters. The Loch Leven has since been crossed and recrossed with the original Von Behr export; the characteristics once believed to distinguish the two have not persisted, and ichthyologists have agreed on the practicality of designating the fish as one species. The name Loch Leven or, popularly, "Lock," for the brown trout persists in Montana, Wyoming, and other parts of the West. In the East, brown trout is the usual designation.

The adaptable brown has probably a wider range in North America than any of the salmonid family except the rainbow trout. *Salmo trutta*[2] thrives today in all states except those of the extreme Southeast and middle South, where the water warms to temperatures too high for even this fish's broad range of tolerance. The brown trout does well in streams and lakes throughout the Rocky Mountain area from New Mexico to Montana, in the Pacific Coast states, in the Black Hills of South Dakota, in Michigan, Wisconsin, and Minnesota, and in several Canadian provinces.

Like all the trouts and chars, the brown is native only to the Northern Hemisphere. Today's fabulous fishing for this species in the waters of Chile, Argentina, New Zealand, and Tasmania, stems from exports of brown-trout eggs. Long-distance shipments of the eggs are practicable: packed in ice they are capable of being kept alive for several weeks.

Probably no other trout has such wide color variations as the brown. A "wild" brown—born and growing to maturity in a cold stream—is as lovely to behold as any of the Salmonidae. The olive-brown or bronze-green along the back fades lighter on the sides, flames into a brilliant golden yellow on the underbody. The upper flanks are bedecked with numerous black or dark brown spots; these extend into the dorsal fin, and sometimes a few are present in the upper caudal. Along the lateral line and below is a sprinkling of brilliant red spots, some of them encircled by wide bluish rings. The fins are yellowish green, the lower fins unspotted, the adipose marked sometimes with perhaps three or four brown or red spots.

[2] Ichthyologists are at odds over the scientific name of the brown trout. *Salmo trutta* is ascribed by Linnaeus. Some authorities maintain that *Salmo trutta* is appropriate only to the sea-run phase, and that *Salmo fario* should designate the freshwater brown trout.

That today's angler seldom sees the wild brown trout in all its glory is one of the sadder aspects of modern hatchery-based fly-fishing. Virtually all the browns of our present-day synthetic fishing are raised to maturity in the state hatcheries, and often they are taken by anglers only a few days after they are stocked. These fish, though handsome enough to adorn the interior of any creel, are pale specimens by comparison with their brethren who were born in the stream. Indeed the difference can be so broad that an angler accustomed only to the hatchery fish and taking his first wild brown, may wonder what sort of trout this beauty may be.

Like the brook trout, the brown spawns in the fall. Stream fish migrate upriver, though usually they do not ascend to the tiny upper rills as the brook trout is inclined to do. Brown trout in lakes may enter a tributary to spawn, or merely move into the shoreward shallows. In northern waters the time is October through February. A large female may fan out three or four nests, spotted over a stream-bottom area of 20 to 30 feet. Here she will deposit up to 6000 large and non-adhesive eggs. The incubation period is said to be around fifty days in hatcheries maintaining a water temperature of 50° F. In streams and lakes it is variable, depending upon water temperatures.

Young brown trout born of lake parents that have entered a tributary for spawning normally spend two or three years in the stream of their birth, feeding chiefly on insects. Descending to the lake as they grow larger, they feed increasingly on fish.

The brown trout's growth potential gives it a positive attraction from the angling standpoint. Its life span is longer than the brook trout's, and in lakes and the larger rivers it achieves a size unattainable by the brookie. Very large browns are by no means rare, even in the lakes and streams of quite populous areas, and the known presence of large trout of course lends a sporting appeal to waters inhabited by the brown. Fish of four to eight pounds are taken each season in rivers, lakes, and reservoirs of New York, New Jersey, Pennsylvania, and New England. In the West, the browns seem to wax even larger: the California Department of Fish and Game reports specimens of fifteen pounds and up. The record brown of all time is said to be a 39½-pound monster taken by W. Muir in Loch Awe, Scotland, in 1866. Several American specimens have weighed over twenty pounds each.

But such extravagant dimensions are rare. The brown trout known to most fishermen is hardly larger than the average brookie. Creel contents along any brown-trout stream will disclose a thousand fish of eight to twelve inches, to one that weighs two pounds or more.

Brown trout are known to be sea-run in some rivers of the northeastern United States and in Canada. Edward C. Migdalski writes[3] of the almost identical color and form of the sea-run brown trout and the Atlantic salmon. "Several times in Connecticut I have had to identify specimens taken in traps by commercial fishermen," he states. "The caudal peduncle on the Atlantic salmon is narrower; scales are smaller; its upper jaw does not usually extend as far back beyond the eye as the brown trout's, and the tail is slightly emarginate or concave in the adult."

In Europe, where the sea-run brown appears to be well known, the same confusion of this species with the Atlantic salmon is evident. Many European fishermen call the sea-run *Salmo trutta* a "salmon trout." (Certainly this is the meaning of the scientific name, and it seems to justify the contention that it should apply only to the sea-run phase of the brown.)

Sea-run populations of brown trout, stemming from plantings in Newfoundland in the 1880's, are well established today in the rivers of Newfoundland's Avalon Peninsula.

It is interesting to note that the brown trout may fertilize a female salmon's eggs in the temporary absence of the male salmon; indeed this extracurricular use of the male milt is said to be quite common practice among many of the trouts and chars.

The brown trout's prey is much the same as that of the brook trout: stream insects, crustaceans, smaller fish. The fauna against which it must constantly be on guard comprise the same predatory birds, reptiles, and beasts—chiefly, of course, man. Legend persists that the brown eludes anglers more successfully than do other trouts and chars. The brown trout is smarter, in a word. Doubtless this belief is justified when applied to older and larger brown trout. It can scarcely be valid, however, for the great majority of eight- to twelve-inch stockees over which most of the flies are cast.

[3] *Angler's Guide to the Fresh Water Sport Fishes of North America* (Ronald Press Co., New York, 1962).

There is another legend along the brown-trout rivers, and it concerns this fish's uncanny selectivity in feeding. When it is taking the light Cahill, for instance, the angler had better fish this fly if he wants anything in his creel but much air. Yet all fishermen who have sought the brown trout for even a few seasons have seen those odd and inexplicable hours when the stream suddenly comes alive with rising and moving fish. In such an interval (it will vanish as suddenly and strangely as it came) the brown trout will literally take anything—wet fly, nymph, streamer, or bait. The brook trout and rainbow seldom or never indulge such unbridled sprees of feeding.

There are, to be sure, serious indictments against the brown trout. It will eventually take over in a brook-trout stream, ousting the brookie instead of practicing peaceful coexistence.

But most American fly-fishermen will concede that the brown has contributed more to their sport than has any other trout. By all odds the greatest surface-feeder among the trouts and chars, it can justly be credited with the progress and current advanced state of dry-fly fishing in America.

This is not to say, of course, that the dry fly is always the most lethal brown-trout lure. Worm fishermen account for many browns, in the high and cold water of the early season. Adherents of the spinning-rig (outlawed on a few stretches of eastern rivers) can place their assorted lures almost anywhere, even on the largest stream, penetrating trout sanctuaries inaccessible to the man with a fly rod. The large specimens of *Salmo trutta*, whether in stream or lake, are taken mostly at night and on such bait as nightcrawlers or minnows. These outsize browns are notable for their nocturnal feeding. Indeed, some of them seem to feed *only* between nightfall and dawn, holing up in the deep pools or the depths of a lake by day and cruising into the shallows at dusk. In this hour, the well-fished streamer or bucktail, imitating the swimming minnow, has been the undoing of many a brown.

Though in common with many fishes it is vulnerable to a deftly manipulated lure or bait, the brown remains the classic dry-fly quarry. It is the fish not only of Walton and Cotton, but of Theodore Gordon,[4]

---

[4] For whom the Quill Gordon, possibly the most widely used of all trout flies, was named.

Edward Hewitt, George M. L. LaBranche, and a host of other dry-fly students and practitioners whose writings have helped to make the floating fly a high expression of angling. The rivers on which these men practiced their art—New York's Beaverkill, Willowemoc, Neversink, and Esopus, Pennsylvania's Brodhead, and others—probably held many native brook trout a century ago, but they have been essentially brown-trout rivers for decades past. And as such they have been the cradles of dry-fly fishing in America. The tactics studiously learned upon their pools and riffles have spread, with the gradual extension of the brown trout itself, to the rivers and lakes of forty-odd states and of Canada.

The Von Behr export of 1883 has surely proved itself worthy of every mile of water in its present enormous range.

Chapter 2

RAINBOW,
CUTTHROAT, AND
GOLDEN TROUT

RAINBOW TROUT
Salmo gairdneri Richardson

This great fish of the West has in its being all of the wild rampaging character of its native rivers. It is tough and strong and far-ranging, attains much greater size than the eastern brook trout, and, in both the freshwater and sea-run phases, exceeds the brown trout in average dimensions. It is perhaps the most spectacular fighter of all the Salmonidae, not excepting the Atlantic salmon.

The sea-run rainbow is the steelhead of the West. Originally the steelhead was classified as a different fish: scientists called the non-migratory rainbow *Salmo irideus*, and the anadromous steelhead *Salmo gairdneri*. Today the two are known to be one species, and the specific name *gairdneri* is applied to both.

Probably the term "non-migratory" is a misnomer for the rainbow. It serves to distinguish the freshwater fish from the ocean-going steelhead, yet all rainbows are essentially migratory. Those without access to the sea seek the largest habitable fresh water they can find, though they ascend to the upper brooks at spawning time.

The Kamloops trout, *Salmo kamloops*, is a variety of the rainbow, native to the rivers of British Columbia. Some ichthyologists include the western golden trout, *Salmo aguabonita*, in the rainbow clan, but this fish has authoritative status as a distinct species.

The rainbow's original range was confined to the steep charging rivers of the Pacific coast, from southern California to the Bristol Bay area of Alaska. The fish is native, too, to rivers on the Asian shores of the Bering Sea.

Plantings of the rainbow have established it over a tremendous range. In the United States it thrives today throughout the Rocky Mountain region, in the East and the central West, and as far south as the mountainous areas of North Carolina and Tennessee. From introductions in 1920 it is present on the island of Kauai, Hawaii. Canada has planted the rainbow from Newfoundland to the Hudson Bay and James Bay drainages, and westward. Introduced into Europe, it has successfully competed with the brown trout. In the Southern Hemisphere it has flourished and grown large, providing superb fishing in the fast Andean streams of Chile and Argentina, and the lakes of New Zealand.

The rainbow's western origin and persistent anadromous character have given it many names: steelhead trout, steelhead salmon, hardhead, salmon trout. Place names of the West designate the fish in certain areas: Shasta trout, Klamath River trout, and McCloud River trout are a few.

Salmo gairdneri is a fine example of the striking beauty that characterizes all the trouts and chars. The name "rainbow" is misleading, however. It derives from a broad band, not rainbow-hued but pinkish lavender, running the length of the fish's lateral line and extending over the gill covers and cheeks. Though this trout's color varies widely with environment, the characteristic freshwater pattern is featured by this pinkish stripe. Above it, the back and upper sides are greenish bronze, dotted with many small darker spots which spread into the dorsal, adipose, and upper and lower caudal fins. The spots are sparse along the pinkish band, absent from the silvery white underbody. As spawning time approaches, the rainbow becomes a darker fish, the male developing a hooked lower jaw and a brighter red in the lateral band. In salt water the steelhead acquires a silvery overcast and loses the vividness of its distinguishing stripe. Like other sea-run trout, it takes on the characteristic freshwater coloration shortly after entering a river.

Any month from February to June may be the rainbow's spawning time, depending on latitude, altitude, and other factors influencing water temperature. April is probably the peak of the season in temperate waters. The fish is mature and ready for its first spawning at the age of three. Thereafter it may spawn, at yearly intervals, twice or even three times more, but the great majority of rainbows in spawning runs are first-time spawners.

The spawning site may be a fast riffle over a gravel bottom; but often the tail of a pool is chosen, for here a flow of water is assured if the stream level recedes. Two imperatives of a good nest (and they surely are recognized in the fish's terms) are a supply of oxygen for the eggs and a minimum danger of silting. Flowing water provides both.

The female digs out a nest with powerful thrusts of her tail; the male hovers near, ready and eager with his fertilizing milt and quick to chase off any rival male. When the female is ready to shed eggs in the nest the male draws next to her; to any observer his cloud of milt now signals the act of spawning. A large hen fish will make several nests in a straight upcurrent line, covering the eggs of each with gravel from the next upstream, and composing a redd over a bottom area perhaps two feet wide and ten feet long. In this process she often suffers body bruises and a badly frayed tail. Her original mate may be spent, and other males attend her, before she completes spawning.

A ten-inch female deposits about 600 eggs; a fish of five pounds may shed 6000. The eggs, large and non-adhesive, remain safe under the gravel through an incubation period of thirty to fifty days.

Probably in all normal spawning of the nest-building trouts and chars, fertilization of the eggs is extremely efficient—98 per cent or better—and the proportion of eggs lodging in the prepared nests, covered by gravel and thus protected until they hatch, is estimated at 90 per cent or more. So far, the process of reproduction leaves almost nothing to be desired. Immediately after the emergence of free-swimming fry, however, the damage begins. Predators are every-where: fish, snakes, birds. The mortality now is tremendous. Of ten thousand fertilized eggs, perhaps not more than two ever become mature fish which live to spawn in their turn and so perpetuate their kind.

Attaining a length of about six inches in its second summer, the rainbow lives on much the same diet as the brown and brook trout: insects, crustaceans, worms, small fish. The rainbow seems to develop a marked preference for fish at an earlier age than does the brown trout. Many anglers who commonly fish dry flies for browns of ten to fifteen inches believe the streamer, bucktail, or other minnow-imitator a superior lure for rainbows of the same size.

Though less a surface-feeder than the brown trout, the rainbow is the greatest surface fighter of all the Salmonidae. When hooked on a fly it goes at once into the air and leaps again and again, sometimes literally dancing on its tail all over the surface of a pool.

Ichthyologists hold that the rainbows do not feed on their spawn-ing runs. Whether they "feed" or not, they do take baits and artificial lures with a seemingly ravenous appetite. On Catherine Creek, in western New York, the annual upstream migration of rainbows resident in Seneca Lake has provided in recent years a sort of rainbow-trout derby. The sensational spawning run draws fishermen from afar, and the numbers of trout taken attests the fact that the rainbow en route to breed will seize a variety of offerings, whether the motive be hunger or something else. Fishing on New York's Esopus River and its tributaries reaches an April–May peak when the rainbows move upstream from Ashokan Reservoir to spawn.

Eastern United States streams first saw the flash of the rainbow trout in the early 1880's. The first shipment of rainbow eggs is said to have come from the McCloud River in California to a hatchery in Wytheville, Virginia.

Protests against the rainbow's eastern introduction, similar to those which greeted the first importations of brown trout, were short-lived. Anglers not only admired the rainbow's way with a fly but soon saw that this fish was tolerant of warmer water than the brook trout could abide, and capable of attaining a size that classed it as big game on fly-fishing tackle. Eastern anglers were taking rainbows of five to eight pounds not many years after the first introductions from the West.

Back home on the Pacific coast, among the sea-run steelheads, fish of fifteen pounds have long been common; some of the recorded weights of lake rainbows and Kamloops trout in the West have been sensational. The record to date belongs to a specimen taken from Lake Pend Oreille, Idaho by W. Hamlet on November 25, 1947. This giant of a trout weighed 37 pounds and was 40½ inches long.

One objection to the rainbow persists, however, and justly so from the standpoint of stream stocking. The fish has a downstream obsession, an urge to seek a lake or the biggest habitable reach of the river it can find. Michigan fish culturists realized as long ago as the 1890's that rainbows previously planted in rivers were appearing in the Great Lakes.

Because of the rainbow's fondness for big water, eastern state hatcheries and private clubs have largely given up stocking it for stream fishing. The brook trout will invariably remain where planted in smallish rivers, if the water is cold and pure, and the brown trout will not wander far. Both are thus better adapted than the rainbow for stream stocking.

The rainbow can be exceptional, however, sometimes flouting all the rules which are supposed to govern its species. This writer was once fishing the headwaters of a small eastern river, armed with a tiny dry fly and thinking only of brook trout or the occasional brown which ventured this far upstream.

The lush August growth afforded little casting space anywhere. But here a deep narrow run was spanned in its middle by a windfall, a barkless oak trunk which had been there for years. This natural bridge afforded a slippery but strategic casting position, for there was trouty water above and below it, and uncluttered space for the back-cast in each direction.

I crept out to the middle of the log, crouching to minimize my silhouette against the sky, and lengthened line for my first cast up-stream. Even in such shaky and cramped casting there is little excuse for allowing a backcast to touch the fly to the water, but I was guilty of just that. As the fly dimpled the surface behind me there was the eruption of a rising trout. Turning to face the action downstream, I slid off the log into waist-deep water, realizing at the same time, as the fish went into the air and lashed across the surface of the narrow run, that it was a rainbow of perhaps a pound and a half.

What is remarkable in this incident is not the trout's acceptance of the fly on the backcast, or the angler's fall from his casting perch, or even, finally, the landing of the fish. Such little asides are common in trout fishing. What is remarkable is that the trout was a rainbow of good size, in this small headwater, three or four months after its spawning time. No planting of rainbows had been made in this stream for many years. Previously stocked fish had become resident and grown large in a lake ten miles downstream. In August this rainbow should have been there, with its kindred. Its presence upstream merely con-firmed that the habits of fish are not infallibly predictable.

Utilizing the rainbow's tendency to run out of small streams, conservationists have done remarkably good jobs of stocking, pro-viding brief periods of stream fishing and establishing permanent populations of large rainbows in lakes fed by the streams.

In Missouri, a state whose waters seem hardly suitable to any of the trouts, the Conservation Commission predicated a rainbow-trout program on a candid put-and-take basis: fish hatchery-grown to maturity and stocked as catchable (ten-inch) trout. Revenue from special licenses pays the relatively high cost of this fishing. The spring-spawning habit of the rainbow is by no means an unchangeable con-dition, and man has monkeyed with it to his advantage. The Missouri procedure entails artificial spawning (stripping of eggs and milt) in November, and a growing season of sixteen months, to March of the second following year. In this period Missouri rainbows, fed a highly nutritive ration, achieve the planting size of ten inches or more. These fish are stocked in time for a March-first opening date, and somewhat larger fish are placed in streams and lakes during the open season. The program is based on the concept that most but not all of the trout will be caught soon after stocking, but a limit of five a day precludes any wanton slaughter. The few that are not stream-caught have given, over the past few seasons, a potent angling appeal to many of Missouri's lakes to which they have migrated. Today, some lakes in this "unlikely" trout state contain rainbows of eight or nine pounds.

The steelhead trout, or sea-run phase of the rainbow, returns big and silvery to its parent river after the rich and abundant fare of the ocean. Fresh-run and heading upstream, it is a strong, tremendously active fish, capable of ascending falls ten feet high. The larger specimens, weighing twenty pounds or more and striking savagely at flies and salmon-egg clusters, provide angling excitement unexcelled by any fish.

Among the trouts and chars, the steelhead and the Arctic char are outstandingly anadromous. These two seem to confirm the theory that trouts and chars in the northerly range have a greater tendency to become sea-run than those farther south. Probably the primary factor is temperature: the warmth of the lower reaches of southerly rivers is an effective barrier against a downstream migration. Rainbows were stocked several years ago in the high cold headwaters of a river in Colombia which flows for many miles at high altitudes before dropping to the hot tropical lowlands, to merge eventually with the Orinoco. The planted rainbows established a permanent population in the upper waters. They will never become sea-run steelheads, however, for the barrier of temperature keeps them upriver as effectively as would a high dam.

Harbor and big-city pollution, notoriously heavy in eastern U.S. rivers and estuaries, could well be an equal barrier. The Delaware River, for example, has fair populations of rainbows and brown trout in its upper branches and tributaries, but to become sea-run these fish would have to migrate for many miles through the sewage and industrial effluents of Trenton, Philadelphia, Camden, and Wilmington —an unimaginable assignment for any trout.

The rivers of Maine and eastern Canada are much cleaner, yet there is no record of steelheads in these waters. Along the Pacific coast from California to Alaska, however, migrations of the steelhead from river to sea and back to the river are as historic as the migrations of salmon.

The upstream runs occur at different times in a given river, and from one river to another. The motivation is not necessarily the attainment of sexual maturity, for some spring-run steelheads are still immature. More probably, the upstream urge is linked to the fish's movements in salt water. Steelheads not yet ripe, which have remained in estuaries or traveled only a short distance to sea after their downstream migration as juveniles, may start back upriver in April or May. Such fish remain through the summer in the larger pools, become mature, and proceed upstream in the fall to spawn in November or December.

Large steelheads which have had two years in the ocean enter the rivers in the fall. These are ripe fish, full of the purpose of reproduction. They travel chiefly in the daytime, stopping at night but taking no prolonged rest, and sometimes migrate hundreds of miles to their upriver spawning grounds to breed in the late winter or early spring.

Like the salmon, the steelhead does not truly feed on its spawning migration. This fact is at odds with angling experience, for the fresh-run steelhead seems to have an insatiable appetite for flies and other lures.

The steelheads' cycles of freshwater life and sea life are so varied and apparently haphazard as almost to defy definition. Its extreme irregularity in keeping its appointments makes it a difficult fish for historians.

Yet a great deal has been learned about this fish, particularly of its spawning and its life in the river. Leo Shapovalov and Alan C. Taft, studying the steelhead and its migrations in Waddell Creek, California, have reported its freshwater habits with great thoroughness.[1]

As juvenile fish, steelheads migrate to sea at different ages and at different times within a single season. In rivers holding optimum conditions for survival and growth, some of the young fish rapidly attain above-average size and head seaward when less than a year old, still

[1] *The Life Histories of the Steelhead Rainbow Trout and Silver Salmon* (State of California Department of Fish and Game, Fish Bulletin No. 98, 1954).

with visible parr marks. These exhibit a quickened tempo throughout the fresh- and saltwater periods, sometimes returning to the river after only eight months in salt water, perhaps not venturing into the open sea at all but merely moving in and out with the estuarial tides. Others lose themselves for two years or more in the unknown areas and depths of the ocean. Still others remain in fresh water, feeding on insects, crustaceans, and small fish, for one to four years. Northern steelheads, notably in the Alaskan rivers, may remain inland for five years and spawn a second time before migrating to sea. A few—possibly but not necessarily the progeny of non-sea-run males—complete their life cycles in the river without ever going to sea.

In the usual pattern, however, the young fish remain in the river for one to two years, descend to the sea, and return to the parent river two years later as sexually mature fish. After that, the river-to-sea-to-river cycle is annual, but only a minority survive to make a second return.

Great quantities of immature steelheads, eight or nine inches long, going to sea in the spring of their second year, have been killed by anglers. Acting to prevent such destruction, the Washington State Department of Game has closed some streams to fishing until June or July, when most of the young downstream migrants have reached salt water. Washington conservationists believe that these measures have saved thousands of immature fish for a return later as adult trout.

Protection of the juveniles is imperative to offset, even in slight degree, the very heavy natural predations to which they are vulnerable. Mortality among young steelheads in fresh water, caused by predatory fish, birds, and snakes, is so great that only about 3 per cent of the fry survive to make a seaward migration. The ocean enemies, chiefly fish of many kinds (the seal and sea lion are discounted as major predators) take a further toll. It is estimated that total survival—adult fish returning as first-spawners from the number of eggs produced—is about .02 per cent, or *one* returning spawner out of five thousand fertilized eggs.

Unlike the Pacific salmons, the steelhead lives after its spawning to return to the sea. The majority, however, spawn only once. Third-time spawners are rare, fourth- and fifth-spawners almost nonexistent.

Coming in from the sea, the steelheads lose the silvery color

typical of all salmonids after a stay in the ocean. In fresh water t\
develop the pink stripe of the rainbow trout resident in rivers a\
lakes; in the males particularly this band becomes vivid and pr\
nounced. As spawning time approaches, the males develop elongated
jaws and large canine teeth.

The spawning procedure of steelheads is very similar to that of
the freshwater rainbows. Sometimes, however, the female picks a site
that seems far from ideal to the human observer. Shapovalov and Taft
cite a case in which a spawning fish in the East Branch of Waddell
Creek chose to dig her nests on "a hard, gravelly, semi-cemented mix-
ture of decomposing rock forming a portion of a ford built for auto-
mobile passage." The trout crumbled this hardpan with her digging.

Males among the stream trout—freshwater rainbows and occasionally other resident species—may attempt to participate in the steelhead spawning, and sometimes succeed in fertilizing the eggs of the
sea-run female. The mating of sea-run males with stream females is
not reported.

Egg-shedding is virtually a complete process: a typical count on a
spawned-out, 24-inch female which had cast about 5500 eggs found
only seven eggs remaining in her body.

The post-spawning movements of the steelhead seem as random
and unplanned as the other phases of its life cycle. In some rivers the
spent fish start immediately upon their return to the sea; in others
they may delay this journey for weeks, lingering in the larger pools
singly or in schools. These upriver loiterers, exhausted from the spawning, become weak, emaciated, and pale, losing the reddish flush of the
freshwater coloration.

The incubation period of steelhead eggs can be as brief as nineteen days in water at 60° F., and as long as three months at 40° or
lower. The fry begin to emerge from the redds when the yolk sac is
absorbed, two to three weeks after hatching.

Virtually nothing is known of the steelhead's travels at sea. It is
probable that the young fish move in schools for some time after reaching salt water. The adults, however, may well be lone wolves, fending
for themselves without benefit of a school. For, though the steelhead
at sea is largely piscivorous, very few are caught by commercial
trollers who take thousands of chinook and coho salmon.

Most scientific opinion holds that the steelhead seldom migrates more than twenty miles out from the coast and never travels beyond the continental shelf. There is no doubt, however, that this fish, like the salmon, attains its greatest growth in the ocean, for it averages much heavier than its rainbow kindred which spend all their lives in the rivers. A scale reading on a spawned-out, 28-pound female showed that she had returned from the sea for her third spawning and was seven years old. By comparison, a five-year-old river rainbow which had never migrated to sea was only 17½ inches long and weighed less than two pounds.

A large lake can be the "ocean" for some rainbows, and produce growth comparable to that of the sea-run fish. The rainbows of Michigan, following their downstream urge, become "steelheads" (as they are quite justly called by the state's anglers) by migrating to the Great Lakes and returning to the rivers. They have never been numerous, and today are diminished, probably because of sea-lamprey predations, but those which survive have average intervals in the rivers and Great Lakes paralleling the river and ocean cycles of the Pacific coast steelheads. The "ocean," here, is fresh water, yet the spawning migrations are comparable. Thus the influencing factor would seem to be big water, rather than salinity or the lack of it.

Returning to the natal river, the steelhead exercises a homing sense comparable to that of the Pacific salmons. Shapovalov and Taft report that experiments during nine seasons with steelheads marked at Waddell Creek and Scott Creek, on the north-central California coast, "show conclusively that the rate of straying among steelheads is considerably less than among silver (coho) salmon for the streams involved." One could surmise, however, that this homing faculty is greatly helped if, as supposed, the steelhead does not wander far at sea and, in some cases, hardly moves out of the estuary of the parent river.

The Kamloops trout is an upcountry cousin of the rainbow. Originally native to the lakes and streams of the upper Fraser and Columbia River systems of British Columbia, the Kamloops has been quite widely distributed throughout the western states and Canadian provinces.

This member of the rainbow clan has a dark green or bluish back, abruptly defined and strikingly contrasted to the broad pink band along the lateral line. Extending over the gill covers and cheeks, this band is a more vivid pink than the lavender-tinted stripe of the rainbow. The Kamloops's back, lateral-line area, dorsal and caudal fins are well sprinkled with dark spots. The lower flanks and belly are silvery white.

The Kamloops trout was planted in approximately two hundred British Columbia lakes, previously barren of other fish, fifty-five or sixty years ago. In some of the lakes, this attempted distribution met with marked success—trout of five or six pounds three years after stocking. In others it failed completely.[2] Ecological factors normally propitious proved the opposite in a number of these efforts to establish the Kamloops. As this trout is a stream spawner, high hopes were held for certain lakes with excellent spawning tributaries. These promising facilities, however, eventually produced an overpopulation of the Kamloops, with many fish of such small size (eight to twelve inches) as to discourage angling.

Where the Kamloops thrives under optimum conditions it achieves great size. Fish of fifteen pounds are not uncommon, and specimens of more than thirty pounds have been reported.

Plantings of forage fish as food for the Kamloops trout, in British Columbia's previously barren lakes, have yielded only spotty returns. The kokanee, a non-migratory form of the sockeye salmon (see Pacific Salmon, Chapter 6), is the natural food of the Kamloops trout. Yet, in several of the lakes where the kokanee has been introduced to feed the Kamloops, the forage fish has eventually taken over, apparently utilizing the lake's food resources more efficiently than the trout it was intended to support.

The rainbow trout is constantly beset by a host of enemies. The inland predators against the brook trout and brown are impartial, attacking the rainbow, too, wherever they can find it. At sea, the steelhead's existence depends upon its ability to elude several varieties of sharks and other predatory fishes. Bears take their toll of migrating salmon and steelheads alike in Alaska and British Columbia waters.

[2] Reported by the Canadian Department of Fisheries, Ottawa.

Man has been exceptionally harsh with the steelhead and freshwater rainbow, polluting their rivers, thwarting their spawning runs with dams, and in past years netting the steelhead commercially in many rivers and bays of the West. Dams not only impede the upstream migrations but impose perhaps impassable barriers against the downstream runs. Can young fish, heading down to the sea, negotiate to its outlet a lake thirty miles long? Answers to a host of questions posed by industrial and water-supply dams are being sought by fish culturists.

Meanwhile, the rainbow's innate strength and tenacity continue to multiply its kind against all the ravages of nature and of man, and to maintain its high place in any ranking of game fish.

CUTTHROAT TROUT
Salmo clarki   Richardson

More than a century ago, Charles Darwin expressed wonder that one freshwater lake or river could hold a species of fish common to another that was far distant and separated by barriers of land. In *The Origin of Species* Darwin wrote:

It is probable that they [fishes] are occasionally transported by what may be called accidental means. Thus fishes still alive are not very rarely dropped at distant points by whirlwinds; and it is known that the ova retain their vitality for a considerable time after removal from the water. This dispersal may, however, be mainly attributed to changes in the level of the land within the recent period, causing rivers to flow into each other. Instances, also, could be given of this having occurred during floods, without any change of level. The wide difference of the fish on the opposite sides of most mountain ranges, which are continuous, and which consequently must from an early period have completely prevented the inosculation of the river systems on the two sides, leads to the same conclusion.

Darwin's wonder could have been greater still had he known of the tremendous native western range of the cutthroat trout, *Salmo clarki*. For in 1859, when *The Origin of Species* was published, the cutthroat swam as it had for centuries in the cold rivers and lakes of a triangular area eleven hundred miles wide at its base and extending

Trouts and Char

Top to bottom: Rainbow, Brown,
Cutthroat, Dolly Varden

sixteen hundred miles north. On today's map, this enormous native habitat of the cutthroat runs from the western Dakotas across Wyoming, Montana, Idaho, and Washington to the Pacific Ocean. It reaches southward through Colorado to northern New Mexico; it includes Utah, Nevada, Oregon, and California from the Eel River north. The giant triangle narrows northward through British Columbia and Alberta to southern Alaska and Yukon. It is perhaps the greatest native range of any of the trouts. Significantly, from the Darwin reference, it is not confined by major mountain ranges. In the steep whitewater streams of both the eastern and the western slopes, in the long gradual down-drifts of the intermountain rivers, and in the coastal estuaries, the cutthroat assaults the flies of anglers and fights like the fine game fish it is.

The Indians knew the cutthroat long before the westward-migrating white man[3] came to esteem it as a fish to catch and a fish to eat. Later, where its populations became sharply diminished, it became a fish to protect.

Perhaps because of its wide distribution, the cutthroat has more names than any of the trouts. Local names, nicknames, appellations such as flat trout, salmon trout, black trout, bluenose trout, and even porgy—altogether nearly a hundred oddments of nomenclature—designate it throughout its range. Among them, that of "native trout" seems apt, for the cutthroat is the native trout of the inland West.

The cutthroat breed is fuzzy with subspecies, variants, and hybrids. The Montana black-spotted trout, distinguished by large black spots scattered over its body, is a kind of second cousin once removed. Another is the "crescenti" trout, found only in Lake Crescent, Washington. A couple of the in-laws have earned distinct scientific designations: the Lake Tahoe cutthroat, *Salmo clarki henshawi*, and the Piute trout, *Salmo clarki selineris*. The Lake Tahoe cutthroat is native to the lake it was named for, and to the waters of the Truckee River system of Nevada and California. The neighboring Piute trout, believed to be a variant of the Tahoe, is an isolated fish, belonging essentially to the upper drainage of the Fish River valley in Alpine County, California.

---

[3] Including Captain William Clark, of the Lewis and Clark Expedition, for whom *Salmo clarki* is named.

Interbreeding of one cutthroat strain with another, and of cut-throats with rainbows, has occurred all over the West. From point to point in the far-flung range the chemistries of air, water, altitude, and natural food have worked their changes in the cutthroat's coloration and spawning habits. This fish in an Oregon coastal river may look quite different from its back-country relative in a high Wyoming lake.

Probably the most reliable mark of distinction is that which gives the fish its name—a reddish brush-stroke under the lower jaw—but in some waters even that is absent. Another clue is the presence of hyoid teeth back of the tongue, yet a good many genuine cutthroats lack them.

The next time you take a trout in the western high country, look first for the red mark on the lower jaw. Then note, perhaps, that your fish has a gray-greenish back and upper sides, a quite abrupt fading to pinkish along the lateral line and lower flanks, and a white belly. Many dark spots may cover the fish from gill cover to tail, including all fins. If your fish is a cutthroat, the pectoral and ventral fins should be pinkish, the dorsal, caudal, and anal darker.

Even without these colors, your fish may well be a cutthroat. It may be quite dark, from back down to belly; it may have golden spots as well as dark ones, and the spots may be comparatively few, oc-curring chiefly on the posterior flanks. Your fish could even have a longitudinal stripe, like a rainbow's, and still be a cutthroat. It may even fight like a rainbow, too, with leaps and surface thrashing, or possibly bore deep without ever jumping at all, reminding you of an eastern brook trout. But whatever its tactics, if you take it on a fly you will probably agree that it is a fighter all the way to your net.

Your cutthroat may not be more than a foot long, for the frying-pan sizes are usual in the inland streams. But you cannot identify it that way, either, for it could measure twenty inches. Even in this unlikely but possible event, your cutthroat doesn't approach the rod-and-reel record for the species. That was a fish of 41 pounds, 39 inches over all, taken from Pyramid Lake, Nevada, inside an Indian reserva-tion, by an Indian named John Skimmerhorn, in December 1925.

The lake fish average larger than the stream residents. The sea-run cutthroats of the coastal rivers attain sizes appreciably greater than do the river fish of the vast upland range, yet the latter tend to be deeper and heavier, inch for inch, than their anadromous counterparts. In the Alaska and Yukon rivers and lakes, from Ketchikan to White Horse, twenty-inch cutthroats are not uncommon. Throughout its habitat, growth rates and maximum size vary widely according to the extent of the range and the food supply.

These basic conditions, plus altitude and water temperature, also affect the cutthroat's age at sexual maturity, which can be anywhere from three to five years. The fish is highly variable in its spawning habits. Breeding time is January and February in some of the Oregon and Washington rivers where the cutthroat comes up from the Pacific. In the inland rivers, and in many of the lakes, spawning may start in February, and occur, from one river or lake to another, in all months from February to August. The river fish seek shallow, clear, fast water for their spawning beds; lake fish usually migrate up a tributary to the same type of spawning bottom.

The female cutthroat makes one or more nests, inches deep, preferably in pea-size gravel. She extrudes 350 to 500 eggs if she is a ten- to twelve-inch fish, as many as 10,000 if she is an eight- or ten-pounder. The eggs, carefully covered, hatch in six to eight weeks, and the fry emerge into the cold eternal current.

The majority of cutthroats spawn only once, a minor percentage two or three times. Four-time spawners are very rare.

Most of the young fish that survive their many predators stay in the parent stream for two years before descending, usually in April of the second year, to the lake or the sea. They are feeding, now, on insects, small crustaceans, worms. As they grow, they become more piscivorous, in fresh or salt water. In the springtime estuaries they take a heavy toll of young salmon migrating seaward.

The entire range of the river-to-sea migration, and the return, is far shorter than that of the steelhead or the salmon. Once it has descended to the ocean, the cutthroat is a frequenter of the estuaries, never venturing far out to sea. Schooling in the tidal bays, these trout move in and out with the tide, or perhaps cruise along shore to the next inlet.

An occasional cutthroat with access to the sea will make no attempt to reach it, living out its life in fresh water. The usual log, however, is two years in fresh water, two in salt. Individual fish may remain only a few months in salt water, then essay a "feeding run" upstream (not a true spawning migration) in late September or October. They will remain in the river, however, for the spawning, which may be in January or much later. These "feeding run" migrants are big and tough, bluish above, silvery below, sometimes so closely resembling the steelhead that identification is difficult. Called "green fish" in the Northwest, they afford the best of all fly-fishing for cutthroats.

Fly-fishermen in Washington and Oregon say the first late-summer hatch of flying ants is the signal to try for the cutthroats returning from the sea. To fly purist and bait-user alike, this trout is an angler's joy. On days unpropitious for the fly, it will attack spinners, salmon eggs, night crawlers and live bait. The lake cutthroats further accommodate the angler, especially him without a boat, by their habit of feeding chiefly in the shoal water along shore.

The cutthroat seems a poor mixer with other trouts and chars. The Montana Academy of Sciences notes that *Salmo clarki* originally inhabited virtually all the waters of Montana but has gradually dwindled because of plantings of exotics (rainbows, browns, and eastern brook trout).

The State of Washington has utilized this character of the cutthroat to great advantage in at least one outstanding instance of fishery management. Blue Lake, a native cutthroat water in remote north central Washington, was stocked with eastern brook trout in 1933, and later with rainbows. For a few years it provided some of the best fly-fishing in Washington. But by 1939 the increase of "scrap" fish—suckers, carp, squawfish, and chub—and a proportional decline in the trout were evident; by 1949 this imbalance was so marked that *all* trout were believed gone. Treated with rotenone in August 1949, Blue Lake yielded up thousands of dead scrap fish but not a single trout. Later it was restocked with cutthroats only. Today it is a natural cutthroat hatchery, posted against all fishing, the home of thousands of mature fish that are the breeding stock for Washington's cutthroat-planting program.

Anglers and wildlife lovers may take heart from such conservation practice, in a day when trout populations are declining everywhere through increasing land use, pollution, and dams which impede migrations and flood spawning grounds.

GOLDEN TROUT
Salmo aguabonita Jordan

The warmth of spring ascends slowly to the upper levels of California's High Sierras. But usually by early June the ice is crumbling along the margins of the lofty lakes and has already gone from the swift little inlet and outlet streams. At this season, one of the rarest jewels among all trouts seeks the shallow waters to spawn.

The golden trout, *Salmo aguabonita*, is California's own fish. Originally it was found in a tight little range confined not only horizontally but vertically. It is native to streams and lakes of the Sierran crest from California's Kern River watershed north to El Dorado County, but only at altitudes above 8000 feet. The golden has been transplanted, with varying degrees of success, into the high lakes of Wyoming, Montana, Washington, and a few other western states having water sufficiently clear, cold, and elevated to meet this trout's fastidious needs.

Where the golden flashes its brilliance in the lofty Sierran brooks it averages eight to ten inches. In the lakes it grows to a size to lead many an angler on an arduous trip, on horseback or afoot, up into the rare airs of this trout's spectacular haunts. Goldens of eighteen to twenty inches come to the fly or the spinner in Reflection Lake and other waters cupped among the two-mile-high crests.

The largest golden taken on sporting tackle was not a California fish but a descendant of Wyoming transplants. This one's size would justly be rated as big for any species of trout; for a golden it was prodigious—11 pounds in weight, 28 inches in length. This record fish fell to the rod of Charles S. Reed in Cook's Lake, Wyoming, on August 5, 1948.

The golden trout is well named. Below its dark gray-greenish dorsal surface its upper sides are olive-yellow, sparsely covered with dark spots. A broad deep-pink or reddish band runs the length of the lateral line and extends over the gill covers. Spaced at even intervals along this band are nine to eleven blue-black parr marks. This stripe and its overlaid parr marks may be spotted too, but usually the spots are only on the posterior section, from the anal fin to the tail. Below the red band the fish is pale to bright yellow down to the belly, which may be yellow, orange, or pinkish. The ventral and anal fins are pink to orange, unspotted, with a white tip separated by a well-defined, curving black line. The dorsal and caudal, dusky to olive-yellow, are well covered with dark spots, and the dorsal exhibits an orange or pinkish tip.

The broad reddish band and the parr marks may be less distinct on the larger lake fish. The over-all color scheme, strikingly brilliant throughout the golden's narrow range, is enhanced in the smaller fish in brooks at extreme altitudes, and in the males at spawning time. The meat of a fresh-caught golden is pinkish red.

The June or early July spawning is in shallow fast water. The eggs are dropped in nests cleared by the female's tail, and covered with gravel or sand. Lake-dwelling goldens prefer to migrate up an inlet stream or a short way down an outlet, if one is available; if not, they will spawn in shoal water of the lake. The fry of lake parents may go to the lake as early as a month after hatching, but probably most of the new generation of lake goldens remain for a year in the stream of their birth.

Small golden trout in the upcountry rivulets feed chiefly on aquatic insects and small crustaceans; larger ones in the lakes become fish-eaters to a degree but are ready takers of a well-placed fly or nymph.

Some anglers report that the golden is an inferior fighter by comparison with the cutthroat and rainbow of comparable size. Such comparisons, however, seem idle; the opinions pro and con are based largely upon sentiment. Whatever the degree of the golden's gameness, those who cherish our remaining wilderness areas may well be thankful for this trout's presence in its remote, above-the-clouds range. It is a fish to protect and to nurture, in those relatively few waters of the West which meet its rare ecological demands.

Chapter 3

LAKE TROUT

Salvelinus namaycush (Walbaum)

A surprising number of people believe a lake trout to be any trout that happens to live in a lake. All of the trouts and chars do live in lakes, as well as in streams, and grow to greater size in the lake environment. But only *Salvelinus namaycush* is properly called the lake trout.

This is a distinct and eminently distinguished member of the salmonid family. In appearance, size, spawning habits, and fighting ability it exhibits a set of contradictions, variations, and unorthodoxy that often upset the nice calculations of ichthyologists and fishermen.

The lake trout is not a trout at all, but a char, as *Salvelinus* denotes. Some scientists prefer *Christivomer* rather than *Salvelinus* as the designation of charhood. Anglers have several names for this fish. While it is a lake trout or "laker" over a great deal of its range, fishermen in the West and in Alaska call it a mackinaw trout; in Maine and eastern Canada it is a togue or a gray trout. Elsewhere it is known as the Great Lakes trout, salmon trout, namaycush, forktail trout, and even longue.

By whatever name, it is an impressive fish. Its average size makes it the second largest of the Salmonidae, exceeded only by the chinook salmon; in an occasional instance of prodigious growth it has outdone even the chinook. The record lake trout on rod and line was a Lake Superior specimen 63 pounds 2 ounces heavy, 51½ inches long, taken by H. Hammers on May 25, 1952. The Great Lakes have long been famous for their outsize lake trout. Prior to the devastation wrought by the sea lamprey, lakers of 80 pounds were occasionally taken by commercial netters in Lakes Superior, Michigan, and Huron. The big lakes of Manitoba, Saskatchewan, Alberta, Yukon, and the Northwest Territories are noted, too, for their giant "mackinaws." Canada's Department of Fisheries reports one of 102 pounds, probably the largest on record, taken in a net in Lake Athabaska.

Such figures are far above the average, but in many waters fish of 15 to 25 pounds are not uncommon. As with most fishes, the available range and food are the growth determinants. The larger lakes, with abundant populations of forage fish such as ciscoes, whitefish, smelts, and alewives, produce the larger lake trout.

This fish's natural range runs from Labrador (but not the island of Newfoundland), Quebec, Nova Scotia, and New Brunswick south to upper New York and New England, thence west and north across the Great Lakes region and western Canada's vast sweep of geography to British Columbia, Yukon, and Alaska. The namaycush has been introduced quite widely into deep lakes of the western United States and even in such eastern states as Connecticut. Though it is traditionally a lake fish, it is frequently found in northern rivers, but does not migrate to the sea.

Deep water is essential to the lake trout. A lake without one or more areas of depth—50 feet at least, preferably 200 or more—is not for namaycush, no matter how extensive its area. The lake trout spends the warm summer months deep down; it has been taken by anglers at the bottom of veritable freshwater abysses exceeding 300 feet. Yet, as becomes its heterodox nature, it is fond of life in the shallows in the springtime. Though the lake trout usually ascends again to the shoals for the autumn spawning, the female not infrequently drops her eggs in deep water.

Throughout its vast habitat, the lake trout varies greatly in color but has a few distinctive touches to identify it almost everywhere. It has the most deeply forked tail of all the Salmonidae, and the abundant spots are pale—whitish, cream-colored, or washed-out yellow —though in some lakes of Alaska they are reddish. A more minute inspection will reveal that the teeth on the roof of the mouth are set in a sort of crest.

The color background can be grayish, or decidedly brown, or gray-green to greenish blue on the back, fading to paler bluish irides-cent sides and a white, or sometimes pinkish, belly. The back, in some waters, has vaguely vermiculate markings resembling those of the laker's char relative, the brook trout. Occasionally these vermiculations will be pronounced and extreme, covering even the lower sides, as if the traditional spots had run together. Such spots among the namaycush clan seem further to demonstrate this fish's propensity for departing from the norm. On most lake trout, however, the spots are clearly defined. They extend over the entire body, gill covers, jaws, head, dorsal fin, adipose and caudal fins, but are absent from the pectoral and ventral fins, and merely suggested on the anal. These lower fins are pale, pinkish in some fish, edged with yellow or dull orange in others. Unlike other trouts and chars, the male laker in most parts of his range changes color but slightly at spawning time. Investi-gators at Cold Stream Pond, Maine, however, reported that spawning male lakers showed a wide black band running horizontally along the sides, and that the females took on a bright strawberry color. These spawning signals were plainly visible under water.

This nonconformist among fish is singularly casual and haphazard in its spawning habits. The spawning lakers do not build nests, though the males have been observed busily clearing silt from a bottom area by moving rocks with their tails. At this stage of the reproduction process, the males are alone on the spawning grounds. The females follow in two to five days. The spawning migration to shoal water may consume ten to fifteen autumn days, and is the shortest spawning run of any of the Salmonidae. Sometimes, in fact, there appears to be no spawning run at all, the female simply dropping her eggs in deep water. In Seneca Lake, New York, ripe lake trout have been taken, for the stripping of eggs, from good spawning bottoms 200 feet down; and in Lake Superior this fish has been known to spawn at depths as great as 480 feet.

On the other extreme, the chosen spawning ground is sometimes as shallow as that selected by a small brook trout in a mountain rill. In Lake Louisa, Ontario, lake trout have been observed spawning in eight inches of water, their backs frequently visible above the surface.

The common spawning depth, however, is at fifteen to twenty feet. Preferred bottoms are rocky and rough, full of crevices into which the eggs can settle and be protected against most predators. The common eel, and to a lesser degree the sucker, are able to burrow into the rocky nooks and crannies, and are notorious eaters of lake-trout eggs.

Some of the deep-spawning Great Lakes trout, however, seek hard clay bottoms, possibly at depths which eels and suckers cannot tolerate. According to some ichthyologists, the species consists of various races or "subpopulations," which may be distinguished by their physical characteristics or their spawning habits. In Lake Superior, particularly, the lake trout seems to be greatly diversified. There is, for instance, the siscowet, or "fat" lake trout, whose breeding season extends over a six-months' period from June through November. Certain of these subspecific lakers spawn in shoals on rocky bottoms, others at great depths on smooth bottoms. The Michigan Department of Conservation reports lake trout entering streams to spawn, particularly along the east shore of Lake Superior.

The usual spawning ceremony occurs in October or November. It may include a kind of preparatory period of ten days to two weeks, after the trout arrive on the shoals but before active courting and egg-laying begin.

Anglers at Lake Simcoe, Ontario, have long contended that the wind must blow hard for a day or more before lake trout will enter the shoals to spawn. This theory seems well supported by a six-year study of the Simcoe trouts' spawning habits, conducted by the Canadian Department of Fisheries. In each of the six years, the trout arrived on the spawning shoals following one or more days of strong autumnal winds, and when the water temperature had dropped to a range of 50° to 57° F. This fishermen's theory doubtless has a basis in fact, for a hard blow and rough water help clear the silt from the rocks on a shoal bottom, saving the male trout the trouble. A second and similar contention of anglers is that heavy winds and rough water mean a short spawning period, whereas persistent calm weather means prolonged spawning.

Studies of the lake trout in Cold Stream Pond, Maine, bear out the wind hypothesis. The Maine Department of Inland Fisheries and Game reports: "The only known spawning area utilized by the lake trout (in Cold Stream Pond) is located on the southeast shore in Webb Cove. This shore is windswept for the most part during the summer and fall months, leaving the rock-bottomed area free of mud and sand."

Once the eggs are dropped, no attempt is made by the parent fish to cover them. The eggs hatch in 140 to 166 days, at a water temperature of 37° F, the Maine authorities state. Other sources report hatching in as short a period as fifty days, in water at 50° F. Emerging from the sac-fry stage, young lake trout apparently head for deep water at once, for they are not found in the shallows.

The female is sexually mature at the age of six or seven years, the male at four or five. In her first spawning, the female is perhaps seventeen to nineteen inches long,[1] and may drop 2000 eggs. Much larger and older fish, the big ones of 25 to 30 pounds, will lay perhaps 15,000 to 18,000 eggs in a single spawning.

The laker is potentially a long-lived fish; specimens estimated to be twenty to forty years old have been taken from the large lakes of northwest Canada. Few individuals reach even the age of twenty, however. Heavy natural mortality accounts for most of them by the ninth or tenth year, and hence records of spawning beyond the third time are rare.

The young trout feed on insects, small crustaceans, and worms. The so-called opossum shrimp, *Mysis relicta*, is a preferred food wher-

---

[1] In the Great Lakes and other large bodies, a female lake trout of this age may be 24 inches long and capable of extruding 3500 eggs.

ever it is plentiful. The mature fish are almost exclusively piscivorous. Ciscoes, alewives, smelts, whitefish, suckers, and yellow perch are the common fare in those ideal lake-trout waters which sustain an abundance of such forage fish. The lake trout eats its own eggs, but this may be deemed its caviar rather than a staple. In lakes where other fish are scarce, the namaycush must subsist largely on insects and plankton, and in such waters the age-weight relation reflects the inadequate diet.

Once the annual business of spawning is over, the laker goes back to the deeps and resumes its customary ways. It is a school fish though its schools are less numerous and compact than those of the lake herring and others. The schools or groups travel in more or less predictable lanes, hence commercial fisherman know the best locations for their gill nets.

Whether or not the lake trout returns to the same spawning shoal a year later seems a moot question. Some authorities hold that this trout exhibits a homing tendency only when it must—that is, in lakes containing only one or perhaps two spawning shoals. Lake trout tagged in Lake Superior, however, have shown "a marked tendency to return during successive years to the spawning grounds on which they were tagged," according to Michigan conservationists. Conversely, in Ontario's Lake Simcoe, a body far smaller than Superior but one holding an unusual number of good spawning beds, Canada's Department of Fisheries found "no evidence of a homing behavior of the adult lake trout."

With namaycush, the most careful studies in a given area seem contradicted in another. One point of behavior, however, appears consistent. In large lakes and small, the lake trout is a great wanderer in its post-spawning movements. Fish tagged on spawning shoals have been recaptured later about as far as they could possibly travel from the tagging point. Reported post-spawning trips in Lake Superior are sensational in the distances covered. In October 1950, 116 large (average, 27 inches) lake trout were tagged and released near Keeweenaw Point, Michigan. Within a year, fifteen were recovered. These had ranged as far as 190 miles west, 95 miles north, and 100 miles east.

Even the smaller lake trout exhibit an insatiable wanderlust. Of 617 fish (average size 18 inches) tagged and released in the Apostle

Islands (Wisconsin) region of western Lake Superior, in the summer of 1951, 140 were recovered within a year. Though 90 per cent were taken within fifty miles of the point of release, nine per cent had gone 120 to 255 miles.[2]

Observations on much smaller lakes have shown that namaycush moves from its spawning ground to the extreme limit of travel within its lake.

Green Lake, Wisconsin, is the source of a classic mystery story concerning the resident lake trout. The tale, involving extreme angling frustration, is told by Vernon A. Hacker, of the Wisconsin Conservation Department at Oshkosh.[3] Green Lake is the deepest (maximum, 221 feet) and the fourth largest (7325 acres) in Wisconsin. Lake trout were stocked in it from 1886 to 1944. These fish, it is pertinent to note, were of Great Lakes stock, from the deep, hard-clay spawning beds of Lake Michigan, 180 to 360 feet down.

Plantings were discontinued after 1944, for the excellent reason that no lake trout had been taken by anglers for years. Nets, however, regularly took large trout but never a small one. Ultimately, in 1952, a lone angler began to take the Green Lake trout. His lure was a chrome-plated Sutton spoon in conjunction with a set of flashing spinners called "cowbells," and a four- to eight-ounce weight. This assortment of hardware was trolled slowly, by rowboat, in 45 to 100 feet of water, at the end of a lead-core line.

Other anglers started using this rig, and with comparable success. The captured fish, like those taken in the nets, were all large: they averaged 16 pounds; a few were as heavy as 34 pounds, and none was under 6½.

Questions immediately confronted the Wisconsin Conservation Department: Are small trout present? Do the big ones spawn? If so, why the apparent lack of small fish?

A spawning ground, evidently the only one in the lake (nets set in other areas failed to take a fish), was discovered in 60 to 100 feet of water at what is known as the Sugarloaf Bar. Dredgings revealed a dubious spawning bottom—pure silt over blue clay, with occasional

[2] Reported in "The Movements of Tagged Lake Trout in Lake Superior, 1950–1952," by Paul H. Eschmeyer, Russell Daly, and Leo F. Erkkila, reprinted from *Transactions of the American Fisheries Society*, Vol. 82 (1952).

[3] "Biology and Management of Lake Trout in Green Lake, Wisconsin," reprinted from *Transactions of the American Fisheries Society*, Vol. 86 (1956).

small patches of egg-size gravel embedded in sand. Such bottoms are not favorable (except at depth beyond reach of most predators), since they offer few or no protective crevices for the eggs. Wisconsin scientists believe the Green Lake trout chose the deep Sugarloaf Bar because they derived from deep-spawning Lake Michigan stock, and an inherited tendency to seek the deep smooth bottom had persisted.

In April 1953 a number of small, marked (fin-clipped) lake trout were planted in Green Lake.

The state conservationists then contrived some big boxes of supposedly good spawning-bed stuff—large rocks and gravel—and lowered them to the bottom at Sugarloaf Bar prior to spawning time. When lifted, in November, one box contained lake-trout eggs. It contained also, and revealingly, three specimens of the small amphibian salamander, *Necturus maculosis*, locally called the "mud puppy"—and the stomachs of all three held lake-trout eggs.

Continuing their sleuthing, the Wisconsin men set mud-puppy traps at Sugarloaf Bar and elsewhere in the lake. Several hundred of the salamanders were caught, of which nearly 70 per cent had eaten lake-trout eggs. Significantly, however, none caught on shoals other than the Sugarloaf Bar had trout eggs in their stomachs. Of further interest was the fact that mud puppies caught at Sugarloaf after mid-December had not eaten trout eggs, indicating that their predation had cleaned all trout eggs from the shoals a month after spawning.

There was still no proof that a single trout egg had hatched. Maybe the trouble was not only the predatory mud puppies but a lack of bottom currents and oxygen. In January 1955, a fully screened, predator-proof box containing gravel and several hundred live, fertilized lake-trout eggs, was dropped to the bottom of the spawning ground. Lifted thirty-nine days later, it held 205 live lake-trout fry. Here was proof enough, the experimenters thought, that the Sugarloaf Bar was suitable for spawning except for its deficiency in egg-hiding rock crevices.

L'affaire namaycush at Green Lake had by now become a civic issue, and the people were not letting it go by default. The Green Lake County Board of Supervisors now purchased, with federal-aid funds, 210 tons of granite rock. This was hauled out on the lake ice in March 1955. When the ice melted, the rock settled upon 6000 square feet of the Sugarloaf Bar. Lake trout used this "artificial bottom" for spawning in the following November. In February 1956, the stomachs of trapped mud puppies and yellow perch revealed freshly eaten trout eggs in an advanced stage of development, proving that these predators could no longer clean out the trout eggs a month after spawning.

In March, skin-divers of the Midwest Amphibian Club, equipped with pumping devices to suck trout eggs out of the rocky grottoes, descended to the Sugarloaf Bar bottom. Emerging, they reported "bushels of eggs" in the rocky crevices. In May they went down again. This time, four newly hatched, live lake-trout fry were brought up. These little fellows represented what is believed to be the *first successful hatch* of lake trout in Green Lake, at least within the memory of the present generation.

Meanwhile, the fin-clipped stockees of the 1953 plantings have grown well. A few of 24 inches and four pounds have been taken by anglers. More significantly, the first unclipped, legal-size (17 inches) laker was taken in a net in 1962, and since then other unmarked trout of legal length have been captured. These lake trout are progeny of natural breeding in Green Lake, and hence are proof of the success of the artificial spawning ground.

The Green Lake angler's "cowbell" string of spinners, and such fish-simulators as the large spoons and plugs, are commonly trolled deep, with a metal-core line, in the summer months and close to bottom in the shoals during the spring and fall. Live bait, usually a fish, is similarly trolled. The sewed-on smelt is popular in Maine waters. Excellent, too, are the alewife and the cisco, for these fish are probably the lake trout's preferred food wherever abundant.[4]

Still-fishing on bottom, with dead smelts or shiners as bait, has proved in some lakes much more effective than trolling. The troller covers more water, but according to the still-fishermen, he goes through it too fast. Anglers who know the best spots in a lake and concentrate on them with the still-fishing method, have proved so deadly to the lake trout in Maine that this practice is now illegal in certain lakes of that state.

Ice-fishing for lakers, with tip-ups and other rigs, the angler

---

[4] Ciscoes constituted 96.5 per cent of food found in the stomachs of 72 large (27 to 43½ inches) lake trout taken from Green Lake, Wisconsin, in 1953. Of 86 fish positively identified in these trouts' stomachs, 83 were ciscoes.

cozily ensconced in his stove-heated mobile hut, is a great winter sport on many of the midwestern lakes.

Even fly-fishing for namaycush has its devotees. The fish is a good fly-taker in shoal water during the spring and fall. Anglers who seek it with the fly and the light terminal gear of fly-fishing are its staunch supporters in the age-old debate on its sporting qualities. So taken, the lake trout is free to fight its best.

Deepwater fishing for the laker, on the other hand, involves tackle as heavy as that of salt water: a stout rod, star-drag reel, metal-core line, a heavy lure or bait, and a sinker to keep it deep when trolled. Against such derricking equipment the courage and strength of any trout, char, or salmon would avail little.

Many inland lakes still support thriving populations of lake trout. In some the namaycush has maintained itself by natural reproduction; in others, such as Cayuga Lake, New York, lake trout numbers have been substantially increased by hatchery-bred plantings. But in the Great Lakes, particularly lakes Michigan and Huron, the once-numerous lake trout has been almost exterminated by a killer whose destruction is probably unequaled by any fish predator in fresh water. This is the sea lamprey. The facts of this parasite's predations in the Great Lakes, and of the current campaign to control it, are given in the final chapter of this book.

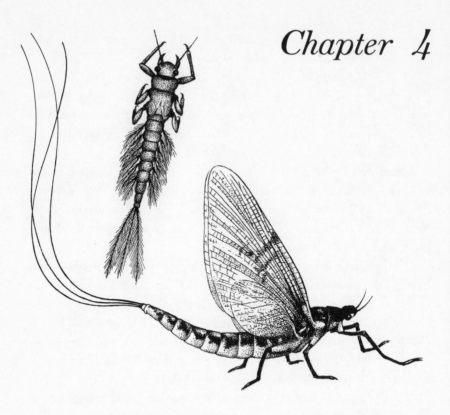

Chapter 4

OTHER CHARS

DOLLY VARDEN
Salvelinus malma (Walbaum)

The great rivers that drain the Pacific slopes, the tributaries of their steep upper valleys, and their headwater lakes, from northern California to the polar seas above Bering Strait, constitute the North American range of Dolly Varden, *Salvelinus malma*. In Asia this fish extends its residence down the shores of the Pacific to Kamchatka and beyond. It is scarce today in its southerly U.S. range.

Popularly called a trout but actually a char, the Dolly Varden is a controversial figure among the freshwater fishes of America. This

NOTE: Illustration is of mayfly nymph and subimago.

scintillant creature of the cold northwestern waters has a reputation that belies its outward charm and grace. In Alaska particularly, the Dolly Varden is a hated fish. Commercial salmon fishermen in Alaska's Bristol Bay country have long held the Dolly Varden to be a wanton killer of the red or sockeye salmon—Alaska's most valuable species. Ascending the rivers on its fall spawning migrations, the Dolly Varden is accused of taking heavy toll of freshly spawned salmon eggs. In the spring, schooling in vast numbers in the tidal estuaries, this fish is reported to be highly destructive of young salmon migrating to sea. Years ago, seeking to kill off this predator, the then Territory of Alaska paid a bounty of 2½ cents for every Dolly Varden tail turned in at coastwise and upriver stores. The campaign was short-lived, however; the caudals of steelheads were not unlike the Dolly Varden's, and presumably the Territorial treasury could not long support the drain.

Elsewhere than in Alaska, the Dolly Varden has been branded as a killer of small salmon and trout. These accusations are doubtless just, but could be applied also to steelheads, cutthroats, and others.

Up and down its long but narrow range the Dolly Varden has various names: bull trout, bull char, western char, Oregon char, golden fin, red-spotted trout, golet. The origin of its best-know name is somewhat obscured by time. In Dickens's *Barnaby Rudge* (1841), Dolly Varden was a gay, enchanting, beautiful young girl, fond of clothes as colorful as her character. Her impress upon the times was such that "Dolly Varden" expressed all that was young, bright, spirited and feminine. A gown of gay-flowered material, widely popular in the 1860's, was called a "Dolly Varden." Later a large hat, flower-trimmed, acquired the same name. The identity of the man (or woman) who first applied "Dolly Varden" to the western char is lost to history, but doubtless the motive behind this christening was the bright beauty of the fish.

In its coloration the Dolly Varden varies considerably, though less widely than the cutthroat, from one river or lake to another. Usually the dorsal surface is dark green to brownish, sometimes almost black; the upper sides are an iridescent bronze down to the lateral line, the lower sides gray-green, the belly white. The upper spots are pale or white; those lower on the sides are orange or reddish. The spots are numerous but do not extend over the head or gill covers, and are not present on the fins. The ventral and anal fins resemble the brook trout's in their pink to carmine color; the ventral has even the white edge and the black pencil line next to it, as on *fontinalis*. The dorsal, pectoral, and caudal fins often show a reddish outer edge.

The sea-run Dolly Vardens are silvery, and inclined to be slimmer than the same species in the mountain streams and lakes. Their spots are pale, sometimes totally absent, and the fins show no red.

The American Fisheries Society gives the Dolly Varden distinct classification as *Salvelinus malma*. Some scientists believe it to be a subspecies of the Arctic char, *Salvelinus alpinus*. Though the Dolly Varden is not so exclusively a northern fish as the Arctic char, it does reach its greatest abundance in Alaska, where it inhabits some waters jointly with *alpinus*. In the extreme northern range the Dolly Varden closely resembles the Arctic char and reaches comparable sizes. Above the Bering Strait, in such Alaskan rivers as the Kobuk and Noatak, and in the waters of Kotzebue Sound, sea-run Dolly Vardens of ten pounds are not uncommon.

Occasional huge specimens, of twenty pounds or more, are taken in the larger lakes of Alaska and British Columbia, and south to Washington, Oregon, and Idaho. The record Dolly Varden came out of that famous natural hatchery of giant trouts and chars, Lake Pend Oreille, Idaho. This fish, weighing 32 pounds and measuring 40½ inches over all, was taken by N. L. Higgins on October 27, 1949. Two years before, the same lake had yielded the record rod-and-reel rainbow trout, of exactly the same length as the prize Dolly Varden, but five pounds heavier.

A much smaller Dolly, usually less than a foot long but ideal game for the wet and dry fly on the lightest of tackle, inhabits the higher mountain streams and lakes of Alaska, This fish has various local names, and is believed by some anglers to be a distinct and isolated variety.

The Dolly Varden is an autumnal or early-winter spawner, seeking shallow water over a gravelly, stony, or sandy bottom. Lake-dwellers may spawn on a shoal bottom of the lake but usually ascend a tributary stream.

The new generation of this species remains upstream for an indeterminate period, one or two years, before migrating to the lake or perhaps to salt water. The immature fish subsist on insects, crustaceans, and small aquatic invertebrates. Later, they become one of the most carnivorous of all the Salmonidae, feeding on small fish, fish eggs, frogs—virtually anything that is animal life.

Its voracious appetite and its tendency to school in great numbers have made the Dolly Varden relatively easy to catch. Fishermen have decimated it along the lower reaches of many Alaskan rivers, where it sometimes swarms by the thousands in a single pool.

Anglers express various degrees of enthusiasm for the Dolly Varden's gameness. Some belittle it as an indifferent fighter, by comparison to others of the Salmonidae. The Canadian Department of Fisheries, in "Trout and Char in British Columbia," notes that the Dolly Varden, as a sport fish, "is given a second-class rating by those anglers whose standards are based on Kamloops and cutthroat trout." Echoing this sentiment, the Oregon State Game Commission says the Dolly Varden "lacks the dash and zip of other trout."

The Dolly's supporters, however, are legion. Many anglers who have fished widely for this western char compare it to its eastern cousin, the brook trout, in its strong subsurface tactics when hooked on a fly.

Regrettably, however, this beautiful fish is not always caught in the delicate way of the fly. In the tidal bays, the lower reaches of the coastal rivers, and many of the lakes, the Dolly Varden is taken on heavy tackle with trolling spoons, or with herring strips, live bait, or salmon eggs. Fly-fishing for the Dolly is largely a sport of the rivers, especially the high smaller tributaries where the fish average only eight to twelve inches.

ARCTIC CHAR
Salvelinus alpinus (Linnaeus)

Salvelinus alpinus is essentially a group designation, including several other chars whose taxonomic status is not fully determined. Some are far-northern fish; others are found in the latitudes of the 40's. The name is applied specifically, however, to the polar fish known as the Arctic char, much of whose range is above the Arctic Circle.

Until relatively recent times this fish had little documentation in the scientific tracts or the angling literature. For it swims in many a tidal bay and little nameless river that no white man has ever seen. For centuries it has been landlocked in countless remote northern lakes. Even today it is known only to the Eskimo, the ichthyologist, and the few sportsmen who have penetrated its fastnesses. Probably because it is so little known, it is unique among all the chars in being the only one called by its correct name. The more familiar chars— *namaycush, fontinalis,* and *malma*—are known to everyone as the lake trout, eastern brook trout, and Dolly Varden trout. Even those specialty chars of the narrow confined ranges, such as *aureolus, oquassa,* and *marstoni,* are quite generally called the Sunapee trout, the blueback trout, and the Quebec red trout. Apparently fishermen love the word "trout" but are allergic to the word "char." Give them a little more time to seek out the Arctic char and it will become some sort of trout in the angler's lexicon. Indeed, it has already acquired such names as Arctic trout, Alpine trout, sea trout, and salmon trout.

Despite this fish's current isolation it cannot be ignored among the *familiar* freshwater fishes of America. The very vastness of its range, which is not only circumpolar but subpolar, precludes its continuing obscurity in an age when jet air travel is bringing the ultimate Arctic reaches within a few hours of the centers of population.

To trace the complete range of *Salvelinus alpinus* you need a map of the Arctic Ocean and all its bordering lands. You begin at Kodiak Island, Alaska, and proceed north and east around the top of Alaska and the entire Arctic drainage of Canada, including the vast complex of islands belonging to the District of Franklin of the Northwest Territories. Continuing east, this fabulous range encompasses Greenland, Iceland, Spitzbergen, Norway, Finland (with an Arctic drainage though it has no Arctic coast), Franz Josef Land, the northward-piercing islands and the entire mainland Arctic coasts of European Russia and Siberia.

Around this periphery of the northern ocean there are thrusts of land above the 82nd parallel of latitude, and the Arctic char is there, in the estuaries and rivers that are ice-locked more than half the year.

Along the polar coasts of North America, the Arctic char fills the gap between the Atlantic and Pacific salmon. The Pacific chinook and its *Oncorhynchus* cousins range all the way up the west coast from California to Alaska, but with limited occurrence north of the Bering Strait. The Atlantic *Salmo salar* has its northerly limit at Ungava Bay, though perhaps a few penetrate the entrances to Hudson Bay. In between, for a 3000-mile straight-line stretch, and for tens of thousands of miles of mainland and island coasts, the sea-run Arctic char takes over as the salmonid which migrates from the sea to the rivers to spawn. It does not die after spawning, but returns to the sea, and may spawn two or three times again in its life span.

Significantly, there is no Antarctic char or native salmonid of any kind in all the Southern Hemisphere.

The enormous beat of the *alpinus* has its odd ecological confinements and extensions. On the Pacific side of North America the Arctic char apparently does not occur along the southeast coast of Alaska below the 60th parallel. On the Atlantic side, however, it is known along the entire Labrador coast; it is landlocked on the island of Newfoundland, and is recorded even in some lakes and streams of the St. Lawrence River drainage, below the 50th degree of latitude. Indeed, this far-ranging char has been reported in New Brunswick, below the 48th parallel, but perhaps this extreme instance concerns one of the many subspecies.

As may be expected with a fish of such wide occurrence and recent history, the Arctic char is the despair of the systematist. Its taxonomic position is murky with the shadows of other fishes which may be local forms or distinct species. These include several little-known chars of the far north, and others which are more familiar and much more southerly. Among the latter are the aurora trout, *Salvelinus alpinus timagamiensis*, ascribed to the lakes of the Timagami region of Ontario, the Dublin Pond trout of New Hampshire, *Salvelinus agassizii*, and others.

Of all the Salmonidae, the Arctic char perhaps best illustrates the glacial theory of fish distribution. If it came down from the north in great numbers ahead of the advancing ice, it conceivably could have become landlocked in such bodies as Dublin Pond, New Hampshire. Here, reproducing its kind for countless generations in a small but deep lake, it could have developed characteristics reflecting unique environmental factors of depth, flow, bottom, water temperature, and food, until its differences from other chars were too marked to be ignored.

The same sort of speculative sights may be trained upon the Dolly Varden of the West (whose northerly range in Alaska overlaps the southern extremity of the Arctic char's Pacific occurrence), the Sunapee trout of New Hampshire, the blueback trout of Maine, and the red trout of Quebec. Some scientific opinion holds that all four are of the *S. alpinus* grouping, their outward differences attributable to the varying environments of so vast a range. The origin and development of the many char species holds possibilities so numerous as almost to defy any backtracking along the genealogical trails of the past. The American Fisheries Society today includes several chars in the single species *S. alpinus*.

The Arctic char varies widely, in color and size, over the far reaches of its native habitat. All fresh sea-run salmonids tend to be lighter colored, more silvery, and with fewer spots, than those which have been in rivers and lakes for some time. The sea-run Arctic char is no exception. Its freshwater coloration has been variously described. The back is sometimes very dark, bluish to black, or it may be greenish gray. Apparently it never shows the vermiculations of *fontinalis*. The side color fades to lighter gray-green or gray-blue. The belly is usually white, but fish in Alaska and elsewhere have been described as having a reddish-colored lower surface and lower fins at spawning time. The spots may be pale ivory, faintly pink, orange, or even bright red in spawning fish. On larger specimens, the spots may be as big as a dime. In its freshwater phase the Arctic char is abundantly spotted on the sides, but spots are absent from the gill covers and cheeks. The dorsal and adipose fins are of the color of the back; the lower fins are usually pale amber but may turn orange, pink, or red in the spawning males. All fins are unspotted. The caudals of small char tend to be deeply forked; as the fish grows larger this fork is less pronounced, but the tail is never fully "square."

Though the landlocked and upriver char average only about a foot long in some parts of the range, this fish is capable of attaining great size. Sea-run specimens of two feet and five pounds are not uncommon. The official rod-and-reel record is a fish of 27 pounds, measuring 40¼ inches, taken at Tree River, Northwest Territories, by

William Murphy on September 2, 1963. There are a few documented records of larger fish, captured in nets.

The Arctic char is a fall spawner. In the ice-free months of July and August the sea-run fish enter the tidal bays prior to the upstream migration. Reaching the spawning grounds in September or October, the female extrudes her eggs on a gravel bottom in shallow water. The lake char may migrate up a tributary to spawn, or select a shoal of the lake at depths of five feet or more. Landlocked Arctic char prepare no nests, merely dropping their eggs over a rocky bottom where the mortality percentage for all eggs spawned must be extremely high.

The surviving eggs hatch in the following spring, with the breakup of ice, and at this time the adult sea-run char migrate to salt water. Landlocked char that have ascended a lake tributary to spawn probably return to the lake shortly after spawning. Young fish of sea-run parents are believed to spend a year in fresh water before going to sea. The salt-to-fresh cycle is not well defined; some fish do not undertake an annual spawning migration but stay in the sea two or three years after returning from the first spawning.

The char is believed to abstain from feeding during its upstream spawning run. At other times and places its principal food is fish and small crustaceans. At various points on a 250-mile stretch of the northern Labrador coast, the stomachs of more than 600 Arctic char were examined, during the summer of 1953, by workers of the Fisheries Research Board of Canada. Capelin, launce, young mailed sculpins, Amphipoda (sand fleas and similar small crustacea), and Euphausiacea (opossum shrimp) constituted the bulk of the stomach contents. At one station, Okkak Bay, capelin composed 99.3 per cent of the entire food intake, as found in the stomachs of 120 chars. Farther north, the major fare was the Amphipoda and the Euphausiacea. At Okkak Bay, the preponderance of capelin as a food item was attributed to shallower coastal waters which afforded spawning grounds for the capelin.[1]

This study was one of several. Another, concerning the age attained by the Arctic char, found that some fish were fourteen or fifteen years old at the time of capture. Age was determined by counting the rings or bands on the otoliths (calcareous concretions in the

[1] C. W. Andrews and E. Lear: *The Biology of the Arctic Char in Northern Labrador* (Fisheries Research Board of Canada Biological Station, St. John's, Newfoundland).

head of the fish). Opaque bands in the otolith represent summer growth; hyaline or translucent bands mark the slower growth of winter. Otoliths revealed the age of five to seven years in some of the smaller char; these fish with an exceptionally slow growth rate were believed to have spent their entire lives in fresh water.

In most waters the Arctic char must be wary of predators which cannot molest more southerly species. The polar bear, various seals, the beluga whale, and the Greenland shark are believed to take a heavy toll of S. alpinus. On the other hand, it may be unique among chars in having man as a minor enemy, if only because man is not numerous anywhere in the range and totally absent from much of it.

Here and there, however, Eskimo Arctic char fisheries have assumed some commercial importance in recent years. The Canadian scientists investigating the Arctic char in northern Labrador have reported details of one enterprise.

From Hopedale to Hebron (a 200-mile stretch of the Labrador coast), 6282 barrels (220 pounds each) of pickled Arctic char were marketed in the years 1944 to 1954 inclusive. The average of 571 barrels a year, at $30 a barrel, represented an annual gross of $17,130. This catch averaged ten to twenty barrels a season, per fisherman, or a per-capita gross income of $300 to $600. By salmon-cannery standards this is a niggling business, yet it is important in the economy of the Labrador native.

The char in this fishery are taken in gill nets set in estuaries, coves, around headlands, and for some distance at sea. The Eskimo fishermen report that the char begin entering the sea when the river ice breaks up in the spring. Fishing reaches its peak during July, when the total downstream run of char is in salt water. A lull then ensues, between the outward migration and the return upriver in September. The largest char so captured were of ten to fourteen pounds.

Variation in the flesh color from white to deep red is a distinct characteristic of the Arctic char of northern Labrador. The deep-red char bring the highest prices, the pink is second in value, the white is the least desired. Since 1949 only the red- and pink-fleshed char have been sent to market, the white being dried for home consumption.

Another thriving Arctic char fishery, conducted by Eskimos, is situated at Fort Chimo, Quebec, on the southern end of Ungava Bay (latitude 58° N.), at about the point where the Atlantic salmon reaches its northerly limit on the American continent. Relatively unimportant a decade ago, this fishery has now attained some commercial stature under the aegis of the Fort Chimo Cooperative Association. In the summer of 1962, two Eskimos representing the cooperative flew to Ottawa to publicize their product. Previously frozen and shipped by sea, it was now available as fresh char, via regular air flights.

The total commercial catch of Arctic char in Labrador amounted to about 200,000 pounds in 1959, 160,000 pounds in 1960, and 300,000 pounds in 1961. Probably these totals have since been exceeded.

That the Arctic char is a distinguished fighter is attested by the few anglers who have felt its power on a light rod. The most effective artificial lures are the fish-simulators—large bright-colored streamer flies, bucktails rigged behind spinners, and various wobbling spoons.

The Arctic char waters of the North offer an exciting prospect to anglers able and willing to meet the expense and to chance the hazards of this wilderness fishing. One may hope that the airplane will not eventually destroy the virgin appeal of such sport.

SUNAPEE TROUT
Salvelinus aureolus Bean

On a still morning of heavy frost, when little eddies of vapor are over the lake surface and the last of the leaves are falling from the New Hampshire hardwoods along shore, you might see the black autumnal water disturbed by the swirl of a fish.

The water could be a shoal of Sunapee Lake. The swirl could have been caused by a spawning Sunapee trout, *Salvelinus aureolus*, and you could be witnessing one of the last chapters of a long and tragic story.

To say that the Sunapee trout may be nearing extinction is hardly an exaggeration. In 1958 Arthur E. Newell wrote, "The population of this species has diminished to the point where it is nearly extinct in Sunapee Lake," and again, "The yield of Sunapee trout fishing is at the present time practically nil."[2]

[2] *The Life History and Ecology of the Sunapee Trout* (New Hampshire Fish and Game Department, Management and Research Division).

In November 1962 Bernard W. Corson, Chief of Fisheries, New Hampshire Fish and Game Department, said in a letter to this writer, "It is difficult for us to say that there are no golden trout in Sunapee Lake; however, we do know that they are headed for extinction there."

The Sunapee trout, also called golden trout and white trout, is a char with an ecology very similar to that of another char called "trout," the lake trout. The Sunapee's status as a distinct species seems still unproved. Some ichthyologists have stoutly proclaimed its specific identity. Others contend that the Sunapee trout belongs to the complex Arctic char group; still others hold that it may once have been a species unto itself but has become so hybridized with its char cousins, the lake trout and the brook trout, that its original identity has been lost. The American Fisheries Society does not list the Sunapee trout as a separate species.

Whatever this fish may be, it has existed as a distinct native char in Sunapee Lake, New Hampshire, after which it was named, and in a few other small but deep lakes in New Hampshire, Maine, and Vermont. It is known to have occurred in Big Dan Hole Pond, at Ossipee, New Hampshire. Now and then it is reported taken by anglers from Conner Pond, at Ossipee. It was once established in the Third Connecticut Lake, one of the source waters of the Connecticut River at the extreme northerly point of New Hampshire, but it disappeared from this body after lake trout were introduced.

Historically, the lake trout has been a serious predator upon the Sunapee. In waters inhabited by both, any substantial increase in the former has meant the disappearance of the latter.

A pure population of *Salvelinus aureolus* is said to exist in Floods Pond, near Otis, Maine, a 654-acre lake with a maximum depth of 133 feet. The Maine Department of Inland Fisheries and Game reports "good catches of Sunapee trout by fishermen who know the lake and are willing to fish deep." Among twenty-four captured specimens were fish five and six years old, measuring 16½ to 19½ inches.[3]

In northern Vermont, the Averill Lakes once held the Sunapee. A letter from George W. Davis, Commissioner of the Vermont Fish and Game Department, states, "It is my understanding that the last Sunapee trout was taken from Little Averill Lake about 1933 or '34."

[3] W. Harry Everhart, *Fishes of Maine* (1961).

Here, too, the lake trout is believed to be largely responsible for the disappearance of the Sunapee.

There is today a unique body of water in New Hampshire, for it has been planted and managed expressly to save the Sunapee trout from extinction. For this sanctuary, which is Tewksbury Pond at Grafton, anglers and naturalists may thank the New Hampshire Fish and Game Department.

The Tewksbury Pond project grew out of the threat of extinction of the Sunapee or golden trout in Sunapee Lake. Several years ago, the existing population of the *aureolus* in Sunapee Lake was known to be menaced when a surprisingly large number of lake trout were seen spawning on a reef which hitherto had been the breeding ground of the Sunapee trout. Knowing that this fish could not long survive in the presence of a heavy population of lake trout, the New Hampshire conservationists decided to reclaim nearby Tewksbury Pond and then to stock it with Sunapee trout and with smelt as a forage fish.[4]

Tewksbury Pond is forty-six acres in extent, with a maximum depth of 48 feet. Approximately 95 per cent of the bottom consists of a heavy organic muck. In a survey conducted during 1961, the water temperature in mid-July, at depths of 40 to 48 feet, was found to be 47° F.

In the spring of 1955, after reclaiming Tewksbury Pond the previous year, New Hampshire stocked 6300 Sunapee trout fingerlings and 1500 yearlings. At about the same time, 20,000 adult smelt and 14,000,000 smelt eggs were planted as forage. Further plantings of Sunapee fingerlings and yearlings, and of smelt eggs, followed. Trout fingerlings planted in recent years were grown from eggs extruded from captured mature fish and incubated at the state hatchery.

The survey of 1961 revealed an apparently thriving population of Sunapee trout in Tewksbury Pond. Gill nets set at depths of 30 to 48 feet captured twenty-six trout, eighteen of which were kept for examination. Of these fish, eight were two-year olds, six were three-year fish, two were of four years, and one each were of five and six years. The oldest trout was a three-pound specimen measuring 21¾

[4] This report of the Tewksbury Pond work is drawn from *Observations on the Golden Trout,* Salvelinus aureolus, *in Tewksbury Pond, Grafton, New Hampshire,* by Peter E. Brezosky, Supervisor of Fisheries Coordination, New Hampshire Fish and Game Department.

inches. Stomach-content analyses proved that the smelt were being utilized. Smelt are the chief fare of the mature Sunapee trout; indeed the presence or absence of smelt is the only known factor influencing the Sunapee's growth rate. Crayfish are abundant in Tewksbury Pond, and probably contributed to the trout's diet.

For some time conclusive evidence of natural reproduction of Sunapee trout in Tewksbury Pond was lacking. It was believed that the absence of a suitable spawning shoal in the almost 100 per cent muck bottom of the pond inhibited natural breeding. As a result of the 1961 survey, an artificial spawning reef of rocks and coarse gravel was laid down in five to ten feet of water. A late report (November 1963) states that this reef is clean of silt but that no positive evidence yet exists that the reef is used by the Sunapee trout for spawning. However, the netting of several trout in the two- to three-year-old class has proved for the first time that they are reproducing naturally, either on the man-made reef or another spawning ground, for the last planting of Sunapee trout in Tewksbury Pond was made in 1959.

Tewksbury Pond is not posted against fishing, but the angling pressure has been light. Access to the pond is possible only via boat, at a single difficult launching area. The creel limit has been held at two trout per day. Further, the Sunapee trout is not generally receptive to artificial lures; it is usually taken by trolling or still-fishing in deep water with smelt or other bait.

The Sunapee trout's over-all coloration, as seen in various waters, has been subject to somewhat conflicting descriptions. Some observers have noted dorsal-surface vermiculations; others have denied the existence of these markings, stating that the back and dorsal fin are of solid color, usually a dark olive-green or sea-green. There seems general agreement on the orange lower flanks, whence the name "golden trout," though carmine sides have been noted in spawning males. Herbert E. Warfel wrote in 1939, "The brilliant red bellies of breeding males render this species among the most beautiful of the native fishes. . . . In non-breeding adults the red is replaced by a golden yellow."[5] On the other hand, the Sunapee's belly has been described as "conspicuously white," and the local name of "white trout" at

[5] *Biological Survey of the Connecticut Watershed* (Survey Report No. 4, New Hampshire Fish and Game Department).

Sunapee Lake is attributed to this feature. The Sunapee's spots may be whitish, pale yellow, orange, or occasionally pinkish. The tail is *deeply* forked in the opinion of some observers, *moderately* forked according to others. Most agree that the lower fins are orange or reddish with white margins; some have noted a black band posterior to the white margin on the anal, while others have not. Small specimens of seven inches or less may show parr marks along the sides.

In a fish with so confined a range one would expect concurrence, rather than controversy, upon the details of its color. The conclusion is inescapable that some of the fish described as Sunapee trout were in reality hybrids. It is known that the Sunapee has bred with the eastern brook trout and with the lake trout; indeed, successful hybridizing has been accomplished in hatcheries.

The Sunapee's size, too, has been subject to dispute. New Hampshire specimens of 30 inches, weighing over eight pounds, have been recorded. There is an official record of a Sunapee trout of 11 pounds 8 ounces, 33 inches long, taken from Sunapee Lake by Ernest Theoharis on August 1, 1954. Some contend, however, that any so-called Sunapee trout weighing over five pounds will be found to have characteristics of the lake trout, proving it a hybrid and not a true Sunapee.

The probability of widespread hybridization seems to have tarnished the bright legend of a fish whose rarity made it a treasure of our eastern waters.

Considering the Sunapee's marked tendency to fertilize the eggs of the lake trout, and vice versa, the latter's historic predation upon the former may seem anomalous, but is doubtless attributable to the ecological kinship of the two fish. Like the lake trout, the Sunapee must have deep water, where the temperature is 50° F. or lower, and both species spend their summers in these chilly grottoes. From mid-October to mid-November both ascend to shoal water for their spawning. A small lake may have only one suitable spawning bottom—a reef of rocks, rubble, and coarse gravel, affording protective crevices for the eggs. Since both the Sunapee and the lake trout favor this type of breeding ground, they will spawn at the same site and at approximately the same time. The spawning-habit resemblance goes even further. The female Sunapee, like the lake trout, makes no nest, merely casting her eggs over the bottom and then returning to deep water, with no attempt at postpartum care.

The pre-spawning courtship period doubtless effects a kind of truce in the lake trout's predation, but throughout most of the year, cruising their common deeps, the marauding of the larger lake trout upon the smaller Sunapee is presumably habitual. *Namaycush* certainly eats the eggs of *aureolus*, but probably this compliment is returned.

The male Sunapee matures sometimes at the age of two years, but usually at three or four. The female probably matures earlier. Data on 237 female Sunapees stripped during the period 1951–55 showed an average of 938 eggs per fish. Fisheries scientist John Duncan Quackenbos wrote many years ago that the Sunapee trout "is one of the most prolific of our salmonoids, the female averaging 1200 eggs to the pound, and casting spawn when only two ounces in weight." As the Sunapee is capable of spawning several times in its life span, this fish should maintain itself naturally in suitable waters.

Despite its inability to exist with the lake trout, the *aureolus* seems to get along well with many other species. In Sunapee Lake, prior to the sudden explosion of the lake-trout population, the Sunapee lived with brook trout, rainbow trout, landlocked salmon, smallmouth black bass, and once, for a brief space, with a few chinook salmon introduced from the Pacific coast.

The Tewksbury Pond experiment in New Hampshire, and the existing Sunapee trout population in Floods Pond, Maine, seem today the only bases for hope that this rare coinage among the chars may be saved for future generations of anglers and naturalists.

BLUEBACK TROUT
Salvelinus oquassa (Girard)

The small and beautiful char called the blueback trout is Maine's own fish, native only to a few deep lakes and ponds in the remote backwoods of the Pine Tree State.

Salvelinus oquassa was once abundant in the Rangeley Lakes of Maine, and was named for Oquossoc Lake in the Rangeley system. These waters were the only known habitat of the blueback trout when this fish was first described by Charles Girard in 1853. Heavy and heedless fishing in the late 1890's, coupled with predation by increasing numbers of landlocked salmon, brought about the decline of the Rangeley bluebacks almost to the point of extinction. Protective legislation, enacted in 1899, may have delayed but did not prevent the blueback's final disappearance from the Rangeleys, for in 1939 a biological survey recorded no specimen of S. *oquassa* in these waters.

Subsequent studies of other Maine areas have revealed, however, that the blueback exists in several deep, cold ponds and small lakes. Four of these are in Aroostook County, two in Piscataquis, and at least one in Somerset. The Maine Department of Inland Fisheries and Game has encouragingly stated that "other populations will undoubtedly be discovered as more remote water areas are studied." The habitat of the blueback is a true wilderness, studded with hundreds of lakes and ponds, many of which are accessible only by canoe or a small airplane with pontoons.

Take from your wallet an ordinary credit card or the like, measuring 2½ by 3½ inches, and place it upon the northerly part of a full-page, atlas-size map of the State of Maine. Your card will cover the entire known range of the blueback trout—an area about 100 miles east to west and 60 miles north to south.

In this closely circumscribed area the blueback is another specialty char, like the Sunapee and the Quebec red trout, and its taxonomic position seems equally uncertain. Some students believe it to be a distinct species, though the American Fisheries Society does not accord it that dignity. Others hold that the blueback is another landlocked form of the Arctic char.

The blueback seems to be the smallest of all chars. The Rangeley Lakes adults were reported as six to nine inches long. Charles A. Waters, in a thesis entitled *A Study of the Life History and Taxonomic Position of the Blueback Trout*,[6] states that in 1874 E. M. Stilwell and Henry O. Stanley, commissioners of fisheries for the State of Maine, attributed the large size of Rangeley Lakes brook trout to the availability of the blueback as a forage fish. In this sense the Rangeley bluebacks were likened to the smelt of Sebago Lake. Mr. Waters suggests that the small size of the blueback, in the few small lakes of the present known range, may be due to overabundance and underfishing. In these

[6] University of Maine, 1960.

waters, brook trout are co-residents, yet they are not suspected of serious predation upon the blueback. Captured specimens of the blueback have rarely measured as much as 14 inches, and never more than that. The blueback is, furthermore, a slim fish: inch for inch it weighs considerably less than the *fontinalis*. A fourteen-inch blueback would probably tip a small and accurate balance at less than one pound. So far, there is no official record of the largest blueback to be taken on sporting tackle.

But like many another miniature, the blueback trout is a gemlike thing. Its back is a steely, iridescent blue, inclining to brownish in some specimens, without spots or the vermicular markings of the brook trout. This color fades to lighter blue and silvery along the sides, and to a pale yellowish-pink or salmon color on the belly. The spots are pale cream or whitish, quite numerous but almost invisible in some fish. The top of the head, snout, and upper jaw may be a deep, metallic blue-black, lightening over the gill covers. The dorsal fin carries the color of the back and is similarly without spots. The lower fins are orange to pink; in the males these become deep red, as does the belly, just prior to spawning. The pale spots become orange in spawning males. Female fish show little if any color change at spawning time. The tail, somewhat forked, is dusky bluish in both sexes.

By nature the blueback seems to be a shy fish, rarely seen during most of the year. Its summer residence, like that of the Sunapee and the lake trout, is deep down in fifty or so feet of water, where the temperature is 50° F or lower. Out of these depths it may be lured by anglers using a worm-baited hook and a sinker.

Studies by Mr. Waters and his co-workers indicate that the majority of blueback trout attain sexual maturity in their fourth year. Little is known of their spawning habits, however. At the time of their abundance in the Rangeley Lakes, they migrated up the tributary streams, about mid-October, seeking shallow-water spawning beds not far from the lakes. As the blueback spawners moved into the tributaries they were killed in vast numbers by spearing and netting. This wanton slaughter was described, according to Maine fisheries reports, in terms of "bushels and cartloads."

Mr. Waters states in his thesis, however, that tributaries suitable for the reproduction of salmonids are not available in the present blueback habitats. He concludes that spawning is confined to the lakes.

The food of the blueback is mainly plankton and small crustacea, to a lesser extent insects and fish, as shown by examination of stomach contents. Certainly the chief predator upon the little Maine char is the landlocked salmon. Mr. Waters writes, "An ominous threat to the welfare of four blueback populations was recorded during this study, when landlocked salmon were observed at the foot of Red River Falls, six miles below Pushineer Pond. It may be more than coincidence, then, that natural barriers obstruct the outlet streams of all blueback lakes, preventing the immigration of predatory salmonids which occur elsewhere in the same drainages."

Again in the spring, as the ice disappears, the blueback trout seeks the shallower waters of its lake or pond. At this time it is taken by anglers with dry or wet flies. So far, the blueback has little reputation as a game fish. In all the blueback lakes and ponds the co-resident brook trout grow to greater sizes, feed during the summer in shallower water that is more easily fished, and take flies and bait more readily. Waters's data showed that 86 per cent of all captured adult bluebacks were taken at depths of 30 to 50 feet, while 93 per cent of the brook trout were caught in less than 30 feet of water. Thus, in the summer at least, the two species are not in competition for space.

Like the Sunapee trout, the blueback is a fish to wonder about. Its distinctive color and markings, small size, possible kinship with the Sunapee and other rare chars, and its confinement to a few small lakes in Maine, pose obvious but difficult questions.

Though the blueback's range is extremely circumscribed, its remoteness and inaccessibility should long preserve this fish. Fortunately conservationists are alert to prevent another such debacle as that at the Rangeley Lakes in the last century.

QUEBEC RED TROUT
Salvelinus marstoni (Garman)

The Quebec red trout is closely related to the Sunapee and blueback, and its taxonomic position is similarly clouded. Some authors hold it to be a separate species and refer to it by the scientific name *Salvelinus marstoni*. Others maintain that it is a subspecies of the Arctic char, *S. alpinus*. The American Fisheries Society concurs in the latter view, giving the Quebec red no listing as a separate species. Other popular names are Marston's trout and red trout.

It is of course a char, not a trout. The Quebec fisheries scientist Vadim D. Vladykov reports that for many years it was considered a very rare fish, limited to a few lakes of the river systems north of the St. Lawrence. Later, experimental fishing with nets showed it to be quite widespread in Laurentides Park and the Gaspé Peninsula.[7] This is a narrow range, geographically, yet the word "rare" can hardly apply to the Quebec red as it does to the Sunapee and blueback. There are perhaps two thousand lakes and ponds in the 3700 square miles of Laurentides Park alone, and all of them were once believed to hold the Quebec red trout. That was doubtless a sweeping assumption, but probably at least one hundred deepwater lakes in the Laurentides and the Gaspé have populations of S. marstoni.

Similar exaggerations have been made on the weights attained by this fish. The occasionally reported specimens of eight and ten pounds were almost certainly Arctic chars incorrectly identified. The Quebec red is a smallish fish, infrequently exceeding a pound and averaging less, though individuals of slightly over two pounds have been taken by anglers.

The Quebec red is a slim fish and has a deeply forked tail. Its chief feature, however, is the rose to red color suffusing the flanks and underparts of both sexes. This color deepens at spawning time, in both males and females, to a brilliant deep red. The spots are pale; the pectoral, ventral, and anal fins are carmine with a narrow white anterior edge.

The Quebec red trout is a lover of cold water, and like its char cousins the Sunapee, blueback, and lake trout, is found only in lakes with considerable depth. Virtually all of the lakes containing the Quebec red have populations of the eastern brook trout too, but the two live at different levels most of the year. The Quebec red trout inhabits the cold depths except in the spring and fall, when it ascends to the shallows for brief periods.

It is said to thrive best in lakes containing such fish as suckers and chubs, suggesting that the young of these species are a major item of the red trout's food.

[7] *Les Formes Locales de la Truite Rouge du Québec* (Département des Pécheries, Province de Québec, 1957).

S. *marstoni* spawns later than the brook trout in the same waters, its season being late October to December. Not a great deal is known of its spawning habits, except that it is believed to spawn in the shoals of the lake itself, rather than in the tributary streams. Apparently its breeding practices are similar to those of the lake trout (which exists with it in some waters), the Quebec-red female making no attempt to dig a nest and merely dropping her eggs into the crevices of rocks. The eggs number about 400 for a 9½-inch female, as many as 1000 for a 13-incher.

Fly fishing for S. *marstoni* is best in the spring, when the fish come into the lake shoals immediately after the breakup of ice. This char is said to have a special fondness for a touch of yellow in the fly. In the fall, with the red trout again ascending to the shallows, fly-fishing could be productive, but in most or all of the range the legal season is then closed. Through the summer this fish may be taken by trolling various lures, or still-fishing with bait, in deep water.

Chapter 5

ATLANTIC SALMON

Salmo salar Linnaeus

Impelled by a transcendent need to reproduce their kind, the Atlantic salmon come in from the sea in the spring. They are river-bound now, heading for the smell of fresh water, the keen land smells, the component earth, rocks, roots, gravel, and grass that distinguish a river from the sea. This was the smell of their birth and early life, and they sense it now, like a beacon, even while still they are miles from shore. As they cruise the shoreline it becomes intermittently strong and fading and strong again, its accents occurring where the brackish estuaries meet the sea.

For days and weeks as the salmon have coursed the coast, members of the school have peeled off at one tidal bay after another, homing where each river discharged from the land. Then, on an evening different from all others, those remaining in the school pause, knowing the sea journey is done. The differences here are many and certain; in other features than its smell this place is in the salmons' sense of the past. This is the slope of the bottom; these are the rocks, the shell beds, the pilings, the sunken wreckage, the weeds. But above all, coming out of the land is an emanation, the smell of the river of their birth and their first few years of life as parrs.

The school is still large—a hundred or more salmon left of twice that many before they neared the offshore nets. Most of them have been three years at sea and are of about the same size. Anglers up the river, who will reduce the school in the succeeding weeks, will call them 18- to 25-pounders. In the lexicon of men, they are "bright" salmon, the "fresh-run," and they are "maiden" fish too. They are blue- or green-bronze above, silvery below, with a few dark spots on the head and gill covers, and sparse X-shaped marks along the back and upper sides. Some are net-marked, others show the scars of seal bites, but all are in the ultimate prime of a salmon's condition, heavy with muscle and fat, fortified against the long fasting of the upstream journey. They will be followed, in a few weeks, by the much smaller grilse who have had only a year at sea; the grilse will be followed by later runs of salmon as large or larger than these first migrants to the river.

Ashore, it could be called a balmy evening in late May, with an after-rain freshness upon the blossoms and the leaves. Out here, even at the flood tide, the cool oxygen-charged fresh water is perceptible, foaming down from the land. The school points to it, swimming easily on the flood, herding to the narrowing of the sea at the river mouth. The school will wait out the tide, enter the river when the tide begins to fall.

It will be a long upriver trek—seventy-five miles as a few anglers know it, from the estuary under the railroad bridge to the spawning shallows in a forest-gloomed rivulet far upstream. But if the summer is kind with rainfall the journey should be easy, taken stage by stage, without haste, resting in the long pools for days at a time, and pushing on a mile, two miles, at night. By late September they should be up there. Let the late-coming grilse pass them, as they will, in a frantic rush to even higher spawning beds. This early-run school could take its time.

There would be moments, though, to draw on the ultimate resources of courage and strength. Moments of knifing upstream against the violence of rapids, the long downgrade pitches of the river without a single slack-water resting place in a quarter mile, and perhaps with only one navigable channel, boulder-studded, through which the entire school must pass. Here some will drop out, slammed against rocks by the fury of the water. Stunned and helpless, they will be propelled back downstream, the great bodies turning over and over. In the slack at the tail of the rapids one will be deftly scooped by a waiting bear who knows the feeding potentials of this place. In the still pool below, there will be a swift dark shadow and a surface eruption as an otter seizes another of the great fish.

And the moments of the falls, where the river narrows to a tight and furious channel and plunges vertically ten feet down. The salmon can make it if the pool below is long and deep, affording a run before the takeoff, and depth for purchase against the spasmodic clutch of all the strength of tail and body muscles for the upward thrust, the clearance into air, and the fight, up and up, as if the pectoral and ventral fins were wings fighting gravity and the thin medium of air, and struggling still, at the top, against the charge of water at the brink. But here, as in the rapids, some among the school will fall back stunned or hurt. Others, falling but unharmed, will surrender the ascent of the river until rain raises its level and gives passage over the falls.

Changes are evident in the diminishing school, as many weeks pass. The last of the sea lice have died in the fresh water and dropped away. But the bright silver of the sea has become flushed with a dull red; large black spots are showing; the males are becoming mottled and blotchy, and a slimy coat now covers the scales. The stomachs of all in the school are shrunken after the long fast, but their body cavities are filling with the stuff of reproduction: the milt of the cock fish and the eggs of the females.

By mid-September the thinned-out company has reached its journey's end, the upper pools and shallows of the narrowed river. This is the natal place: in these gravel bottoms most if not all of these survivors were born, six or seven years ago. They are tired now, weak and bruised by the long upriver haul; but they have arrived in plenty of time and they can rest, above or below the chosen spawning grounds. Some of the male fish now begin a kind of courtship, seeking out their mates in a preliminary pairing. Sexually edged, and armed now with the elongated and hooked lower jaw, the cock fish begin to fight with one another.

The deterioration of both males and females has progressed hideously by mid-October. They are very dark now, the females almost black, the males rusty. Many have torn fins; spreading areas of fungus over a skin soft and pulpy appear to embed the scales. The males' kypes—the hooked lower jaws—are so accentuated that their mouths cannot close, and their teeth have grown large and canine. Such wastage and distortion seemingly cannot proceed further without being fatal to all the fish of the school. But it is time, now, for the climax and the end of the long travail.

As if to mock the far-gone decay of the breeding adults, the river here is active with young salmon, red-spotted troutlike parr only inches long, one to three years old, quick and darting and brilliant with health. Some of the males among these miniature salmon are sexually mature, perhaps anticipating their role in the approaching drama.

The adult females come now to the digging of a series of nests, using their tails and bodies to scoop out hollows in the bottom gravel. The chosen spots are the heads of riffles or the tails of pools, where the water is accelerating. Some females work out their hollows in only a foot of water, making the first hollow at the downstream end of the series that will compose the complete redd. The male of one pair, having fought off all others, hovers near his mate, quivering occasionally with his mounting excitement. The cutting of a single nest may take hours or even days, the female leaving her work at intervals to ease back into the lower pool and rest. When at last she is ready she hovers over the hollow or may sink into it. The male consort, vibrant with his purpose, comes alongside; now the eggs and the milt are almost simultaneously extruded.

This act may be repeated five, six, or more times before the female's spawn is completely shed. It entails a series of nests, the gravel from the second hollow covering the eggs in the first, each hollow a couple of feet upstream from the previous digging. Into these nests a twenty-pound female will drop 14,000 to 16,000 large adhesive eggs, and bury them in six to twelve inches of gravel.

Now and then, intruding himself upon the adult salmon's climacteric, a tiny quick parr, unseen by the big fish, will flash under their bodies and discharge his sperm as the female looses her eggs. This little emission is as potent as the large male's; if the big fish misses or is already spent, the parr's contribution will fertilize the eggs. The presence of the large male is needed, however, for the parr's company alone will not excite the female to the point of extrusion.

The spawning is usually finished by mid-November. Some of the spent fish die—a few on the spawning grounds, more on the downstream drift to the sea. Some will begin the return trip at once, feeding now, going slowly, often tail first in the swifter water, gradually strengthening, with luck eluding their many predators all the way to the ocean. Others will winter in the upper river and return as "black" salmon, or "slinks," in the early spring. Among the few fish surviving to reach the sea and returning to spawn again, the ratio will be about nine females to one male.

The river in which we have looked briefly at the cycle of *Salmo salar* or the Atlantic salmon—from the ocean to the spawning ground and back to the sea—could be one in Newfoundland, New Brunswick, Nova Scotia, Quebec, or Maine. With the time of entry changed from late May to July, the river could be in Labrador, as far up as the top of the Ungava Peninsula, at latitude 61° N., the northerly limit of the Atlantic salmon's range in North America. Current scientific opinion holds that the range does not include Hudson Bay and its tributary rivers. Abroad, the Atlantic salmon enters the rivers of Greenland, Iceland, the British Isles, Norway, France, Belgium, Holland, Germany, the northwestern extremity of Spain, and the Baltic Sea drainages of Sweden and the Soviet Union. It is seldom if ever reported in an Arctic river and never in those of the Mediterranean. Like the other salmonids, the Atlantic salmon is native only to the Northern Hemi-

Atlantic Salmon
Salmo salar

sphere. It is believed to be another relic of the vast glacial reshaping of the land.

Eastern Canada has today more than two hundred salmon rivers. Maine once had over twenty, now has perhaps only eight.

Formerly the range on this side of the Atlantic extended as far south as Delaware Bay and its river. The Hudson was a salmon river of considerable repute when the Dutch founded New Amsterdam, and long afterward. As late as 1895, Article VI, Section 137 of the Fish and Game Laws of New York State prohibited the taking of Hudson River salmon in nets while fishing for other species. The Housatonic and Connecticut rivers had salmon populations into the 1800's. Thoreau, in *A Week on the Concord and Merrimack Rivers* (1839), recalled that salmon "were formerly abundant here." In seventeenth-century England salmon were a stable food. Even the Thames had its spawning runs. Izaak Walton observed, three hundred years ago, "Though some of our northern counties have as fat and as large salmon as the River Thames, yet none are of as excellent a taste."

Salmo salar's former abundance throughout its range made it a familiar fish to everyone. Its annals go back to remote antiquity. Perhaps the oldest known salmon artifact was unearthed by archeologists in the Pyrenees of southern France. It is a piece of reindeer bone bearing the likeness of a salmon, estimated to have been carved about 12,000 B.C. The word *salmo* has been attributed by some to Caesar's armies in Gaul who saw hordes of the fish leaping in rivers and coined its name from the Latin verb *salire* ("to leap"). This origin is uncertain however. In the first century A.D., Pliny wrote, "In Aquitania the river salmon surpasseth all the fishes of the sea."

Over the last thousand years, hardly a generation has been without its chroniclers of the salmon. Because of its abundance, large size, value as a food resource, and spectacular fighting qualities, *Salmo salar* invites inquiry, both scientific and sporting. Students of the salmon have learned a great deal about its life in fresh water. Of its day-by-day history at sea, however, very little is known beyond its basic feeding habits and the prodigious distances of some of its salt-water journeys.

The Atlantic salmon's closest relatives are not the various Pacific salmons, but the trouts—the *Salmo* tribe which includes the brown,

rainbow, and cutthroat. Next in the order of kinship are the chars—
the genus *Salvelinus*, the brook trout, and others. Much farther removed are the Pacific salmons, with the generic name *Oncorhynchus*.

The river is the birthplace, cradle, and nursery of the salmon, and
the fish's sole habitat for perhaps half its life. Yet virtually all the
salmon's growth is made at sea. A four-year-old parr, becoming a
smolt and descending to the ocean for the first time, may be only
seven inches long. Three years later, returning to the river for its first
spawning, the same fish weighs eighteen to twenty-five pounds.

No other fish has so many special and picturesque names to designate it in the various stages of its life and health. From birth to death
the salmon swims through more than a dozen stages of its elaborate
nomenclature. Whether the egg or the adult fish came first is still as
obscure as the counterpart question concerning the chicken. Starting
with the *egg*, as probably one must, there is next the *alevin*, after the
egg is hatched but is still under inches of gravel, with the salmon-to-be
attached to the yolk sac underneath, feeding on the sac's nutriment
for a month or more, until it is absorbed. Now it emerges from the
bottom to swim in the open water as a *fry*, little more than an inch
long. The fry stay together in great schools, unlike the trouts, which
are inclined to make their individual ways soon after emergence.

As the little fish attains a length of three or four inches it becomes
a *parr*, looking like a trout with its dark back and black-spotted silvery
sides. Along its lateral line are a few brilliant red spots, alternating
with ten or eleven regularly spaced dark smudges called parr marks.
In this bright raiment the fish lives in the river for two, three, or four
years. Many of the males, though none of the females, here become
sexually mature. In northerly rivers—those above Labrador's Hamilton
Inlet and those forming the Ungava Bay drainage in Quebec—a five-
year parrhood is not unusual.[1] Yet after all this time, feeding on
aquatic insects and other minute life of the river, the fish is still only
five to eight inches long.

At a seemingly variable stage of its growth, or perhaps of its
precociousness, the parr has an urge for the sea change. Now its parr

[1] In rivers of northern Scandinavia, parr are said to have a seven- or eight-year
residence.

coloration becomes obscured by a kind of silvery coating,[2] and the little fish is developing chloride-secreting cells in its gills to enable it to accept the change from fresh to salt water. It is a *smolt* now, ready for the sea, and in its new coat less visible to saltwater predators. Shoals of smolt, numbering thousands, descend to the lower river and may linger in the brackish estuary for hours or days, becoming accustomed to the change from sweet water to salt. Then, on a single tide, they will take the sea, losing themselves in the vast dimensions of the ocean for one to five years. This historic farewell to the mother river may occur from April to mid-September, though the spring is the peak season. Spates and freshets were once believed essential to the smolts' entrance to the sea; now it is thought that a rise in temperature and a lowering of light intensity are equal factors.

Once in the ocean, the real growth of the salmon begins. Among the fish that are now smolts, weighing a few ounces after three years of river life, some will return the following year as *grilse*, mostly males, and weighing 2½ to 5 pounds each, after one winter at sea. These are mostly the progeny of grilse, for one of the facts of salmon life is that grilse usually beget grilse. An occasional grilse, however, may be the offspring of a precocious cock parr and an adult hen salmon. A grilse is defined not by its size but on the strict basis of a one-winter sea life before returning to its river to spawn. Further to complicate the terminology, the grilse has such regional names as "jumper" and "racer." On its return to the river it is a fine, strong, silvery fish, handsome as any large fresh-run salmon, its tail more deeply forked than those of its elders. It is inclined to enter the rivers later than the first run of large salmon, and it races upstream, passing the larger first-run fish en route and pointing for spawning beds in the extreme headwaters.

Salmon returning to the river two years after their sea baptism are *small summer* fish, of 9½ to 12 pounds. Those with three winters in the ocean are *large summer* fish, 18 to 25 pounds. *Very large* salmon are those which have spent four to six years cruising the ocean before their *first* spawning migration. In this class the 35- to 45-pounders are not

[2] J. W. Jones, in *The Salmon* (Harper & Row, New York, 1959), attributes this appearance to the deposition of the substance guanine on the scales.

uncommon in some rivers, but the 50- and 60-pounders are very rare in fresh water. Usually these outsize specimens are virgin females, coming upriver for their first spawning. Indeed, all of these salmon, from the grilse to the very large, have still another term, *maiden fish*, applying to both sexes. They are all first-time spawners, regardless of the length of sea life.

The largest Atlantic salmon recorded as killed on a rod was a 79-pound 2-ounce fish taken from the Tana River, Norway, in 1928, by Henrik Henriksen. It was doubtless a maiden fish, though the available data do not say. With the salmon, as indeed with some other fishes, "records" seem meaningless, for many huge fish have been caught in remote areas by anglers who did not trouble to record weights and measurements or even to photograph the catch. Information on the extreme maximum growth of salmon is better supplied by the commercial net fishermen who traditionally take the largest fish. Sixty-pound salmon are not uncommon in the ocean drift nets on this side of the Atlantic. In Scotland's River Devon a 103-pounder was duly recorded some years ago.

Perhaps 90 per cent of all Atlantic salmon entering a river to spawn are maiden fish. Exactitude in these things is impossible, but of a hundred fresh-run salmon in a resting pool not far from the sea, perhaps ninety are seeing the river for the first time since going to sea as smolts, and ten have been in this pool before as fresh-run fish. These ten are *previous spawners* (still another classification of *Salmo salar*), and probably nine of them are females. The previous spawners are less silvery than the maiden fish; a reddish-golden cast is upon them even as they come in from the sea, and they have more spots along the back, upper sides, and gill covers. They are not necessarily the largest fish in the pool; in fact they are usually smaller than a maiden salmon of three years' sea life.

The salmon attains its growth by *continuous* life in the sea. A previous spawner is likely to have had two years in salt water, from the time of its descent as a smolt to its *first* spawning run, and *only one* year at sea—rarely two, but never more than two—between its first and second spawnings. In this year it grows but little; indeed, it may have failed to regain all it lost after spawning the first time. Third-time spawners are probably less than one per cent of all spawning salmon; fourth-time spawners are so rare as to be almost nonexistent.

After spawning and while still in the river, the salmon is a *kelt*, a *spent* salmon, a *black* salmon, or a *slink*. The last appellation is slangy and irreverent, but certainly it is almost onomatopoetic. The fish at this stage are usually wasted, ugly, and unfit to eat. A *mended kelt*, however, may be a quite passable fish. This one is a salmon which has probably entered the river late and spawned not far from the sea. Such a fish has had a short upstream migration and a relatively brief fast prior to spawning. Hence it was in fair condition at spawning time and has improved, since, on the river's food. A mended kelt, idling in a pool on its return to sea in the spring, may be in good enough shape to be mistaken for a fresh-run salmon.

Among salmon returning to the sea are a very few females that have not spawned. Still full of ova, they may have failed to attract a male, but more probably they are physiologically unable to shed their eggs. Eventually the eggs are absorbed within the body.

Much of the life history of an individual salmon is apparent to an expert reader of the rings on its scales. Scales are usually taken from the upper sides, below and slightly forward of the dorsal fin, and are read under a microscope at thirty or more magnifications. A salmon's scale is almost a chronicle of its life, telling of the fish as the rings of a tree trunk tell of the tree. The scale rings represent intervals of time. Wide spaces between the rings denote the periods of fast summer growth; narrow spaces mark the slower winter growth. The age of the salmon, the number of times it has spawned, and the elapsed time since its last spawning, are all evident.

Surely the habits of no other fish are more strenuously debated wherever anglers meet. Among the perennial questions: Does the adult salmon feed in fresh water, and if not, why does it take a fly? Does the salmon really return to the river of its birth? How high can the salmon leap, in negotiating falls on its upstream run?

Vadim D. Vladykov writes in *Fishes of Quebec*,[3] "It is an established fact that salmon do not feed in rivers." Inbound from the sea, they are fat, their flesh is red and rich in oil, and they draw upon this

[3] "Atlantic Salmon," Album No. 2, Department of Fisheries, Quebec.

reserve until spawning is over. Few if any ichthyologists believe that salmon feed voraciously on the upriver run, but some aver stoutly that they feed "a little." These point to the fact that food occasionally has been found in the stomachs of salmon running upstream. The usually empty stomachs of salmon killed by anglers are attributed to the disgorging of food during the salmon's struggle, or to the fish's very short intestinal tract and rapid digestion. Fly-fishermen have cited instances of digested food being found in the mouths of salmon which could not disgorge it because the leader had become wrapped around the salmon's jaws.

Despite the almost unanimous opinion that salmon do not truly feed on their upriver run, they take not only flies but various baits with apparent avidity. In the British Isles, where bait-fishing for salmon is quite widely practiced, baits include minnows, prawns, shrimp, and worms. The fact that salmon do take such baits is evidence that they really feed, according to those on this side of the debate.

Various reasons have been adduced to explain the nonfeeding salmon's taking of a fly. The fish is excited or exasperated, some say, by the gaudy concoction of feathers, or is merely playful or curious. Yet the salmon will sometimes rise to a small dull-colored nymph, or a No. 10 dry fly tied in imitation of a natural dun. Probably the most logical reason is one often cited by anglers and guides: as a parr in the river, the fish fed on stream insects, and now as an adult salmon it instinctively follows the ingrained impulse of its parrhood.

Of the ability of salmon to return to the river of their birth there can be no doubt. Tagged fish have done it again and again; indeed, the evidence indicates that nearly all salmon come home to spawn. It can be said that *all* adult Atlantic salmon *seek* the home river. The few that miss are called "lost" fish. Even hatchery-reared parr, planted in a given river, will return to that river as adult salmon.

The proponents of the "zone of influence" theory contend that a river exerts its influence—that is, the effect of its smell—for miles at sea, and that salmon may stay in this zone during their entire sojourn in salt water. Hence their "return" is merely an about-face within the stream at sea. Considering the known sea-distances traveled by salmon, this theory, plausible as it may be, poses a few questions. Though many salmon may not venture more than twenty-five or fifty miles beyond the home-river estuary, tagged specimens have occasionally been recaptured at points ranging from two hundred to more than a thousand miles from the point of tagging. Furthermore, many salmon enter the Gulf of St. Lawrence from the outer ocean, via the Strait of Belle Isle or the Cabot Strait, and cruise the shores of the Gulf and the St. Lawrence River estuary for five hundred miles before entering the home river.

The environmental influence—in other words, the character of the river—seems nevertheless a stronger homing factor than heredity. There are "early" rivers and "late" rivers, so designated according to the larger migrations of salmon which are said to belong to "early" or "late" groups or "families." Also, there are "big fish" rivers, "small fish" rivers, and even rivers where grilse are the chief migrants. The Restigouche in New Brunswick, the Grand Cascapedia in Quebec, and the St. Mary's in Nova Scotia are typical "big fish" rivers. Occasionally a big-fish river will be within a few miles of a small-fish river; indeed, there are instances of the two kinds entering the same estuary, and even of small-fish branches of big-fish rivers. The Upsalquitch, a branch of the big-fish Restigouche, is said to hold salmon of the eight- to ten-pound class almost exclusively.

Nova Scotia experiments cited by Percy S. Nobbs[4] indicate that environment and not heredity is the influence beckoning the salmon home. Early fish from an early river were stripped, and their young progeny were tagged and released in a late river. Then stock from late fish belonging to a late river were released in an early river. The late stock planted in the early river returned early; the early fish planted in the late river returned late.

One wonders, however, how the "zone of influence," or the smell of a river, can persist through some harbor pollutions. But whether it be smell, sight, or another sense not susceptible to human measurement or comprehension, some perception of the salmon leads it back to the river of its birth.

Though the ability of salmon to negotiate high falls has been exaggerated in some accounts, the truth, as J. W. Jones observes in *The Salmon*, is spectacular enough. He cites a perpendicular leap of 11 feet 4 inches, as measured from the pool below to the water level

4 Atlantic Salmon Association, Document No. 6 (Montreal, July 1949).

above. The majority of salmon essaying this barrier did not make it, but about one in every twenty managed to get over. Mr. Jones adds that smaller falls may sometimes be more difficult, or even insurmountable if the water below them is shallow. The salmon needs depth to gain momentum and purchase for the airborne act.

The LaHave River in Nova Scotia contains a long, deep pool, at the head of which is Indian Falls. This barrier is a narrow and steep but not perpendicular drop of about 15 feet at summer stages. Today a fishway is there, but before it was built some salmon effected the ascent. Many others failed, but now and then a prodigious initial leap, followed by a tremendous show of power swimming at the top, would take a salmon over. Describing this feat, F. H. Wooding justly terms it "a humbling experience to watch."[5]

The ultimate reward for the high endeavor of the spawning run seems sadly incommensurate with the effort. A female salmon produces 600 to 800 eggs to the pound. Even at the top figure, a 20-pound female will deposit 16,000 eggs, as compared to about 6½ million for a 20-pound cod. With the salmon, survival of eggs is highly efficient. Deep under gravel, the eggs are well protected. Even after the long winter period of incubation 90 per cent or more hatch in the spring. So far, the exhausting labor of the spawning run seems well repaid. But later the fry and the parr are vulnerable to a great horde of predators, headed by the kingfisher, merganser, and trout. Probably less than 10 per cent of the fry will reach the sea as smolts. Then, in the ocean, another set of killers—conger eels, swordfish, tuna, sharks, seals, and even cod—takes up the work of destruction. The salmon that succeed in eluding these enemies grow large and fat on the abundant food of the sea: several small-fish species, shrimp and other crustacea, marine worms.

But the survivors are a minute percentage of the original upriver deposits of eggs. If in each spawning season each pair of adult salmon produces just two progeny (out of 2400 to 24,000 eggs) that escape the manifold hazards and return to their home rivers to spawn, the salmon population of that river obviously remains stable. Yet how many rivers have shown this stability, over the past twenty-five or

[5] In "Canada's Atlantic Salmon," reprinted from *Canadian Geographical Journal* by the Department of Fisheries of Canada (Ottawa, 1956).

fifty years? Most of them, despite occasional extraordinary peaks, have suffered significant declines in their salmon numbers. Therefore, even the two-for-two ratio is not being upheld. If the average yield of hatched fry per breeding pair is 5000 (a conservative figure), two surviving progeny would be only $\frac{1}{25}$ of 1 per cent; but even that minute fraction is higher than the actual rate of production of fish which do survive to return upriver and spawn.

Despite such gloomy arithmetic, the Atlantic salmon do continue to enter the rivers of Maine and eastern Canada, year after year, in sufficient numbers to attract anglers from afar. The annual recurrence of their spawning runs is thus a source of considerable revenue to the Maritime Provinces and Quebec and, to a lesser extent, to Maine.

Fly-fishing for salmon is for thousands of anglers the ultimate of all fishing. In no other freshwater angling is so large a fish taken on such light and delicate gear. A 30-pound salmon killed on a 9-foot, 5-ounce fly rod, and such terminal equipment as an O-X tippet and a No. 8 fly, represents an extreme ratio in the weight of the quarry to the weight of the gear.

Salmon rods today, particularly on the western side of the Atlantic, are much shorter than the rods of two generations ago. Old-style rods were two-handed weapons, twelve, fourteen, even twenty feet long, weighing a full pound in extreme cases. Today many are single-handed trout rods, of eight, nine, or ten feet, and five to six ounces. Wulff, one of the best-known salmon fishermen, reports: "By 1940 In expert hands the salmon rod can be very slight, yet effective. Lee I had come down to a seven-foot, 2½-ounce fly rod, and since then have rarely used anything heavier."[6]

Wet flies are still preferred by most anglers most of the time. Dry flies, rarely seen on salmon waters until the 1920's, are winning more and more adherents. In the opinion of some old trout hands (such as this writer, who perhaps should have no salmon opinions at all), the dry-fly technique is easier than the wet in trout fishing, more difficult in salmon fishing, more fun in both.

Flies that are deemed killers in New Brunswick may be avoided like the plague by Newfoundland guides. Color preferences vary widely and often quite abruptly. A reddish fly may be liked on one

[6] *The Atlantic Salmon* (A. S. Barnes & Co., New York, 1958).

Nova Scotia river but be rated far below white or yellow on the next river, only fifteen miles away.

Salmon-fishing techniques vary greatly, too, and their elucidation must be left to abler salmon anglers than this writer. On a pool where salmon are visible, particularly in low water, you may work over a single fish, or two or three, with whatever wet or dry fly your fancy or your guide may dictate. Few pools are without their irregularities, and no two are alike. As you work a pool down, where salmon are unseen, you will pay particular attention to rock outcroppings and other natural features that cause their own individual eddies and backwaters.

Unless one is expert, he should watch such a man as Lew Freeman, a veteran salmon fisherman and guide on Nova Scotia's Medway River. To watch Freeman cast is to gain not only a lesson but some sense of fellowship with style and rhythm and a profound appreciation of what a fly rod can do in a knowing hand. Freeman's cast is left-handed, as is everything else he does, because his left hand is the only hand he has. His right hand and arm had been his casting side until he lost them both in an accident years ago. But watching Freeman cast, or reel and strip in line with the upper stump of his right arm—watching him tie a fly to a leader, or pole his 16-foot skiff upstream through heavy rapids, you see only an unassuming deftness and forget the handicap that would have ended salmon fishing for many a man.

Where no boat is available you cover a pool as best you can from your stance on two felt-soled wader shoes. Wading the large-river pools, you cannot fish as thoroughly as from a boat, yet a few inshore runs and eddies and pockets, perhaps the narrow head of the pool and the lip at its outlet—spots where salmon often lie—may be worked out better in waders than from a skiff or canoe. On the smaller, steeper rivers a boat may be impracticable, and here wading is the better way. Along certain stretches of the North River in Cape Breton Island wading is a pleasant sport, reminiscent of trout fishing. All of the water is accessible to your fly. Here, however, you can be in trouble once a salmon takes hold. Following a salmon in a boat on a long pool is one thing; on foot it is quite another. Even a four-pound grilse may be impossible to play out to the end, once he runs out of a small pool and plunges into the long brawl of a rapids below.

Those who start their salmon fishing cold have an advantage denied to the old trout hands. Superficially, the two sports seem alike. Actually, much good trout practice is the worst sort of salmon practice. The trout fisherman must unlearn many of his tricks. Fresh-run salmon can be closely approached without being frightened: the great stealth employed in stalking a rising trout is wasted on a salmon pool. A rising trout is a potential fish in the creel; a salmon seen to leap may be in no mood to come to your fly, but one lying quiet and unseen may give you an unexpected strike.

In wet-fly fishing, to strike a salmon immediately it takes the fly, as you strike a trout, is usually to lose it. Do not strike at all, counsel the elders, thereby advising the trout fisherman to go against his most basic instinct. The fish will hook itself against the resistance of the submerged fly and the fairly taut line. With the dry fly, however, and its usually accompanying slack line, this resistance is absent. Some salmon-wise practitioners urge here that the angler's strike be instantaneous.

Though many salmon are lost on the strike itself, perhaps more get away during the battle, and not a few at the very end, by a botched job with gaff or tailer. Once a large salmon is on, what to do? You must have, of course, plenty of backing behind your casting line. A salmon may run 150 yards straight down the pool. If it reaches the end of your backing before you can turn it, something will give, and it may be your rod if you hold it high. If you lower the rod, the leader will part, which is far better. In any case, you have lost your fish.

Trout fishermen are again inclined to err here, by applying too much pressure, overstraining or even breaking the rod, or pulling the fly from the fish. A Nova Scotia guide once counseled a woman angler who, with a big salmon suddenly on, frantically asked him what she should do. "When he pulls, you don't," the guide said. "When he doesn't, you do." Reel in when you can. Never strip in, for the coils of line in the boat will foul or acquire a knot, and the entire business may jam on a thole pin or at your rod's first guide when the salmon again heads away. When the salmon leaps, lower your rod. The rest is a steady, long, wearing game, winning what you can, paying it back when the fish insists, but gradually winning a little more than you lose. That, and perhaps a prayer to whatever god among your cluster may preside over such occasions. You are on your own.

The tight little circles of salmon men—those whose faces brighten in the dead of winter at the mere pronunciation of "Jock Scott" or "Dusty Miller"—never "catch" a salmon. They "kill" salmon, or they "take" salmon and release them. Around their northwoods' campfires and their city clubs any reference to "catching" a salmon may raise a few polite but incredulous eyebrows.

The commercial fishermen "catch" salmon in open-sea and off-shore drift nets, trap nets along shore, and gill nets in the estuaries—but not nearly so many now as in the past. The Atlantic salmon fishery, providing mainly fresh salmon, a limited amount of smoked, salted, frozen, and canned, has declined sadly. The average annual commercial catch in Canada is today around 4½ million pounds, with a value of 2½ million dollars. Newfoundland supplies about half of this total; Nova Scotia, New Brunswick, and Quebec provide the rest. In the decade of 1921–30, Newfoundland alone had a peak year of nearly 7 million pounds. Seemingly at variance with the downward trend in the commercial catch, Newfoundland's anglers recorded an all-time high of about 35,000 salmon in 1963. Doubtless the reason is an increase of anglers rather than of the salmon populations.

The commercial salmon fishery of Maine is negligible, though the sport fishing is improving in some waters through intelligent programs of breeding and river management.

Peak years and cyclical abundance have been noted by conservationists and anglers. The basic causes are not known. A year when many fish are in the upriver spawning beds does not necessarily mean a good return of their progeny later. When too many fish are on the spawning grounds, the redds of some are cut into by others, with a resulting loss of eggs. Further, there may not be enough food for an exceptionally large number of parr. A peak year seems a cheerful omen, but what is significant in the statistics is the gradual waning of salmon numbers from one peak year to the next, at nine- or ten-year intervals.

The story of the salmon's decline is a familiar and dreary recital of the sins of man against his natural resource: overfishing, industrial pollution, lumbering pollution (sawdust and bark), forest fires; dams for power, industry, and logging, dams which impose barriers against the salmon's migration and flood their spawning grounds; poaching and illegal fishing, with spears, nets, and chicken wire, at spawning time; and the spraying of insecticides over watersheds, effectively destroying the aquatic life which is the prime food of the parr.

Added to such man-made destruction, unknown adverse factors are operating at sea to depress salmon populations.

Industrial pollution is perhaps the greatest sinner. Factory wastes in the lower waters and harbors have long since closed off many American rivers and more recently some in Canada. In Quebec alone, the salmon-river mileage has been reduced by 50 per cent within the last century. St. Lawrence River salmon no longer ascend the big stream above its confluence with the Saguenay. In all Canadian waters combined, the commercial catch today is about one-quarter of its volume a hundred years ago.

The problem of salmon restoration is receiving practical attention. Work by government agencies, cooperating scientists, and such organizations as the Atlantic Salmon Association, includes tighter control of pollution, predators and poachers, better regulation of commercial fishing, surveys of rivers, the building of fishways and other stream improvement, and the selective breeding of salmon in hatcheries for larger fish and earlier smolts.

In a very real sense, the angler is the trustee of the salmon's future, and should pay well for his sport. River management and adequate stocking are expensive; state and provincial governments can hardly tax all the people to provide fun for the few anglers and to augment the income of the commercial fishermen. The river, that birthplace and nursery of the salmon, is the scene of the angler's sport. If all is well with the river perhaps the cyclical peaks and valleys will slope upward on the salmon graphs of the future.

LANDLOCKED SALMON
Salmo salar Linnaeus

The so-called landlocked salmon is landlocked by choice rather than by physical barrier, for in much of its habitat it declines a ready access to the sea. Once thought to be a subspecies, this fish is now known to be identical with the sea-run Atlantic salmon, Salmo salar.

The landlocked has other names, among which Sebago salmon and ouananiche are the better known. The former derives from Sebago Lake, Maine, part of the landlocked salmon's original and present range. This name is familiar throughout Maine today, elsewhere in New England, and in northern New York. "Ouananiche" is indigenous to Quebec, less widely used in other Canadian provinces, and infrequently in the United States. In some of its Canadian haunts the ouananiche becomes "quananiche" or "wananiche." It is smaller in average size than the more southerly Sebago.

The landlocked salmon is very similar in color to the sea-run Atlantic, though it has its distinguishing marks. Some of its black spots are irregularly double X-shaped, the eyes and scales are proportionately larger, and the fins longer, than those of the Atlantic salmon. The back varies from steel-gray to almost black, frequently with a bluish or greenish shade. Virtually all the spots are above the lateral line; a few appear on the upper areas of the head, cheek, and gill cover. Below the lateral line the fish is silvery, often with a reddish overcast such as the Atlantic salmon acquires in fresh water. All the fins are dark and unspotted.

Though it does not attain sizes comparable to those of maiden Atlantic salmon with four years' sea life, the landlocked grows to tackle-smashing dimensions and is a highly esteemed game fish. Its average weight, however, seems to have declined since the early years of this century when fifteen-pounders were not uncommon. Most landlockeds taken by anglers today are of two to eight pounds; fish above twelve pounds are increasingly rare. The official rod-and-reel record belongs to Sebago Lake. This specimen, taken by Edward Blakely on August 1, 1907, weighed 22 pounds 8 ounces.

The original range of the landlocked salmon extended from the northern deepwater lakes of New England and New York, north and east to the Maritime Provinces, Quebec, the island of Newfoundland and Labrador, and westward to Ontario. In the early 1800's a large population existed in Lake Ontario; it commenced to decline about 1835, chiefly because of pollution, and was extinct by 1890. The fish has been widely introduced into deep lakes in the general area of its original range.

The landlocked salmon is not exclusively a lake fish, however. It thrives in several Quebec rivers flowing into the Gulf of St. Lawrence. In Labrador it is reported in both branches of the Hamilton River above Grand Falls; still farther north it is said to be plentiful in rivers which empty into Ungava Bay.

The European range of the landlocked includes the British Isles, Norway, Sweden, and Russia.

The origin and distribution of this freshwater *salar* is ascribed, in common with the beginnings of other salmonids, to glaciation and the ensuing changes. Many landlockeds, inhabiting glacial lakes with outlets to the sea, apparently preferred to stay where they were rather than migrate to salt water. Dr. G. Power, of the University of Waterloo (Ontario), writes: "Mere physical isolation does not suffice as explanation of the present distribution and characteristics of the freshwater salmon of eastern North America. Since many of the freshwater populations now have access to the sea but do not take advantage of it, a physiological as well as a physical cause is necessary to explain all the facts."[7]

For the majority of landlocked populations the lake serves as the ocean serves the Atlantic salmon. The lake is the landlocked salmon's adult home and the source of most of its growth; the tributary streams and the outlets are its birthplaces and nurseries.

Perhaps as early as the first week of September, landlockeds in Maine and southern Canada congregate near the tributary inlets or the lake outlets (the latter are preferred) prior to the spawning run.

Some authorities hold that the landlocked will spawn in the shoals of the lake itself if no stream with suitable beds is available; others stoutly maintain that lake spawning never occurs.

Spawning takes place in the latitude of Maine and southern Canada from about mid-October to late November—earlier in the more northerly range. In a gravel or rubble bottom the female builds her redd as the Atlantic salmon does, and deposits a comparable number of eggs. Among the male parr some are sexually mature, as with the sea-run salmon, and may contribute their sperm to an adult female's eggs.

Female landlockeds mature for their first spawning when four or

[7] "The Evolution of Freshwater Races of the Atlantic Salmon," reprinted from *Arctic*, Vol. 11, No. 2.

five years old; sexually mature males are usually aged three or four. Among the spawning runs of the landlocked, about 70 per cent of all fish are first-time spawners. Second, third, and even fourth spawnings are more numerous among the landlockeds than among the sea-run Atlantics, and two or three spawnings may be in consecutive seasons. Some of the fish, however, stay in the lake for two years, or even three, between the first and second spawnings.

The habits and biological processes of the sea-run and freshwater salmons appear basically the same. The landlockeds lose weight at spawning time and afterward. The mortality among the "kelts" is certainly much less than with the sea-run salmon, for the spawning migration, from the lake and back, is much shorter, and the fasting period relatively brief.

The fry emerge in late May or June, in the southerly range, and begin feeding on the minute life of the stream. As parr, they remain in the outlet or tributary for one or two years before migrating to the lake, subsisting on insects and tiny fish. Their growth as parr is appreciably more than that of the Atlantic salmon. As a year-old fish the landlocked may be five to six inches long; at age two it has almost doubled this size. Maine's legal angling length of fourteen inches is obtained by most landlocked salmon in three years.

The chief food of the adult landlocked, where the optimum larder is available, is the freshwater smelt. Other fish readily taken are yellow perch, young alewives, sticklebacks, and minnows. The blueback trout (see Chapter 4) is also a preferred food of the landlocked salmon, and will disappear in any lake jointly inhabited by both fish.

Conclusions from a study of spawning migrations in the chain of lakes of the Fish River system, Maine, in 1953–55, were that most landlocked salmon go downstream from the lake to spawn, and that most will return to the lake of origin.[8] In this study 1239 fish were tagged on spawning runs, and many were recaptured. The resultant data emphasize the importance of fishways in dams at outlets of salmon lakes. On this point the report notes, "Misunderstanding and lack of knowledge concerning the reproduction and migration habits

[8] Kendall Warner: "Migrations of Landlocked Salmon in the Fish River Lakes, Maine," reprinted from the *Journal of Wildlife Management*, Vol. 23, No. 1 (January 1959).

of Maine salmon in past years has led to unfortunate mistakes in management. Installation of fish screens at lake outlets has been widespread and has caused incalculable harm to salmon fisheries by preventing adult salmon from descending into outlet streams to spawn. Prior to 1950, fish screens were a common sight at the outlet of many of Maine's finest salmon lakes. Recent research findings . . . and lake-inventory recommendations have done much to rectify past mistakes. . . . The majority of the outlet spawners will return upstream to contribute to the lake fishery if facilities are provided."

Young Atlantic salmon introduced into lakes lacking outlets to the sea become, in effect, landlocked salmon, and appear to thrive. John R. Greeley, of the New York State Conservation Department, reports an experiment conducted at Lake George, N.Y., during 1948 and 1950.[9] In this study, 9000 yearling Atlantic salmon were planted in six streams tributary to Lake George. These fish were reared at the Washington County hatchery at Cambridge, N.Y., from eggs obtained from New Brunswick, and were marked by fin-clipping. Later recoveries led to the conclusion that "planted Atlantic salmon matured normally and produced normal progeny from stripping."

Maine today has the largest sport fishery for landlocked salmon. In Maine's lakes, as elsewhere, the best fishing is just after the spring breakup of ice. The landlockeds are then in the shallow waters of the lake or near the tributary entrances, feeding on smelt which are beginning their spawning run. At this season the landlocked will take flies or trolled lures just below the surface. Later, when the shallows become warmer, the salmon go down into deep water. Through the summer they can be taken by deep-trolled spoons or spinners, and by still-fishing with bait. In September, fly-fishing has an encore when the landlockeds again ascend to the shallows prior to spawning.

Pound for pound, *Salmo salar* in the landlocked form is equal to its sea-run brother as a game fish. Its strong, spectacular, leaping fight, on a fly rod or other light gear, has put it at or near the top in the estimation of anglers.

[9] *Survivals of Planted Atlantic Salmon in Lake George* (American Fisheries Society, Northeastern Division, Sept. 22, 1953).

Chapter 6

PACIFIC SALMON

The five species of Pacific salmon, belonging to the single genus *Oncorhynchus*, are quite distinct from their Atlantic second cousin. The latter is closer, biologically, to the trouts and chars than to the Pacific fish which bear the same common name.

Though doubtless known to the Asians for many centuries, the Pacific salmon occupies a relatively recent niche in Western culture. The five species were first described by Russian scientists in Kamchatka in 1737, but not until the 1880's were they properly classified in the

West. Still another species, called the cherry salmon, *Oncorhynchus masu*, is a non-American member of the genus, abundant along the Asian shores of the Pacific. The popular kokanee, a dwarf salmon of the western lakes, is not a distinct species but a non-migratory variant of the sockeye. Some scientists prefer to call it *O. nerka kennerlyi*, but the American Fisheries Society gives it no separate listing.

The five Pacific salmons formerly constituted a huge resource. This asset has declined sharply, in the past twenty-five or thirty years, through overfishing, pollution, dams, and other expressions of man's failure to preserve a natural treasure. Despite this wastage the commercial Pacific salmon fishery is still large enough to dwarf the Atlantic by a ratio of about seventy to one. Two of the Pacific species—the chinook and the coho—have a further and incalculable value as sport fish, annually attracting thousands of anglers to the bays and rivers of the far West.

Biologically the salmons of the Pacific differ from their Atlantic relative in one major respect. All of them die after spawning once; no Pacific salmon can be termed a "previous spawner." It has justly been said that the Pacific salmon "is born an orphan and dies childless," for its eggs do not hatch until long after its death. Other differences are interesting to scientists and fishermen. The river life of some Pacific salmon species is very brief; indeed, the fry of the pink and chum salmon start the seaward migration immediately after hatching from the eggs. The young of the other species stay in their native rivers a year; a few remain two years, and very rarely a parr will live three years in fresh water. But there is no history of four-, five-, and six-year old parr in the western rivers. Probably for this reason, there is less evidence of sexual maturity among Pacific parrs.

Of the five Pacific species only one, the chinook, achieves weights comparable to the Atlantic salmon's maximum. The chinook, in fact, exceeds the Atlantic and is the largest of all the salmonid family, occasionally topping even the greatest recorded weights for lake trout.

The total maximum range of the five Pacific species is tremendous. Though it varies among the five in its northern and southern extremes, it extends from southern California to the Bering Strait and down the Asian side to Kamchatka, the Siberian west coast of the Sea of Okhotsk, to Korea and even as far south as Japan. It includes the Aleutian Islands on the eastern side of the Pacific and the Kuriles on the west. Two of the five Pacific species, the pink and the chum salmon, are present north of the Bering Strait.

The character of the Pacific coast and its hinterlands, from Oregon northward to the Yukon River, makes it an ideal habitat for salmon. The many rivers and lakes are fed by heavy rainfall along the coastal strip and by melting snows and glaciers in the high inland country. Discharging a constant flow of fresh water to the ocean, these rivers attract the spawning migrations of salmon and provide ideal spawning grounds and nurseries on the gravel beds far upstream.

Since the Pacific-salmon commercial fishery has been for many years far greater than the Atlantic, an extension of the range of the former from west to east has long occupied the minds of scientists and canners. Several attempts at such transplantings have been made; to date none has been conspicuously successful. W. E. Ricker, of the Fisheries Research Board of Canada, at Nanaino, British Columbia, reports, "The total score is certainly not impressive." Among past attempts to introduce Pacific salmon out of their native range, "there has been only one fully-documented successful experiment," Mr. Ricker writes, "that of chinook salmon transplanted to New Zealand." He adds, "Several other attempts 'succeeded' temporarily, in that adult fish returned to the stream where eggs or fry had been liberated, but no permanent self-sustaining run was established."[1]

The Maine Department of Inland Fisheries and Game reports that each of the five Pacific salmon has been introduced into Maine waters at one time or another, but only a few sparse populations of coho (silver) salmon remain at present. The initial introduction, in May 1905, constituted 1,336,000 coho salmon fry, hatched in Maine from Oregon eggs. These fry were planted in eleven Maine rivers. In the period 1943 to 1952, coho salmon were stocked in five Maine rivers. Some 150 adults from the first planting of this series returned to the Ducktrap River in 1947, and a few were captured. Five mature cohos, ranging from five to nine pounds, were taken in a trap on Cove Brook in 1957. These fish, Maine says, were the progeny of natural propagation and were in excellent condition. Such results are interesting but far from significant.

[1] "Pacific Salmon for Atlantic Waters?," *The Canadian Fish Culturist*, Issue 16 (August 1954).

Attempts to introduce chinook salmon into Lake Ontario, beginning in 1873 and continuing until 1925, met with similar lack of success. Of the later plantings, W. B. Scott writes, "Chinook salmon up to 18 pounds were caught, and many were reported ascending streams in the fall. However, they never became established, and many years have elapsed since the last chinook salmon was captured in Lake Ontario."[2]

Cohos planted in Lake Erie in 1933 have also failed to establish a permanent population.

One wonders why the lake plantings to establish a commercial fishery were not made with the sockeye salmon, a species whose traditional fondness for lakes has produced the non-migratory kokanee.

As a parallel observation, little or no success has rewarded several attempts to introduce the Atlantic salmon into rivers tributary to the Pacific. The landlocked form of the Atlantic, however, has proved itself adaptable to several western lakes.

The Pacific salmon was a major support of the Northwest aborigines and a profound influence upon their culture for hundreds of years. When Captain Robert Gray sailed his ship *Columbia* into the "Great River of the West" in 1792, he named the river after his vessel. He found, too, an Indian tribe called the Chinook living in aboriginal luxury on a species of large salmon that abounded in the river. These fish later became known as chinook salmon. Lewis and Clark, descending the Columbia River in 1805, found the same people and the same good living based upon the spring and fall runs of the salmon, which were welcomed with formal celebrations of rejoicing.

The Indians smoked and dried salmon, pounded the dried meat into powder, and the surplus became an item of trade. So abundant was this food supply, and so easy were the harvests, preservation, and storage, that the coastal Indians had much time for the pursuits of leisure.

Aboriginal methods of catching salmon are still basic to the modern industry, though various improvements and refinements upon the ancient gear have been made. The Indians employed traps, seines, gill nets, and hooks, all of which are used in today's commercial fishery. They had other devices, too—harpoons, dip nets at falls, bows and arrows.

[2] *Freshwater Fishes of Eastern Canada* (University of Toronto Press, 1955).

There is little evidence that the Indians systematically practiced the conservation of salmon for conservation's sake. Almost certainly they had no need to regulate their catch. What is now called the "spawning escapement" (spawners eluding the traps and nets in sufficient numbers to maintain a river's population) probably took care of itself. The Indians were nowhere overwhelmingly numerous; if they caught all the salmon they could on any single upstream migration, the escapees were more than enough to maintain the river's salmon population.

Conservation was effected by some of the aboriginal tribes, however, from religious motives. Philip Drucker, in *Indians of the Northwest Coast*,[3] writes: ". . . the Tlingit and Haida people believed that the salmon were a race of supernatural beings who went about in human form feasting and dancing beneath the sea. When the time came for the annual runs, these 'Salmon People' assumed the form of fish and ascended the streams to sacrifice themselves for the benefit of mankind. . . . An elaborate First Salmon ceremony was held over the first catch from each important stream to honor and welcome the species, and many legends taught the young people that man was totally dependent on the goodwill of the Salmon People which they used for food."

CHINOOK SALMON
Oncorhynchus tschawytscha (Walbaum)

Because the chinook salmon is so much larger than any other of the Pacific species there is a legend in some areas that it does not die after spawning. Evidence is completely lacking to support this belief.

The chinook is called by several other names. This largest of the salmonids is known as the chinook chiefly in the Columbia River area and the adjacent Oregon and Washington coasts. It is the king salmon in California and Alaska, the spring salmon in British Columbia (for its habit of making a spring migration), and the tyee in the Puget Sound region. "Tyee" has an implication of weight in some quarters: the Tyee Club stipulates that a tyee must be thirty pounds or more; below thirty the fish is a spring.

[3] McGraw-Hill, New York, 1955.

The chinook's normal range extends from Monterey Bay, California, to the Yukon River, and southward along the Asian coast to the southerly limits of Kamchatka. In Alaska it is plentiful from Ketchikan north across the Gulf of Alaska and into the Aleutians. North of the Yukon River estuary it is scarce, but the river itself has a heavy migration.

The chinook is a big-river fish by choice, and in such rivers as the Columbia and Yukon it punches its way upstream for tremendous distances on its spawning migrations, moving in the daylight hours and resting at night. On the Columbia it reaches Idaho via the Snake River, a Columbia tributary, and proceeds even farther, up the Salmon River and other feeders of the Snake. In the Yukon the chinook is regularly taken at Eagle, Alaska, 1200 miles above the estuary, and is known to spawn much farther upstream, in Yukon Territory, making an 1800-mile run in sixty to eighty days, for speed is imperative in the short period of ice-free water.

The chinook's spawning journey is doubtless more exhausting than those of other salmon, simply because this species travels so far. None of the salmon feeds on the upriver runs; the chinook's long climb to its breeding and its death kills an occasional fish even before the spawning grounds are attained. In the final reaches, many of the survivors are pushing ahead somehow, with their flesh literally hanging in shreds.

In its saltwater coloration the chinook is a handsome fish. The back and upper sides are a dark greenish blue, lightening toward the lateral line. Numerous black spots on the upper sides extend into the dorsal fin and appear on both lobes of the caudal. The sides are silvery, and this argent brilliance carries forward over the gill covers and cheeks, and aft over the caudal peduncle. The dorsal fin is dusky, the lower fins pale and unspotted. The tail is broad and not deeply forked. A distinguishing mark is the black or dusky appearance of the inside of the mouth; this has given the chinook still another name, "blackmouth," in parts of its range. The chinook darkens after a few days in fresh water; indeed some show a reddish color about the lower fins and belly even before entering the river. By spawning time the males have developed a hooked jaw and acquired a muddy dark red color; the females become similarly dusky but not to so marked a degree. The flesh is not so red as that of the sockeye or the coho.

The chinook is capable of achieving 100 pounds, as authentic records attest. The largest so far verified was a fish of 126½ pounds, commercially-caught at Petersburg, in southeast Alaska. A 95-pounder was reported taken at Tanana, Alaska, 600 miles up the Yukon River. The record chinook on sporting tackle was a 92-pounder taken by Heinz Wichmann on the Skeena River, British Columbia, in July 1959. Such leviathans are of course exceptional, yet chinooks of 40 to 80 pounds are not extremely rare in Alaska. Such fish have lived four to seven years or more in 'the ocean. The average weight, however, up and down the coast, is about 15 to 20 pounds.

Spawning runs of the chinook vary in time, in different parts of the range. Usually both spring and fall runs occur; in the Columbia River there is a "summer" run, between the spring and fall, and in California's Sacramento River and its tributaries a "winter" run occurs. Fish of this winter migration spawn early the following summer. All others spawn in the fall. Usually the spring-run fish go farthest upstream to their breeding grounds. The digging of nests and the extrusion of eggs proceed as with other salmons, including the Atlantic. The average spawning chinook drops five to six thousand large adhesive eggs. They are quite safe, under the gravel, from everything except the action of the river itself. Unusual flood waters can scour them out, baring and scattering them to the predators or perhaps killing them by an overlay of silt; very low water may leave them high and dry.

The adults, male and female, die shortly after spawning; their bodies, stranded or drifting downstream, are devoured by bears and other scavengers of the woods.

The young hatch from the eggs the following spring. In southerly rivers most of them go to salt water soon after hatching, though perhaps 20 per cent remain in the river for a full year. In the Yukon and other northerly rivers young chinooks spend at least a year, occasionally two, before finally drifting to sea in schools, as three-inch fish with distinct parr marks.

The food of chinook fry is chiefly plankton; as the fry grow to parrhood they eat insects, insect larvae, and tiny fish.

Reaching salt water, the young chinooks fatten rapidly on the rich and abundant food of the ocean. In the first year of sea life this

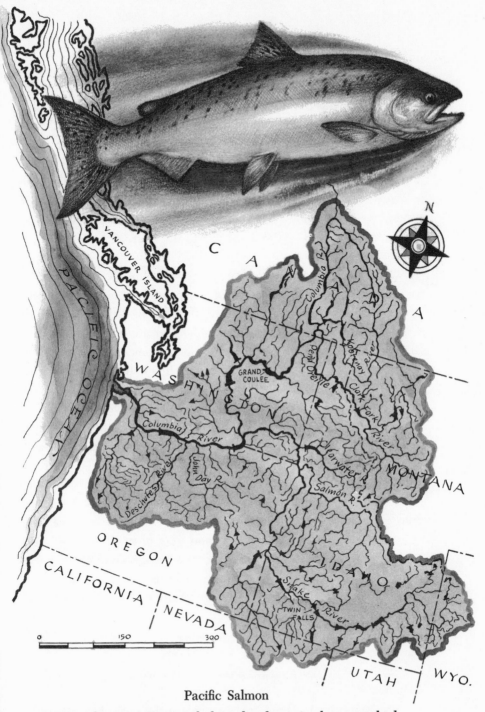

Pacific Salmon

Map shows migration of chinook salmon in the watershed
of the Columbia River system. Some fish migrate to headwaters in
Idaho 1,000 miles inland.

is largely the so-called "red feed," the euphausiid shrimp *Thysanoessa spinifera*, which imparts the red color to the salmon's meat. Later the growing chinooks continue the "red feed" but vary it widely with whatever is abundant in its season: herring, sand launces, needlefish, pilchards, anchovies, rockfishes, and squid.

Four or five years after going to sea, and now weighing fifteen to thirty pounds or more, the adult chinooks return to their native river to spawn and die, completing the immemorial cycle. Among them will perhaps be a few young but mature males, called "jacks." These are similar to the Atlantic grilse, returning to the river after a single year at sea.

Only two of the Pacific salmon species—the chinook and the coho—feed in salt water chiefly on fish, and hence will readily take baits and lures. Pacific-salmon fishing is a far cry from the purist sort of angling, with trout rods and small flies, now widely practiced on the Atlantic-salmon rivers of Quebec and the Maritime Provinces. The chinook is sought mostly in the saltwater bays and brackish lower rivers, by anglers in boats, trolling with stout rods, star-drag reels, and wire leaders. Whole herrings or herring strips are used for bait; the favored artificial lures are large spoons, wobblers, and spinners. In recent years surf fishing for chinooks has become popular on Vancouver Island and other areas, where schools of herring sometimes swim close inshore and draw the chinooks toward the beaches.

Inland, on such rivers as Idaho's Snake, during July and August, there is chinook fishing that resembles the Atlantic-salmon variety, with fly rods and flies, clusters of salmon eggs, or small flashing lures. On such gear, a chinook of 15 or 20 pounds (rarely up to 45) is a fish to challenge the best in angling skill. Indeed this salmon, on any tackle and in any water, is ranked at the very top by many western anglers.

COHO SALMON
Oncorhynchus kisutch   (Walbaum)

The American Fisheries Society terms it the coho, but it is commonly called the silver salmon in many parts of its North American range—middle California to Alaska. It does not enter the Arctic but occurs along the Asian Pacific coast as far south as Japan.

In its saltwater colors the coho resembles the chinook, with slight differences. The spots along the back and upper sides are larger and less numerous, and do not occur on the dorsal fin or the lower caudal, though a few are evident on the upper caudal. The lower sides are brilliantly silvery. The dorsal, adipose, ventrals, and anal fins are pale, the pectorals darker. In fresh water the coho loses its brilliance, turning a dull red, but perhaps retains its ocean cleanness and vigor longer than do other Pacific salmons. Roderick L. Haig-Brown states that spawned-out cohos are sometimes still alive in February, long after the other salmon have died and been washed downstream.[4]

The meat of the coho is a deep salmon color, less red than that of the sockeye, and called "medium red" in the canning industry.

The coho and the chum are about equal as the second largest of the Pacific salmons. The coho averages five to ten or twelve pounds in its southerly waters, slightly more in British Columbia and Alaska. Specimens of twenty pounds are not extremely rare in the north. The record coho on sporting tackle was a 31-pound fish taken in Cowichan Bay, British Columbia, by Mrs. Lee Hallberg, in October 1947.

On its spawning migration the coho will run up the smallest streams as well as the largest rivers, and has been called a "creek fish." It is inclined to spawn not far from the sea, though some of its migrations in larger rivers are long runs, both in miles and in time, carrying the fish far up to the headwaters. Like the chinook, the coho travels by day, rests by night. Spawning runs begin in September, reach their peak in late October or November, and continue even into January. Spring-run cohos are not known, but the spawning itself has been reported as late as March in southeastern Alaska. The first heavy upstream runs usually attend a rising river, especially in some of the California drainages that commonly reach low summer levels. Among the adult fish heading upstream a few "jacks" are usually present— two-year-old, sexually mature males 15 to 18 inches long.

Spawning is perhaps a more violent occasion with the cohos than with the other Pacific salmons, featured by much fighting among the now hook-jawed males. Possibly the cohos' breeding commotion is no greater than that of other salmons, but merely has had more witnesses because of the shallower spawning grounds favored by this fish.

[4] "Canada's Pacific Salmon," reprinted from *Canadian Geographical Journal* and published in booklet form by the Department of Fisheries of Canada, Ottawa.

The female deposits her eggs in a series of nests, after which both male and female die. Degeneration of the gonads and other physiological changes occur even before the death of the fish. Leo Shapovalov and Alan C. Taft have noted, "The occurrence of such changes in a stream such as Waddell Creek (California), where many of the fish spawn within two miles of the stream's mouth, shows conclusively that death is not caused by the rigors of a long journey, but results from independent physiological changes."[5]

The coho's eggs hatch in forty to fifty days or longer, depending upon water temperature. Once free of the yolk sac and swimming as fry, the young cohos' life in the river is fraught with hazards, not only from the usual predators but also from drying stream channels. Coho fry seem to persist in keeping to shallow water, and many are stranded when the river lapses to low summer levels.

Approximately a year after emerging from the gravel as fry, the young survivors start the journey to sea, moving usually in small schools. The vast majority migrate oceanward in their second year of river life; a few stay in fresh water until the third year.

The sea life of the coho is two years, rarely three. Growth is slow in the first saltwater year, very rapid in the second. At sea the coho feeds on much the same fare as the chinook: euphausiid shrimps and other crustaceans, herring, sand launces, squid. Its small-fish diet includes, as does the chinook's, its own species. After a year in the river and two years in the ocean the coho is mature and returns to its river to spawn and die.

Though smaller than the chinook, the coho is equally prized as a game fish. Its savage strike, swift powerful runs, surface-fighting tactics, and repeated leaps have given it a reputation as the sportiest salmon among the Pacific clan. Cohos will frequently strike even when the lure is close to the boat. Late summer and fall are the best fishing times. Then the cohos are congregating in the estuaries, prior to their spawning runs. Effective artificial lures include spoons, wobblers, plugs, and large streamer and bucktail flies. Surf fishing for the coho, with spinning gear or regulation surf rods, can be a rewarding method when the fish are inshore. Later in the fall the coho provides fine upriver fly-fishing.

[5] *The Life Histories of the Steelhead Rainbow Trout and Silver Salmon* (State of California Department of Fish and Game, Fish Bulletin No. 98, 1954).

SOCKEYE SALMON
Oncorhynchus nerka (Walbaum)

Known also as the red salmon in Alaska and the blueback in the Columbia River, the sockeye is of vast importance to the commercial fishery but is seldom taken on sporting gear. It occurs from northern California and Oregon to Alaska, with its greatest concentrations in British Columbia and southeastern Alaska. Above Bristol Bay its populations are sparse; it is rarely reported as far north as Bering Strait and does not enter the Arctic Ocean. On the Asian coast it is known as far south as Japan.

The sockeye in its ocean coloration has a steel-blue to grayish back and upper sides. The top of the head and upper gill covers are often more definitely blue than the dorsal surface. Below the lateral line the sides and underbody are brilliantly silver-white. Spots may be faint or absent entirely. The pectoral fin has a dark anterior margin; the other fins are pale grayish to silvery. Spawning fish turn muddy-red to bright red on the back and sides, dirty-white and blotchy on their once clean silvery-white bellies. The flesh is the deepest red of all the salmons' and commands the highest price per pound.

The sockeye's weight at maturity is five to seven pounds, seldom more, though specimens of twelve to fifteen pounds have occasionally been taken in the commercial nets.

As contrasted to the coho's casual choice of spawning grounds, the sockeye's demands are particular in the extreme. Its spawning migrations are exclusively in rivers that have lakes somewhere along their course, or as their ultimate headwaters. The sockeye will fight its way hundreds of miles inland to a lake and then spawn in the lake's tributaries or outlet.

This salmon enters fresh water usually in June or July; for the next three or four months it dedicates itself to fasting, the exhausting upriver march, the preparation for the fall spawning, and the final act of reproduction and death.

The average female delivers herself of about 3000 eggs. These hatch the following spring; the newborn fry, wriggling out of the gravel nest, move immediately from the tributary to the lake. Here they remain for a full year, sometimes two, and very rarely three, feeding on plankton and tiny water fleas (*Daphnia pulex*). A minor percentage of sockeye fry move to the sea shortly after hatching, but the majority start their seaward migration, as three-inch parr, in the spring of the year following their birth.

The ocean life of the sockeye is three years in the southerly range, four or five years in Alaskan waters. At sea they range far from the home river, feeding on plankton, shrimps, and other small forms of marine life. Four to six years old at maturity, they return to the native river to round out the cycle.

Probably because the sockeye is not a fish-eater, it seldom strikes the angler's lure or bait in salt water. It may be taken in the rivers, however, with fly-fishing tackle, on its summer migration. July fly-fishing for sockeyes in some of Alaska's rivers can be a productive and exciting game. This salmon is accorded status as a sport fish by Alaska's creel limit of two a day.

The sockeye has the distinction of being the only Pacific salmon to produce a non-migratory or "landlocked" variant able to complete its life cycle in fresh water. This fish is the little kokanee salmon, whose native range includes many lakes in the Pacific drainages from Oregon to southeastern Alaska. Introductions have established it in California and elsewhere. Other names are little redfish, kickeninny, and Kennerly's salmon. This bright little eccentric resembles the ocean sockeye in its bluish-and-silver color scheme, with small spots along the upper sides. Upon maturing, and prior to spawning, the males become dull to bright red, the females brownish green.

The kokanee is 10 to 14 inches long, rarely above 16, though occasional specimens of 20 inches and more than two pounds have been reported.

The lake is the little kokanee's "ocean," and in the lake it has the same life cycle as the sea-run sockeye has in salt water. Maturing in its fourth year of lake life, it ascends tributaries in the fall to spawn, and then proves itself to be a genuine Pacific salmon by dying.

The new hatch of fry, appearing the following spring, may migrate at once to the lake or stay in the natal tributary for a year.

In the broad schemes of conservation this little lake salmon plays a valuable role as a forage fish for trout—the primary reason for its introduction and maintenance in many western lakes. This miniature sockeye is also a game fish. Its natural food includes aquatic insects as well as plankton, and it provides excellent sport to the fly-casting angler or the troller of small spinners. Its virtue as a panfish is well known.

PINK SALMON
Oncorhynchus gorbuscha (Walbaum)

The pink salmon, also called the humpback because the male develops a prominent bony hump on its back at spawning time, is the smallest of the Pacific species, averaging three to five pounds, and rarely exceeding seven. It is the most abundant of all the Pacific salmons, in some years accounting for nearly half of the canneries' entire pack.

Though the range of the pink extends as far south as San Francisco, this fish is relatively scarce below Puget Sound. From there northward, especially in Alaska, it is very plentiful. It is one of the two Pacific salmons which enter the Arctic Ocean and spawn in Arctic rivers. The pink is said by some ichthyologists to go only westward from the Bering Strait, entering Siberian rivers as far west as the Lena. Other fishery scientists hold that it also ranges eastward in the Arctic Ocean as far as the Mackenzie delta. In Asia, the pink's range extends southward to Japan.

In the saltwater phase the pink salmon's dorsal surface is dark, brownish gray to greenish blue, quite liberally sprinkled with large dark oval-shaped spots which extend over the caudal peduncle and both lobes of the tail. Below the lateral line this fish is silvery, often with a pinkish cast as it enters the estuaries. The dorsal, anal, and caudal fins are grayish, the other fins pale. All fins except the caudal are unspotted. The males take on the usual reddish color prior to spawning; the females become dusky but not so red as the males. The meat is less red than that of the sockeye or coho.

Fine, small scales—more than 200 in a horizontal row—are a distinguishing mark of the pink salmon.

This fish is one of extremes. It is not only the smallest and most plentiful of the Pacifics, but the least migratory in fresh water. Usually it moves only a few miles upriver to spawn, and is even known to spawn in the brackish waters where the incoming tide mixes with the freshwater discharge of the river. In this intertidal zone the eggs may be covered with salt water much of the time during the autumn-winter incubation. Experiments with screened enclosures have shown that the survival rates of pink salmon spawned in intertidal and in fresh water are comparable.[6]

In the Puget Sound area and parts of British Columbia, commercial catches of pink salmon are heavy in alternate years. Large annual runs, sometimes two runs a year, occur in Alaska, however.

Spawning takes place from July to September. The female drops 1200 to 2000 eggs, which hatch the next spring after an unusually long incubation period. The newly hatched fry start at once to sea.

The ocean life of the pink salmon is uniformly two years, and during this time it is believed to travel great distances in the ocean. At the age of two years the pink attains its maturity and heads back to its river to keep its final rendezvous.

Thus the pink salmon, except in its rare long-distance spawning migrations, is virtually independent of fresh water. During its two years at sea it feeds largely on plankton. Seldom a fish-eater, it does not readily respond to the angler's spoons, spinners, and minnow-imitating flies.

CHUM SALMON
Oncorhynchus keta   (Walbaum)

The distinguishing features of the chum, giving it the popular name of "dog salmon," are its extraordinarily large head and jaws and its outsize caninelike teeth. The angle of the jaw extends back well beyond the eye; in the males both jaws become even more elongate and extremely hooked at spawning time. Aside from this seeming abnormality the chum is quite a handsome fish. Its back is blue-gray, often with a purplish sheen, its sides silvery, its fins unspotted. Spots along the dorsal surface and upper sides are present

---

[6] *Intertidal Spawning of Pink Salmon* (U.S. Fish and Wildlife Service, Fish Bulletin 56).

on some individuals, absent from others. In fresh water the adult migrating chums develop a series of reddish or dark brown vertical bands across the sides.

The chum ranges from the Sacramento River to the Arctic. Like the pink salmon, it is not plentiful south of Puget Sound but is very abundant in northerly waters. It occurs on the Arctic coasts of Alaska and Siberia, east to the Mackenzie River and west to the Lena—the apparent limits of both the pink and the chum. On the Pacific Asian side the chum's range extends southward to Kamchatka or beyond.

The average weight of the mature chum is eight to fifteen pounds, occasionally up to twenty. There is no official sporting record, for the chum is not classed as a game fish.

This salmon breeds in the late fall, usually having migrated up-river only a short distance, sometimes not beyond brackish tidewater. In some rivers, however, it travels far upstream. Eggs number 2400 to 3000 for an average female, and hatch in the spring, whereupon the fry head for the sea.

Plankton and small crustaceans—a diet like the pink salmon's—constitute most of the chum's food in salt water, but the chum lives on such fare much longer than the pink, remaining at sea for three to six years. Most mature in the fourth year of life, then return to their rivers to breed and die.

For nearly all chum and pink salmon, the river is only the birth-place, the breeding ground, and the grave. Virtually the entire life, and all of the growth, is in salt water.

Commercially the chum is important because of its abundance, but its yellowish meat is the least valuable of the five Pacific salmons'. The chum lacks repute as a game fish probably because, like the pink salmon, it is not a great fish-eater and seldom hits a bait or lure. Those who have taken it, however, give its sporting qualities a high rating.

HOMING AND OCEAN TRAVEL

Opinions differ on the homing faculty of the Pacific salmons. Some hold that this instinct, or whatever it may be, is not so marked among the *Oncorhynchus* tribe as with the Atlantic *Salmo salar*. Certain experiments have tended to support this view; others have shown that the Pacific salmons have an acutely developed sense of the parent river and almost unfailingly return, not only to the river but to the precise tributary where they were born.

Possibly those who discount this ability have been influenced by studies of transplanted stocks of salmon rather than native stocks, for there is evidence that the former do not return home with the completeness and accuracy of the latter.

On the affirmative side, Roderick L. Haig-Brown writes (see footnote 4), "It is abundantly clear, both from the results of marking salmon and from the predictable returns of runs, that the fish find their way not merely to their own river system but to a particular branch of it and to the particular tributary of that branch in which their parents spawned and they themselves hatched from the gravel."

Mr. Haig-Brown cites the case of two pink salmon which "have the distinction of being the only salmon in history to be marked as fry before leaving fresh water, caught (as adult fish) in salt water, marked again, and recaptured on their return to spawn in the stream of their birth." Both fish were hatched in Morrison Creek, a small tributary of a small Vancouver Island stream. Both were later caught and tagged at sea, on different days in August, one 45 miles north of the stream, the other 115 miles south. Both reached the Morrison Creek counting fence on the same day, October 6th—"as faithful and dramatic a return from wandering as could well be asked for."

An experiment reported by Lauren R. Donaldson and George H. Allen,[7] on the homing of the coho (silver) salmon in the State of Washington, shows an uncanny ability to find the natal environs. In this test, cohos of the brood year 1950 were reared to fingerling stage at the Soos Creek Hatchery, Washington Department of Fisheries. Two differently marked lots of fingerlings were transferred, in January 1952, to two separate points on a river-and-lake system draining into Puget Sound. In March, after two months in their respective waters, the two lots were released. One lot, with the right ventral fin clipped (called the RV lot), was released thirty-five miles from Puget Sound. Between this release point and the Sound are two large lakes, one

    [7] "Return of Silver Salmon to Point of Release," reprinted from *Transactions of the American Fisheries Society*, Vol. 87 (1957).

small lake, several miles of river, and at least five tributary inlets. The other lot, with the left ventral clipped (LV), was liberated on the small lake, separated from Puget Sound by only a few miles of river.

Many of these fish returned as adults in the fall and winter of 1953–54. A total of 70, all belonging to the RV lot, returned all the way to the point of their release thirty-five miles above Puget Sound, unerringly passing through the three lakes, including the small lake where the LV lot had been released. Just one stray, of the LV group, was among the RV returnees to this point. Of the LV lot, 124 returned to their point of release near the Sound. Significantly, not a single fish in the RV group strayed to this pond, although all of them had to pass it on their way upstream to their own point of release. Also significant is the fact that, although all of these fish had been *reared* at the Soos Creek Hatchery, not one returned to Soos Creek.

Naturally propagated salmon return to their parent stream; those artificially hatched and liberated return to the stream from which they were released, not to the stream to which their parents returned. If released from hatchery ponds with direct access to streams via channel or fish ladder, the adult fish will home to the same ponds, climbing the ladder two to four years later. The usual hatchery procedure with returning ripe salmon is to kill the fish, which would die anyway after spawning, then to strip and fertilize the eggs. The progeny are held in ponds until the fingerling stage, then released, perhaps to join naturally propagated migrants going to sea.

As with the Atlantic salmon, apparently the parr (or fry) environment, rather than heredity, is the influential homing factor.

As yet no one has clearly identified the bases of the homing phenomenon. It has been ascribed by some to the salmon's olfactory sense, the "smell of the river," or to other essential attributes of a river which persist far out to sea. This is the "zone of influence" theory discussed in the Atlantic salmon chapter.

Certainly there is no doubt that salmon have a keen sense of smell. Bear paws and other odor-emanating objects, dipped in the water upcurrent from salmon, will cause them to turn and retreat downstream. That this sense is the agent directing them back to their native streams is debatable, however. Shapovalov and Taft point out (see footnote 5) that the mouths of most California streams supporting the silver (coho) salmon are closed by sandbars during the summer months, and that in some instances the lower rivers are entirely dry, so that no fresh water reaches the ocean. Yet a good percentage of the salmon born in these streams return to spawn.

Once in the river, the salmon's sense of smell may guide it to its native tributary. In an experiment in 1953,[8] adult cohos were captured on their spawning runs in two tributaries of a Washington river, placed in tanks, and returned to the main river below its division into the two tributaries. The nasal sacs of half of these fish were plugged with cotton wool, the other half left unplugged. The great majority of the unplugged fish returned to the tributary of their choice; the plugged-nose fish returned in nearly random fashion.

The homing faculty remains a riddle. The homing migration of salmon may be considered in two phases: (1) travel from the ocean to the zone of the river influence, and (2) travel from the outer limits of this zonal influence to the river itself and thence upriver to the spawning grounds. With the Pacific salmons the first phase of the return home commonly takes a southeasterly direction at sea. The coast may be reached outside the river's zone of influence; then the school cruises the coastline, as Atlantic salmon do, until the sense (believed to be smell) of the native river is encountered, and the second phase of the homing journey begins. Most salmon which stray into a river other than that of their birth become lost in the first phase of the homing migration. Once in the river's zone of influence the sense of smell and, perhaps to a degree, the sense of sight, govern the upriver run to the breeding grounds. Taste is believed to play no part in directing the salmon home.

Equally impressive is the seaward migration of fry and parr. Here is an irresistible compulsion, seizing upon pink and chum salmon very soon after birth, upon the other Pacifics and the Atlantic at later stages. It is as if the ocean were a giant magnet, and the little fry or parr were iron filings. Certainly some sharp physiological change in the fish must generate this action, but such a statement does little to elucidate the basic causes. Specifically, the seaward urge among parr is evoked by many factors. Sunlight and temperature affect the eyes and various developing glands and organs of the little fish, and cause perhaps a restlessness which leads them to swim downstream or simply submit

[8] Reported by J. W. Jones in *The Salmon* (Harper & Row, New York, 1959).

to the current. The ceaseless downstream flow of a river is in itself conceivably a powerful influence beckoning the young salmon to the sea. Once reaching salt water they have undergone organic changes which make life in fresh water impossible and so prevent any return until, years later, other changes shall influence the adults' homing to their river to breed and die.

In their sea lives Pacific salmon may journey only a short way but they are capable of traveling prodigious distances. That some chinooks originating in the Puget Sound drainage system remain in the Sound for most or all of their saltwater existence is perhaps exceptional, for the chinook is a famous coastwise traveler, doubtless the greatest of the five Pacific species. Chinooks tagged off the northerly points of Queen Charlotte Islands, B.C., have been recovered in the Columbia River, 700 miles south, in less than a month, on the spawning return. Others, tagged in the Columbia River, have been recaptured in Alaska.

Pink, chum, and sockeye salmon travel out to sea for hundreds of miles. Alaska-spawned salmon of these species have been caught west of the 175th degree of longitude, a dividing line for U.S.–Canada and Japanese fishing, as set by treaty in 1953. This line is about 250 miles west of Nunivak Island, the extreme westerly point of the Alaskan salmon-fishing grounds. It is 500 to 600 miles west of Bristol Bay, a famous sockeye-fishing area. Prior to the treaty of 1953, Japanese fishermen took large numbers of Alaskan salmon—pinks, chums, and sockeyes—far at sea, well beyond the continental shelf.

While coho salmon are believed to hug the coasts, they have been known to travel great coastal distances. Marked cohos from Waddell Creek, California, have been recaptured 200 miles north. At such a point, the estuaries of many salmon rivers lie behind the migrant, between him and his parent stream, and perhaps all of them are exerting some essential influence seaward. Yet the far adventurer returns, passing them all and entering, finally, his own.

THE COMMERCIAL FISHERY

Drifting with the northerly course of currents along the Pacific coast are myriads of minute organisms that compose the ocean plankton. This massive suspension of nutriment is followed by the plankton-feeders—the herring, other small fishes, and euphausiid shrimps. These, in turn, are followed by the salmon. Upon this ocean pyramid of life, the salmon-fishing and canning industry has been built.

Alaska was discovered by the Russian explorer Vitus Bering in 1741. For more than a hundred years thereafter, salmon played only a minor role in the development of the region. Fur was the major item of trade. Probably the earliest fishing enterprise was set up by another Russian, Grigorii Shelikov, on Kodiak Island in 1785, merely to provide dried salmon for workers of his fur-trading firm.[9]

Salted salmon was the chief product of the early industry; but the discovery of the canning process by the French confectioner Nicolas Appert, in 1809, opened up the true potential. Today, canned salmon constitutes nearly 90 per cent of the entire production, the balance being made up of frozen, cured, and fresh.

The total North American catch of Pacific salmon is currently about 300 million pounds a year, probably 70 times greater than the entire Atlantic-salmon commercial fishery.

Of the total Pacific catch, that which is canned yields an annual pack of about 5½ million cases of 48 pounds each, net. Alaska contributes over 60 per cent of the total pack, British Columbia about 33 per cent, the Washington-Oregon coast about 4½ per cent.[10]

Pink salmon, one of the less valuable species per pound, makes up the major share of the total catch and pack. The sockeye and chinook are the most valuable, but the chinook is a minor factor in the total commercial catch.

The commercial fishery is carried on by three principal methods: gill netting, purse seining, and trolling.

The gill net is a web of netting perhaps 200 feet long and 20 feet deep (maximum dimensions are regulated by law), with a mesh usually of 6½ inches. Resembling an underwater fence, the net is suspended vertically by means of lead weights along the lower edge and of floats along the upper. It is set in bays, estuaries, or offshore, in the salmons' migratory path, and is virtually invisible to the fish. Salmon run into it, thrust their heads into the meshes, and are caught by the

[9] Hubert H. Bancroft, *History of Alaska, 1730–1888* (Antiquarian Press, New York, 1958).

[10] Canned salmon figures based on statistics in *Pacific Fisherman*, January 25, 1963.

gills as they attempt to force their way through. The nets are periodically hauled aboard fishing vessels by power-driven drums, and the salmon removed by hand.

The purse seine is so called because of a purse line running through rings on its bottom edge. The seine is piled in the stern of a fishing vessel which tows a dory or skiff. One end of the seine is attached to the smallboat. To start the set, the dory is dropped astern; the vessel then maneuvers in a circle, paying out the seine to surround a school of salmon. When the circle is completed the purse line is drawn gradually in, preventing the salmon's escape below it. The entire seine with its trapped salmon is then closed, brought alongside, and winched aboard if the vessel is a large one. Smaller fishing boats brail up the catch with huge dip nets.

Cannery-tender vessels, hovering near the fishing fleet, take the netted catch at intervals, hence the fishing boats need not go ashore after each haul.

A trolling vessel is commonly equipped with four long poles, upright when not in use, lowered out and down for trolling. A stainless-steel line from each pole is fitted with a 40-pound weight and rigged with a series of trolling spoons or perhaps whole herrings. Salmon hooked on such lures or bait are brought aboard by power-driven drums. Troll-caught salmon are mostly chinooks and cohos, the two major fish-eating species which are prone to strike a bait or lure.

The salmon trap, once widely used and highly effective, has been outlawed in some areas. An old Indian device, it is used today with various refinements in the Atlantic salmon fishery, where it is sometimes called a "pound net," and in Alaska. The trap is usually a permanent installation of piles, driven into the bottom and extending for hundreds of yards across the line of the salmon migration. Piles and attached netting are so arranged as to lead the fish to a central point or trap, where they are dipped out. Floating traps are contrived with a similar design, but are supported by a floating and anchored structure of logs.

The mechanical magics of industry have been evoked to turn the beautiful sea-run silvery salmon into the contents of cans on the supermarket counters. One machine after another, each running at an incredible speed, reduces the bright fish to its final destiny. Elevators hoist it from the fishing vessels; an ingenious gadget removes head, tail, fins, and viscera at the rate of a fish a second; a can-filling machine cuts and molds cylinders of pink meat into can-fitting shapes, and these are slipped into cans speeding along a line at something like 250 per minute. Other robotlike devices add salt, apply the can's top, seal the whole thing, wash it, cook it, and finally affix a label.

Despite modern efficiencies of gear, machinery, and methods, the total catch and pack of Pacific salmon has declined sharply. Alaska, greatest of all suppliers, opened its first cannery in 1878, only eleven years after the United States purchased Alaska from Russia. Since then, Alaska has had a salmon history that reads, in some of its more anguished chapters, like a series of war dispatches.[11]

It is a story of greed, overfishing, exploitation by large remote-control interests of the basic rights of resident fishermen—the fable of the goose and its golden egg told in terms of the industrial age. As fishing pressures increased, the spawning escapement became less and less, and the salmon runs declined; as the salmon runs declined, the commercial quest concentrated more and more tightly upon such profitable runs as were left. Canneries dwindled from a peak of 160 (many of them small) in 1929 to about 25 large ones in 1959. Mobile gear—gill nets and seines—increased sharply while the total catch was diminishing. Numbers of fishermen doubled, from 6000 in the late 1930's to 12,000 in the late 1950's, and of course the average take per capita dropped sharply.

In Alaska's peak salmon year, 1936, the total catch was 750 million pounds (more than twice the figure for the entire North American Pacific fishery for 1961–62).

In a country blessed, as Alaska was, with some two thousand streams producing significant runs of spawning salmon, the story might have been different. Many people tried to make it different—fought to save what they saw to be a vanishing resource. Yet the fishing pressure expanded, year by year. Individual entrepreneurs, seeing their rights transgressed, fought the large companies. Trap-robbing was common, and an occasional gunfight was the natural consequence. By 1920 the U.S. Navy and Coast Guard had a dozen or

[11] As told in *Politics and Conservation* by Richard A. Cooley (Harper & Row, New York, 1963).

so vessels on active patrol to prevent piracy of traps. Between 1906 and 1924, in the long political fight between the cannery organizations and the people of Alaska, no less than forty-two different bills on the Alaskan fishery were introduced in Congress. President Harding and Secretary of Commerce Hoover personally toured the front lines. As late as 1939, seven members of the House Merchant Marine and Fisheries Committee visited Alaska where they traveled thousands of miles inspecting canneries, traps, and other gear, and even troubled to witness the basic element of the entire rumpus—the innocent salmon on its way to spawn.

The Pacific salmon has always been able to maintain its populations against many natural predators. The survival rates of adult salmon returning to spawn, out of the total eggs hatched, have always been microscopically small. Yet the salmon has held against the inroads of trout, eels, squawfish, kingfishers, diving ducks, herons and gulls, flood and drought, upon fry and parr during the brief freshwater tenure. It has held against the seals, sea lions, sharks, and Beluga whales which devour adult salmon at sea, and against the bears, otters, and mink which await it on the upriver runs. It has held, even, against aboriginal man.

But it does not hold against modern man, with his need to feed 200 million mouths, and his need for hydroelectric dams, and lumber, and other industry that befouls and blocks off the ancient salmon waterways. The Alaska story has been repeated, with differences only in detail, from California to Puget Sound, and even in British Columbia.

Attempting to save the Pacific salmon from further decline, fisheries-management agencies in the West are tightening regulations upon commercial fishing, pollution, erosion, and aerial spraying; selectively breeding salmon for more, larger, earlier-maturing, and hardier fish; creating new fishways and lifts at dams, and new spawning grounds where needed; and screening water diversions where young salmon may be lost. It is to be hoped that there will be few repetitions of such atrocities as the digging up of spawning gravel to build highways.

One cannot be overly sanguine, however. At the current stage of the salmon's decline man's efforts can hardly be expected to hold populations intact. Industry and agriculture on the one hand, and salmon on the other, are historically incompatible. The choice lies between the two, despite the utmost in conservation practices, and the American economic system has always given the choice to industry and agriculture.

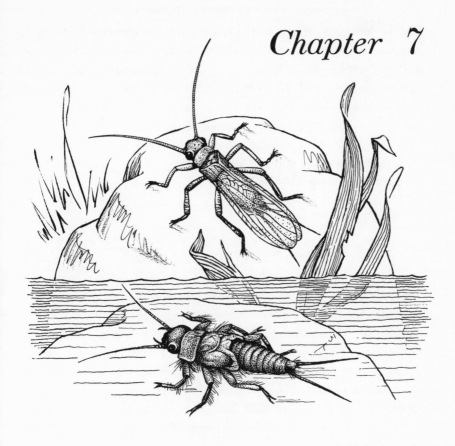

Chapter 7

GRAYLING

The grayling is one of the most colorful and high-spirited of all fresh-water fishes, a creature of the frigid waters of the northern wilds. Where the wilderness has succumbed to man and his works, the grayling has vanished.

This fish has two remarkable and entirely unrelated distinctions. One is its huge flaglike dorsal fin. The other is its ancient and extraordinary reputation of possessing the odor of wild thyme. The second

NOTE: Illustration is of stonefly imago and nymph.

feature has given the fish its generic name, *Thymallus*; the first is responsible for the specific name *signifer*, or "standard-bearer." Some writers currently use *Thymallus signifer* to designate the Arctic or Alaska grayling, and *Thymallus signifer tricolor* to denominate the American subspecies or variants, the Montana and Michigan graylings. Others use *T. arcticus signifer* for the Alaska-Canada fish, *T. arcticus tricolor* for the Montana and Michigan members. Earlier scientists, holding the Montana and Michigan graylings to be separate and distinct species, referred to the former as *T. montanus*, and to the latter as *T. tricolor*.

ARCTIC GRAYLING
Thymallus arcticus (Pallas)

The American Fisheries Society happily chooses to distill this witch's brew of nomenclature into a single component by recognizing only one grayling, with the common name of Arctic grayling and the scientific name *Thymallus arcticus*. This simplification is eminently in agreement with ichthyologists who contend that the grayling is another relic of the last glacial age, and that the several forms are but variants, their relative sizes and color differences the results of environment over countless generations.

The grayling is considered today a member of the salmonid family, along with the trouts, chars, salmons, and whitefishes. Previously only the trouts, chars, and salmons were classed as Salmonidae; the graylings were Thymallidae, the whitefishes Coregonidae.

Various local—and more or less erroneous—names for the grayling are Rocky Mountain whitefish, Colorado grayling, *poisson bleu*, Yellowstone grayling, Manistee herring.

The grayling's range is tremendous, and virtually all of it is in remote wilderness regions away from the haunts of men. *Thymallus* is still abundant in Canada, from the Nelson River drainage of Manitoba westward across northern Saskatchewan, Alberta, and British Columbia, and north to Yukon, the Northwest Territories, and Alaska. On the Alaska Peninsula, Becharof Lake is said to be the home of very large specimens. The grayling is not found in the

Aleutians, but from Bristol Bay north across the Alaskan interior and all the way to the Arctic Ocean, almost all the streams and many of the lakes have their populations. Abroad, the grayling has been known for centuries in northern Europe and Asia.

Oddly, this fish was native to Michigan and Montana but apparently to no state in between. Though believed extinct in Michigan since the late 1930's, the grayling once swarmed in such streams as the Au Sable, Manistee, Muskegon, Hersey, Pine, and Boardman. The town of Grayling, Michigan, on the Au Sable River, was named for the fish. Harold H. Smedley notes, in *Trout of Michigan*,[1] "The grayling was so significantly Michigan that it was once suggested that the 'flag fish' be adopted as part of the State's escutcheon." Thaddeus Norris wrote of grayling on the Au Sable River in the year 1874, "On our second day we killed and salted down, heads and tails off, 120 pounds of fish besides eating all we could."

Norris was a sportsman and conservationist, certainly no fish hog. His 120 pounds of grayling could have made no perceptible dent in the Au Sable's population in 1874. Later, however, the slaughter of grayling on Michigan's rivers was unrestrained. Mr. Smedley writes of fishermen whose pleasure, during the grayling's spawning runs, was "to fill the box of a common lumber wagon full of fish, not just one load but half a dozen each spring for several successive years. All sizes were taken; the larger were kept, the fingerlings thrown on the bank to rot."

Other influences, too, helped to end the grayling in Michigan. Possibly the greatest offender was the lumbering industry. Logging along the river banks opened the cool, wooded streams to the sun, warmed the water, silted the bottoms. Log drives in the springtime breeding season of the grayling destroyed the old spawning beds.

Attempts at artificial propagation, with Michigan native fish and Montana transplants, yielded no permanent population. The haunts of the Michigan fish were far from most of the state hatcheries, and the early-spring spawning season made difficult the capture and transportation of ripe adults. As late as 1936, about 150,000 Montana grayling were stocked in Michigan waters, but the results have been insignificant.

[1] Privately printed, 1938.

In Montana the grayling is native to and was once abundant in the upper Missouri River, above Great Falls, and its diminished numbers still persist in this drainage. Here Lewis and Clark first noted this fish, and believed it to be a species of trout. The Montana grayling's true discoverer, however, was James W. Milner of the United States Fish Commission. Milner found the fish in a tributary of the upper Missouri River, in 1872, and named it *Thymallus montanus*.

The Montana Fish and Game Department reports the native grayling as present today in the headwaters of the Madison and Jefferson rivers, but adds that stocks are badly depleted and may become extinct. One of the sources of the great Missouri River system, the remote Red Rock Lakes in southwestern Montana, also holds a native population of grayling.

The northern grayling shows usually a dark blue back and purplish gray sides, iridescent on fresh-caught fish. Some twelve to eighteen well-spaced bluish black spots appear on the forward sides, both above and below the lateral line. The small head is blue-bronze, with a bright blue marking on each side of the lower jaw. The huge sail-like dorsal fin is grayish, sometimes pale pink on its upper edge, with crossrows of blue spots edged in red. In the Michigan and Montana varieties, the dorsal displays on its upper parts reddish or purple spots encircled by bright green; on its lower areas it has dark roseate lines. The pectoral, anal, and caudal fins are pale gold to greenish, and unmarked; the ventral may be streaked diagonally with deep purple and pale pink.

In all graylings, the male's dorsal fin is larger than the female's; on the male of the Michigan-Montana fish the dorsal when folded down reaches to the adipose. The folded dorsal is the normal or reposed position; it is erected in anger or excitement, as at spawning time or when a hooked grayling is fighting for its freedom.

Probably the average length of the grayling is ten to fourteen inches, the average weight less than a pound. Specimens of two pounds are not uncommon in Alaska and other northern waters. The angling record is a fish of exactly five pounds, taken by William G. Clark in Great Slave Lake, Northwest Territories, on August 5, 1959.

The grayling lives to the age of seven or eight years. Fish of the average size are probably three to four years old. Fishermen have

Arctic Grayling

noted that grayling seem to run to uniform sizes in any given water. If your first fish is a pound and a half you are lucky, for your subsequent strikes will probably be from fish of the same size. Reasons have been advanced for this apparent oddity: different feeding habits of adult and immature fish, or the probability that the large graylings, if present, bully the smaller ones away from the lure.

The grayling's reputed odor of wild thyme has been noted by many writers and denied by a few. Izaak Walton remarked the scent: "And some think he feeds on water-thyme, for he smells of it when first taken out of the water." Some fourteen hundred years before Walton, the writer Æolian (A.D. 170–230) observed the same delicate emanation. An Italian who wrote in Greek, and who is credited as the first in history to describe an artificial fly, Æolian mentioned the *thymallus*, a kind of grayling (of Macedonia) and its odor of a freshly gathered bunch of thyme.

Now and then the picturesque thyme legend has been deprecated by the irreverent. One such dissent was voiced by T. E. Pritt, in the 1880's: "Some writers have compared the odor to freshly-cut cucumber; others, more fanciful, have been undecided whether it was thyme or lemon. I confess my imagination will not reach any of these similes . . . It is a strong, pungent suggestion of fish, not, I think, altogether pleasant."[2]

The majority of grayling mature and spawn at the age of three or four. By mid-March, in more southerly waters, the fish move upstream to spawn. Elsewhere the season may be April or May, or even June in the far north. Lake grayling begin their spawning activities immediately following the breakup of ice, when they migrate usually into tributaries, though some of the lake fish are said to spawn on the inshore shoals. The river fish seek the headwaters or the small feeder streams, sometimes traveling long distances. Shoal water over sand or fine-gravel bottoms is preferred; often the water over the spawning beds is only inches deep, and the great dorsal sails can be seen moving above the surface. The males are now more brilliant than the females and may be easily distinguished.

The grayling makes no attempt to dig nests. As the eggs are extruded the male is with the female, sometimes with his dorsal fin wrapped over her back. The small adhesive eggs are soon covered lightly, not by the female but by current-washed sand or gravel. The average female grayling deposits 2000 to 4000 eggs, but upwards of 8000 have been counted from large fish.

The incubation period is two to three weeks. The unusually small yolk sac is absorbed within a week or ten days, and the free-swimming fry, half an inch long, begin at once to feed voraciously on tiny aquatic life.

[2] *The Book of the Grayling* (Goodall and Suddick, London, 1888).

Later, the grayling's food is composed largely of insects. A study of the food intake of the Montana grayling introduced into Ford Lake, Michigan, in 1936,[3] revealed that well over half the diet was composed of aquatic Diptera. The tabulation included dragonfly nymphs, water fleas, copepods, Mayfly nymphs, water beetles, midge larvae and nymphs, aphids, land beetles, ants, wasps, and spiders.

The grayling is a difficult hatchery fish, according to an early (1907) Bureau of Fisheries Document.[4] Though the ripe eggs lie loosely in the abdominal cavity and are easily stripped, they must be handled with great care. Much more washing is required than with trout eggs because of a glutinous substance that otherwise causes them to bunch and become susceptible to fungus. Because of the brief incubation time, shipments of grayling eggs may hatch in transit if the temperature rises above 42° F.

The dedicated trout angler can take the grayling to his heart as his own fish. The four-ounce trout fly rod, tapered line and leader, and dry or wet flies constitute the ideal gear. Like the brown trout, the grayling may be highly selective at times, and then, for no apparent reason, start hitting almost any fly that is offered. It seems to disdain the cover of overhanging branches, windfalls, and rocky shelves, often congregating in schools plainly visible in open pools or flats with no cover anywhere.

The strike may be spectacular or very quiet. The grayling sometimes leaps completely clear of the surface and takes the fly on the downward arc. Again, the fish may nose up under the fly, seeming to inhale it and merely dimpling the surface.

Once hooked, the grayling is an active fighter. Some anglers pronounce it as game as any fish in fresh water; others say that after a brilliant but brief struggle it is apt to fold and come easily to net. Because of its weak mouth the grayling should be played more carefully than a trout of the same size.

British fishermen have been inclined to scorn the *Thymallus*, but the English fish has had at least one stout defender in T. E. Pritt (see

[3] Justin W. Leonard, "Feeding Habits of the Montana Grayling in Ford Lake, Michigan," reprinted from *Transactions of the American Fisheries Society*, Vol. 68 (1938).

[4] *Culture of the Montana Grayling* (U.S. Fisheries Station, James A. Henshall, Superintendent, Bozeman, Montana, Document No. 628).

footnote 2). This writer contended that the grayling should be caught in the fall or winter—September to February—but not in the spring, to appreciate its game qualities. "The grayling spawns in the spring, and not until the first breath of approaching winter has chilled the rivers . . . does he begin to assert himself as one of the best of the British sporting fish, and by this time the majority of anglers have laid their rods aside." Mr. Pritt cited a popular belief that the grayling was introduced into English rivers by the monks of old, "in order to have at hand a fish which is in its best season when trout and salmon are out of condition."

Chapter 8

WHITEFISHES AND CISCOES

The whitefishes, a coldwater northern tribe belonging to the salmonid family, include fourteen species of the genus *Coregonus* and six of the *Prosopium*. Only a few are still in sufficient abundance to be commercially important; still fewer can be considered game fish. Within the purview of "familiar" fishes, only five—the lake, round, mountain whitefish, cisco, and inconnu—require detailed comment.

119

Among the whitefishes' many similarities to other salmonid forms, probably the most outstanding is their environmental necessity. From Newfoundland and Labrador to the Great Lakes, across the northern tier of states, and from Hudson Bay westward across Canada to Alaska, native or introduced whitefishes live with the trouts, chars, and graylings in the clear, cold lakes and rivers. Along both coasts various species of whitefish are native to the river-and-lake systems entered by the Atlantic and Pacific salmons. In the Great Lakes region particularly, and in many deepwater inland lakes, the lake whitefish, round whitefish, and various shallow and deep varieties of ciscoes and chubs constitute a staple food of the lake trout.

Abroad, the range of the whitefish family includes northern Europe and Asia.

The whitefishes all have the adipose fin and soft-rayed dorsal typical of the Salmonidae. They possess, also, an axillary process or projection of cartilaginous material at the base of the pelvic or ventral fins.

In other respects, the whitefishes differ markedly from the trout-char branch of the family. They are invariably school fish, not given to the lone wandering and individual enterprise of some of the trouts and chars. Because of this gregariousness the formerly abundant white-fish were taken in huge numbers by gill nets set in the school lanes.

The whitefish scales are much larger than the trouts' and chars', numbering about seventy to one hundred in the lateral line. The head and mouth of the whitefishes are proportionally smaller, and the tail more deeply forked. The jaws are usually totally devoid of teeth, though occasionally a few weak teeth are present, and some of the whitefishes have teeth on the tongue. The inconnu of the far north is exceptional, possessing small teeth in its jaws. The whitefishes are generally without body spots but may show spots on the fins. At spawning time one or both sexes may develop small tubercles called "pearl organs" on the head and/or sides.

None of the whitefish clan is anadromous though some of them make quite lengthy upriver migrations to their spawning grounds. The inconnu frequents brackish or salt water in the northern bays but spends most of its life well above the intertidal zones. The lake white-fish is the only one of the group with a saltwater reference in the

American Fisheries Society's listings. There is no record of extensive sea travel for this species, however, or of any phase of its existence that could properly be called a sea life.

Dr. John Van Oosten wrote of the Great Lakes whitefish in 1936:[1]

From evidence, it is assumed that ten distinct species of this group (whitefish, herring, chub) were found in the Great Lakes basin (including Lake Nipigon) before the close of the glacial period. Herring and whitefish survived in all lakes; none of the rest survived in the warmest lake, Lake Erie.

Each group occupies a rather broad zone defined by depths at its margins. . . . These zones overlap at the margins so that different forms are intermingled in small numbers. The selection of a zone by a certain species is influenced by . . . factors such as the character of the bottom, depth, temperature, nearness of shoals or depths, which factors also affect the abundance of organisms on which the various species feed. The majority of the species vary as to spawning season, spawning depths, and spawning grounds. The shoal forms spawn at approximately the same season, late fall and early winter, while deeper-water forms spawn at different times of the year. The spawning season of any species may vary considerably from year to year, and also may occur a month or two earlier or later in the different lakes. . . . It appears that coregonids are spawning in one or more of the lakes during all months except July.

Excellent food fishes, the lake whitefish and the cisco or lake herring were once the basis of a thriving commercial fishery, concentrated chiefly in the Great Lakes area. This plentiful supply, and its proximity to large processing and marketing centers, supported an extensive fishery for several decades. Overfishing, sea-lamprey depredations, pollution, and other factors brought about a sharp decline in whitefish and cisco populations despite the efforts of hatcheries to maintain the fish by artificial propagation. At one time, Upper and Lower Red Lakes in northern Minnesota were important sources of whitefish eggs for hatchery rearing. Millions of fry from Red Lakes eggs were planted in Lake Superior. This work was typical of many efforts to restore the Great Lakes whitefish commercial fishery, but no significant increase resulted.

[1] In charge, Great Lakes Fisheries Investigation, U.S. Bureau of Fisheries, Ann Arbor, Mich. Memorandum published by the Fisheries Division of the Michiban Department of Conservation, March 20, 1936.

LAKE WHITEFISH
Coregonus clupeaformis   (Mitchill)

The lake whitefish, deep-bodied and laterally thin, is the largest of the tribe, with the exception of that odd fellow the inconnu, and the most important of the whitefishes commercially.

Other names for this species are common whitefish, Great Lakes whitefish, and inland whitefish. Various local names denominate the species in different areas.

The lake whitefish's extensive range runs from Newfoundland and Labrador west and north across Canada, and from New England and New York westward across the northern United States. The fish's northern limits extend over the 60th degree of latitude into Yukon, the Northwest Territories, and Alaska. Though it inhabits some very deep lakes it is classed as a shallow-water form, preferring a depth range of 50 to 150 feet.

The lake whitefish can be a handsome specimen when fresh-caught. Though it varies considerably from one water to another, in its better color phases it has a dark bronze to greenish back, a hint of pale pink-orange on the upper sides, bright silver below the lateral line, and white on the belly. A pearly iridescence is on the back and sides. The snout slightly overhangs the lower jaw, and two flaps of membrane are between the openings of the nostrils.

Though this is a delicate species—mature fish frequently die in hatcheries and aquaria if not accorded the gentlest of handling—it is potentially a long-lived fish. Specimens have lived for ten years in captivity, and wild fish estimated to be eighteen years old have been caught.

Two generations ago, the Great Lakes yielded lake whitefish of twenty pounds and over. Official data are lacking on record fish taken on sporting tackle. Today the Great Lakes average is less than three pounds; those over four pounds are commonly called "jumbos" in Lake Erie. Despite the downtrend in the commercial catch, broad fluctuations occur. In a given year the catch may be ten times as great as the previous year's take, only to decline as steeply in the year following.

Inhabiting comparatively deep waters during the summer and winter, the mature lake whitefish ascend to the shallows in the spring and fall. The autumnal migration, in late October or November, is the spawning run. The eggs are often dropped over rocky bottoms of the shoreward or reef shoals similar to those used by lake trout. Indeed, the whitefish and lake trout often spawn on the same shoal at the same time, for eggs of the two species have been found in the same rock crevices. Whitefish make no attempt to build nests, the females merely casting their eggs at random. These unprotected eggs number 15,000 to 20,000 for an average-size female, and mortality among them is doubtless high. Survivers hatch in the late winter or early spring.

Food of the lake whitefish consists chiefly of plankton, mollusks, crustaceans, aquatic insects and their larvae. Though not as piscivorous as the larger trouts and chars, the whitefish preys on small fishes to some degree.

This species is taken by anglers through the summer by deep still-fishing with such baits as grubs, minnows, small strips cut from yellow perch, and dough balls. Small hooks are needed. Some anglers use floats or dobbers, but many contend that only one's fingers on the line can detect the first tentative overtures of the whitefish at the bait. Old hands at whitefishing say that many fish are lost by striking too quickly. The trick is to wait out the whitefish's first gentle nibbling, and to strike only when a harder pull occurs. Even large specimens indulge in very delicate maneuvers with the bait before taking hold. Once hooked, the whitefish must be played with great care because of its tender mouth.

Fly-fishing for lake whitefish is practiced when the spring and fall shoalwater movements are on. But probably more are caught during the winter, by ice fishermen, than in the rest of the year. On many inland lakes of Ontario and the states of the Great Lakes region, ice-fishing for the whitefish has long been a popular sport.

CISCO OR LAKE HERRING
Coregonus artedii Le Sueur

This is another "shallow-water" member of the whitefish clan, usually summering at depths of 30 to 100 feet and entering the shoals in the spring and fall. Other names are freshwater herring, grayback,

Lake Whitefish
with Two Mountain Whitefish

blueback, and tullibee. As its name implies, this fish resembles the common marine herring, but the two are in no way related.

Smaller than the lake whitefish but excellent as food, the cisco is still of commercial significance though its numbers have diminished substantially in the Great Lakes and elsewhere. It is important also in many waters as a forage fish for lake trout.

The cisco is native to the Great Lakes and many coldwater lakes of New England, New York, Quebec, and Ontario, northward to Hudson Bay and west to Saskatchewan.

Deep and laterally compressed, the cisco resembles the lake whitefish in general outline. Its mouth is small and pointed, however, with no overhang of the snout above the lower jaw. The color varies considerably in different waters. The dorsal surface may be green, blue-green, or dark blue; on some ciscoes this dusky shade extends downward halfway to the lateral line. The sides are silvery and iridescent. All fins are pale, the lower ones tipped with dark gray, the dorsal and caudal with wider dusky margins on their posterior edges. Two flaps of skin are between the openings of the nostrils.

Ciscoes

Great Lakes ciscoes occasionally attain weights of five pounds and up. The average, however, is about one pound in the Great Lakes and half a pound in smaller waters.

Mature ciscoes, three to five years old, may enter the lake's shore-line shoals in early fall but do not spawn until late November or December, sometimes after the lake is frozen over. The numerous small eggs are dropped casually, with no preparation of nests, in depths varying from three to twenty feet. Studies by C. J. D. Brown and J. W. Moffett of cisco egg numbers per female in Swains Lake, Michigan, showed a variation between 23,000 and 37,000 for fish of 15¼ to 16¼ inches, and of ages five to nine, the largest number being cast by a six-year-old cisco less than 16 inches long.

The cisco's decline in commercial importance has been compensated to some degree by its growing appeal as a sport fish. The cisco is a fly-taker during its vernal and autumnal periods in shoal water, and is gamy on a light fly rod. Owasco Lake, one of the Finger Lakes of New York, has been the scene of a "cisco derby" in recent years. Ciscoes come into the shoals in great numbers when the June hatch of flies occurs, and many of sixteen inches and up are taken on dry flies. Through the summer deep trolling with small spinners and still-fishing with various baits are effective. Like the lake whitefish, the cisco is good winter game for ice-fishermen. At all seasons its flesh is tasty when fresh or smoked.

ROUND WHITEFISH
Prosopium cylindraceum   (Pallas)

The name round whitefish well describes this species, for the lateral thickness of its body almost equals its vertical depth. Other names are pilot, frostfish, Menominee whitefish, and grayback.

The round whitefish occurs in scattered and thinning populations over a broad range: Labrador to British Columbia, with populations in northern New England, New York and the Great Lakes region. It is said to be absent from Lake Erie.

Though a fine food fish, it is hardly of sufficient abundance in any single area to support a commercial fishery. It is infrequently taken by anglers and has little or no reputation as a sport fish.

The family's characteristic colors are present in the round whitefish: the dark, bronze-green or bluish back, and the silvery sides. The dorsal and tail are gray to brown; the lower fins may show bright pink markings. Rows of dark spots appear on the sides of the young, but fade out as the fish reaches a length of five or six inches. The mouth is small, and the pronounced overhang of the snout gives it almost a suckerlike appearance. A single membrane is present between the nostrils.

The maximum weight of this species is four to five pounds; the average is one to two pounds. It is another "shallow-water" denizen, its schools keeping to depths of 50 to 180 feet during the summer months, and ascending to the lake shoals in the spring and fall. The breeding season is late November or December, sometimes on spawning bottoms 25 to 50 feet below the lake surface, but often in the shallower mouths of tributaries or even well upstream.

The newborn fry move into deeper water not long after hatching in the spring. Their food is chiefly plankton and tiny insect larvae; later they feed on insects, small mollusks and crustaceans.

MOUNTAIN WHITEFISH
Prosopium williamsoni   (Girard)

A western species, the mountain whitefish is native to the cold-water streams and lakes of the Rocky Mountain and northwest coastal states, and north into Alberta and British Columbia, existing in many waters with the cutthroat, Dolly Varden, lake trout, and grayling. The Montana Fish and Game Department rated it a decade ago as "probably the most abundant game fish in the state," and reported it "successful against the competition of exotics, fishing pressure, and agricultural and industrial developments—factors which have greatly reduced the cutthroat, Dolly Varden and grayling."

The mountain whitefish has various local and regional names: Rocky Mountain whitefish, pea nose, stream whitefish, mountain herring, and Williamson's whitefish. Some ichthyologists consider it a variety of the round whitefish.

Its dark dorsal surface and silvery sides are typical, but it differs from the lake whitefish and cisco in having only a single fold of membrane between the nostril openings. Its snout overhangs the lower jaw. Stream fish average less than twelve inches and weigh less than a pound; in the lakes they may attain greater weights. The largest of record was a river fish, however. This specimen, taken by Orville

Welch in the Athabaska River, Alberta, on June 3, 1963, weighed exactly five pounds.

Spawning in the late fall, usually when three years old, the mountain whitefish of the lakes may ascend the tributaries for its egg-laying or merely move into the shallows of the lake itself. Fish in the rivers seek the headwaters or small branch streams. In either event, no nest is made.

This species feeds on aquatic insects to a marked degree. It has a flashing and active response to the artificial fly, fished dry or wet. Perhaps its fastwater habitat has helped the river fish's reputation as a sporty fly-rod fish. In this it is troutlike; in its way of taking bait it is characteristically a whitefish. Anglers are advised to "baby" the tender-mouthed fish once it is hooked. In fast water this need for gentle tactics can impose problems which are of less concern to the angler for cutthroats and Dolly Vardens.

The mountain whitefish lacks importance in the food markets, but its following among anglers is an increasing economic asset to the western states.

INCONNU
Stenodus leucichthys   (Güldenstadt)

The inconnu is called the sheefish in Alaska and along the Canadian Arctic coast, and the nelma or white salmon in Siberia. It is the largest of all the whitefishes, averaging five to ten pounds, and is reported to achieve weights of fifty pounds in exceptional instances.

Comparatively little is known about the inconnu, however. Its range is from the base of the Alaska Peninsula (latitude 60° N.) north to the Arctic, with its most numerous populations above Bering Strait. It frequents the rivers and brackish estuaries of the Arctic drainages on the North American side at least as far as the Mackenzie River delta, and on the Asian side for unknown distances along the Siberian Arctic coast.

The American Fisheries Society lists the inconnu as a freshwater species, with no anadromous reference such as applies to the Atlantic and Pacific salmons and several of the trouts and chars. The inconnu has been reported on its spawning migrations far up the Yukon and Mackenzie rivers, but to measure such distances from the ocean could be misleading, for the runs may begin at points far inland. "Land-locked" or non-migratory inconnu live in some Alaskan lakes and in the large inland seas of the Northwest Territories, such as Great Bear and Great Slave lakes, both accessible via the Mackenzie River.

The inconnu resembles the lesser whitefishes in color, with a dark olive to greenish blue back and silvery sides. It has been reported as having numerous small black spots, and again as being unspotted. The dorsal fin is dark, the forked caudal grayish, and the lower fins pale.

Inconnu

The mouth is large, and the lower jaw projects. Both jaws contain small teeth.

This species may initiate its spawning migration in the summer but does not actually breed until September or October. The lake-dwelling inconnus move into tributaries to spawn; the river fish migrate upstream. Knowledge is scanty regarding the number of eggs deposited, the period of incubation, and the movements of the fry.

Decidedly more piscivorous than other whitefishes, the inconnu is taken on spoons, spinners, bucktail or streamer flies, and baits such as minnows and herring strips. It is generally rated inferior to the chinook and coho salmon as a game fish, but in its larger sizes it has been called, no doubt with justice, an "unexploited tackle buster."

There are conflicting reports on the edibility of the inconnu. Its primary haunts are so far removed from centers of civilization that it has had, to date, no commercial significance.

OTHER WHITEFISHES

Various other ciscoes and chubs of the genus *Coregonus* are common to some or all of the Great Lakes, and to other deep lakes in Quebec, Ontario, Manitoba, and Saskatchewan, and in the northern states from Maine to Montana. These are the longjaw cisco or chub, *C. alpenae*; the bloater, *C. hoyi*; the deepwater cisco or chub, *C. johannae*; the kiyi, *C. kiyi*; the blackfin cisco, *C. nigripinnus*; the Nipigon cisco, *C. nipigon*; the shortnose cisco, *C. reighardi*; and the shortjaw cisco or chub, *C. zenithicus*.

All have the typical whitefish coloration, varying in detail: light green to dark green or olive on the dorsal surface, silvery below. Only two, the Nipigon cisco and the shortnose cisco, are shallow-water species, commonly inhabiting levels from 50 to 200 feet below the surface. The others are deepwater fish, thriving in the abyssal dusks and pressures from 300 to 700 feet down. The Nipigon cisco and the blackfin cisco attain sixteen inches or more; the others are small.

These lesser species have been commercially netted in the past. *C. hoyi* represents a substantial fishery in Lake Michigan today and is expected to increase in commercial importance.

Chapter 9

SHADS, HERRING, ALEWIFE

The shads are of the herring family, the Clupeidae, which includes, other than the freshwater and anadromous species, the strictly marine herrings, menhadens, sardines, and pilchards. All of this family are characterized by a forked tail, a single short, soft-rayed dorsal fin in the middle of the back, and the absence of both an adipose fin and a visible lateral line. The American shad is the largest of the herring family, and among the anadromous species the only one of great importance as a food and game fish.

AMERICAN SHAD
Alosa sapidissima (Wilson)

The story of the American shad parallels that of the salmon. Once tremendously abundant all along the Atlantic coast, the shad has declined because of pollution of rivers and harbors, heavy commercial fishing, and the isolation of spawning grounds by dams. Formerly a staple if seasonal food, the shad and its delectable roe are now approaching the rare-luxury class from New England to Chesapeake Bay.

The natural range of the American shad is the Atlantic coast and its larger rivers from the St. Lawrence in Canada to the St. Johns in Florida. In these waters it has been called the common shad and white shad, and has immemorially acquired the names of its rivers—Hudson River or North River shad, Delaware River shad, Potomac shad, and so on, as if the fish in one river were a different species from those in another. They are all the same, however, as they are on the Pacific coast, where they were introduced in 1871. In that year 12,000 fry from Hudson River stock were planted in the Sacramento River in California. Subsequent transplants in the Sacramento and Columbia rivers proved well adapted to the Pacific waters and eventually spread up and down the coast. Today the American shad is established from San Diego to Cook Inlet, Alaska.

The fresh-run shad in its upstream spawning migration is a bright and gleaming fish, deep blue to blue-green on its back, silvery along the sides. A large dark spot is on the "shoulder," just back of the gill cover, followed by several smaller spots. The anal fin is long, with close-cropped rays. The entire length of the belly is knife-thin, and the scales here give the fish a saw-toothed lower outline characteristic of many of the herring family. The lower jaw fits into a notch in the upper, and weak teeth are present in both.

Male shad taken in nets and by angling average a pound and a half to five pounds; females are slightly larger. In the days of the shad's great abundance, fish of twelve pounds and up were not uncommon; today specimens weighing over eight pounds are rare in east-coast rivers of the United States. Shad of the Pacific coast seem to average somewhat larger than those of the Atlantic. Exceptional are the shad of the St. Lawrence River spawning runs. These fish average appreciably heavier than the shad of Nova Scotia or the Atlantic states, not uncommonly exceeding nine pounds and occasionally reaching twelve. Though many big shad are taken on fly rods and other sporting gear, no official size record is listed.

Like the salmon, the shad spends most of its life and attains most of its growth in the ocean. The ocean food which fattens the shad, however, is a different fare, being almost exclusively plankton.

The upstream spawning runs begin as early as January in the rivers of Florida and Georgia and are progressively later up the coast, occurring in June in Nova Scotia and Quebec. Since some of the spawning migrations are extremely long, water temperatures at the time of the entrance into rivers may be well under the 60°-to-70° F. range which the shad prefers for its egg-laying. Notably long spawning runs are those of the St. Lawrence River, where shad ascend as far upstream as Montreal and even enter the Ottawa River to spawn—at least 500 miles from the Gulf of St. Lawrence—traveling at speeds of 25 to 50 miles a day.[1] Delaware River migrations may be 250 miles from Delaware Bay to spawning beds on the West Branch.

Usually the males are first on the spawning grounds, followed shortly by the females. The reproduction ceremony of the shad is nocturnal and brief. No nest is made. The eggs, non-adhesive and numbering 30,000 to more than 600,000 per female, are shed at random and abandoned. If the river is a northern one, both parents return to the sea. A curious fact, however, is that shad of the southern rivers— North Carolina to Florida—die after spawning.

The eggs sink slowly, swelling as they absorb water, and drifting with the current. They hatch after about a week, at 60° to 65° F., into larval fry that are free-swimming at once, even though part of the eggshell may still be attached.

The young shad remain in the river until fall and then migrate to sea as fingerlings of three to five inches. This first downstream run is a critical time in the life of the shad. Like most young fish they are highly vulnerable to predators, but perhaps the major hazard is pollu-

---

[1] Vadim D. Vladykov, *Movements of Quebec Shad as Demonstrated by Tagging* (Department of Fisheries, Quebec, 1950).

tion in the lower reaches of many rivers. The young shad need more oxygen than is commonly contained in harbor waters of the East. Those surviving the journey to the sea remain there until reaching their maturity in the third, fourth, or fifth year, then return to their native river to spawn.

A curious migratory pattern governs the ocean life of Atlantic coast shad. Gerald B. Talbot of the U.S. Fish and Wildlife Service states that shad spawning in Chesapeake Bay tributaries and northward to New England make a post-spawning migration to the Gulf of Maine, where they feed all summer. In the fall they head south and apparently winter in the middle Atlantic coastal area, moving inshore the following spring and then migrating either north or south to their native streams to spawn. Immature shad which have been born from the Chesapeake Bay drainages northward also travel to the Gulf of Maine each summer until, as mature fish, they are ready for their first spawning ascent of the parent river.[2]

It is believed that the majority of Quebec shad spend the fall, winter, and early spring between the Gulf of Maine and the Nova Scotia banks. Hence the shad's travels, in these instances, are comparable to the longest movements of the salmon. Shad ascending the St. Lawrence River as far as Montreal and making a post-spawning return to the Gulf of Maine cover a distance of fully 1500 miles. (See footnote 1.)

The homing faculty of shad has been less studied than that of salmon but apparently is equally acute. Vladykov reports recaptures of tagged fish clearly indicating that Quebec shad, after spending months in the Atlantic, return to spawning grounds in the St. Lawrence River west of Green Island. One taken in a trap and tagged at Green Island on July 12, 1946 was caught again almost exactly a year later, on July 11, 1947, in the identical trap, set in exactly the same place as the previous year. Lost shad, like lost salmon, are apparently the exceptions.

The history of commercial shad fishing is a sad chronicle of abundance to scarcity. Up to the 1820's the migrating fish ascended the Hudson River as far as Baker's Falls, about fifty miles above Troy.

[2] *The American Shad* (U.S. Fish and Wildlife Service Leaflet No. 504, February 1961).

During the annual run, farmers camping at the falls caught as many as they could and salted them down for home consumption. The building of a dam at Troy in 1825 blocked the upriver migration and ended the spawning above this point.

For nearly a century thereafter, however, the Hudson shad fishery was substantial. In the season of 1895, shad nets in the Hudson numbered 3471 and caught 1,155,610 shad. At Alpine, New Jersey alone, 703 nets accounted for 94,100 shad. The farthest upriver net, at Castleton, New York, nine miles below Albany, took 500 fish. The average price for the entire 1895 season on the Hudson was 20 cents for roe shad, 10 cents for bucks. The total catch weighed 4,044,000 pounds and brought a gross income of $184,897 to fishermen.[3]

The U.S. Fish Commission supplied 54,000,000 shad fry to the Hudson, from Delaware and Susquehanna River stocks, in the years 1882 to 1895. During the same period, New York State hatched and planted over 33,000,000 shad fry in the Hudson. It is doubtful, however, that several billions of fry could have maintained the Hudson stocks against normal mortality, intensive fishing, and a thickening pollution from Albany to New York Bay.

The Hudson's decline as a shad river was more or less paralleled in other streams of the eastern seaboard. The peak year was 1896, when over 50 million pounds were marketed from Canada to Florida. The total held at better than 40 million pounds annually from 1889 to 1901, after which the fishery declined to 20 million pounds by 1912 and to 8 million by 1958.

Figures submitted by Mr. Talbot in *The American Shad* show the steepest declines in the New England and Middle Atlantic areas. The eastern Canada fishery, never above two million pounds since 1895, had extremely low years in 1920 and 1930, but revived from 1950 to 1955 to a yearly level of about 1,600,000 pounds. The Pacific coast fishery had a peak of about 7,500,000 pounds in 1915, declining to about 1,200,000 pounds in 1955.[4] In areas of vast population the shad may well be nearing extinction as a commercial entity, not only in

---

[3] A. N. Cheney, "Shad of the Hudson River," in *First Annual Report of the Commissioner of Fisheries, Game and Forests of the State of New York* (1896).

[4] The Washington State Department of Fisheries reports, as of September 1961, the annual commercial Pacific coast production as approaching three million pounds, with a value of slightly less than a million dollars.

numbers but in quality. Those of the lower Hudson are certainly far inferior in taste today, by comparison with the shad of even twenty-five years ago.

Running counter to the commercial decline, the sport fishery for shad in certain rivers has shown an upsurge. Hardly known as a game fish until recent years, the shad is now earnestly sought by fly-fishermen and others on the Connecticut, Delaware, Susequehanna, and rivers to the south, including particularly the St. Johns in Florida, the Edisto in South Carolina, and the Ogeechee in Georgia. The St. Johns is probably the greatest shad-angling river on the continent, having yielded 60,000 or more shad annually to sports fishermen in recent years.

Though shad are plankton feeders to begin with, and apparently do not feed at all on their spawning migrations, they are comparable to salmon in their willingness to take artificial flies. Other effective lures are small spinners, metal jigs, and colored beads strung upon a hook. The shad is a hard and spectacular fighter, and because of its tender mouth must be handled with extreme care.

A young Canadian guide once told this writer that he would choose a fresh-run shad, for both sport and meat, against a grilse or salmon of equal weight. We of course attributed this incredible pronouncement to youthful heresy—sometimes to be found even in the little upriver villages of the salmon country.

HICKORY SHAD
Alosa mediocris (Mitchill)

This somewhat smaller edition of the American shad is the second-largest of the herring family, reaching three pounds but averaging much less. It ranges from Maine to Florida, with a center of abundance in the Chesapeake Bay area, where it is called the tailor shad or freshwater tailor.

The hickory shad has unique status as an anadromous fish. Apparently it enters rivers to spawn only from Chesapeake Bay to Florida, but is strictly a marine fish in waters north of the Chesapeake.

It is much like the American shad in appearance, including the

Top to bottom: Skipjack Herring,
Shad, Alewife, Hickory Shad

body color and the dark spots behind the opercle, but is distinguished by a projecting lower jaw and by faint stripes along the sides. The hickory shad is much different from the American in its feeding, however, being largely piscivorous. There was formerly quite an extensive market fishery around Chesapeake Bay; today the commerce in hickory shad is negligible.

GIZZARD SHAD
Dorosoma cepedianum (LeSueur)

The gizzard shad, seldom exceeding fifteen inches, is found in fresh waters from the St. Lawrence River west to Minnesota, in parts of the lower Great Lakes region, and thence south to the Gulf states and northeastern Mexico. It is absent from or rare in the northeastern and middle Atlantic states. It inhabits clear to muddy lakes, rivers, bayous, and brackish waters of southern estuaries from which it enters fresh water to spawn.

The distinguishing mark of this fish is the greatly elongated last ray of the dorsal fin. It has the general coloration, long anal fin, sawtoothed belly scales and shoulder spot of the American shad. This spot, however, tends to disappear in older fish. Other differences between young and old gizzard shad are notable. The young have fine teeth on the tongue and a short digestive tract. As the gizzard shad matures, its food is mainly of plant origin. Now the teeth disappear, the intestine becomes greatly lengthened and the stomach thickly muscled like the gizzard of a fowl, giving the fish its name.

The chief value of this fish is as forage for game species. Though largely unknown to anglers, and worthless as food for humans, the gizzard shad is tremendously abundant in some of the southern lakes and impounded reservoirs. There it often waxes so numerous as to become a problem, nullifying its forage value by competition with game fish.

Lake Talquin, an 8800-acre impoundment in northern Florida, had excellent fishing for largemouth bass, bluegills, and crappies until the dam broke in 1957. After the dam was rebuilt and the lake refilled, the once fabulous fishing failed to return. A sampling of the lake's fish populations revealed that the gizzard shad and its close relative, the threadfin shad, constituted 58.4 per cent, by weight, of all fish in the lake. Treatment by rotenone, at the rate of .06 part per million parts of water, killed 500,000 to 600,000 gizzard and threadfin shad. These represented 99.9 per cent of the total kill, with .1 per cent kill of game species.[5]

This report is significant here in revealing how this fish can over-populate a lake if the optimum balance of species is destroyed. Where the balance is maintained, however, the gizzard shad is a vital link in the food chain, converting algae and other plankton into protein for the piscivorous game species.

The similar threadfin shad, *Dorosoma petenense* (Günther), has the elongated dorsal-fin ray. It is abundant in the South, where it has the same ecological niche as the gizzard shad.

ALEWIFE
Alosa pseudoharengus (Wilson)

Usually preceding the shad in its springtime spawning runs, this smallish (under one pound), plankton-feeding member of the herring family enters brooks and rivers of the Atlantic coast from the Gulf of St. Lawrence to the Carolinas. Essentially a marine and anadromous species, the alewife has become landlocked in many waters. It is abundant in Lake Ontario, where it is a principal food of the lake trout.

The alewife has the serrated belly line and dark shoulder spot of the American shad, but is identifiable particularly by its strongly projecting lower jaw. Its back is blue-green to grayish, its sides silvery and often iridescent. It may have indistinct horizontal lines effected by small dark markings on the scales.

In various parts of its range the alewife is called gray herring, branch herring, big-eyed herring, ellwife, and gaspereau. Nova Scotians know it as the kyack, and catch it in dip nets by the thousands on the late-May upstream spawning runs. Many of these fish,

---

[5] John T. Brown, *A Report on Fisheries Investigations and the Selective Treatment of Lake Talquin (Fla.) in 1961* (Florida Game and Fresh Water Fish Commission, April 1962).

averaging eight to ten inches, are dried, salted, and retailed by local stores at five to ten cents each.

Alewives may ascend streams for considerable distances, seeming to prefer upriver ponds and small lakes for their spawning. The eggs are laid during May and June in the northern range, earlier southward, and are abandoned by the parents. The young with access to the sea migrate downstream in the late summer or fall, mature in three or four years, and return upstream to spawn. The prolific females average about 100,000 heavy, adhesive eggs.

Landlocked alewives often die in large numbers during the summer, and their carcasses, washed on shore, impose a considerable nuisance upon lakeshore cottagers and bathers. W. B. Scott, in *Freshwater Fishes of Eastern Canada*,[6] says recent studies indicate this "die-off" is correlated with changes in water temperature.

Closely resembling the alewife in looks and size is the blueback herring or glut herring, *Alosa aestivalis* (Mitchill). The single discernible difference is noted only in dead fish. In the blueback herring the peritoneum or body cavity has a black lining, as compared to the alewife's white interior. The blueback herring also differs from the alewife in seldom spawning very far above brackish water. Its range is approximately Nova Scotia to Florida, with increasing abundance southward.

SKIPJACK HERRING
Alosa chrysochloris (Rafinesque)

Native to the large streams and lakes of the Mississippi Valley southward to the Gulf and Texas, the skipjack herring derives its name from its lively surface action when its schools are herding minnows close inshore.

The skipjack has a projecting lower jaw, weak teeth, and yellowish reflections upon its sides, which give it an alternate name of golden shad.

Though a freshwater species in most of its range, the skipjack is anadromous along the Gulf coast, ascending the rivers to spawn in

[6] University of Toronto Press, 1955.

early spring. It is not a large fish, averaging twelve to fifteen inches, with occasional bigger specimens taken from the salt water of the Gulf. More carnivorous than most of the shads, the skipjack preys actively upon minnows, other small fishes, and insects, and is a more eager taker of baits, artificial flies and other lures. Though a good sporting fish, it is little esteemed as food.

ALABAMA SHAD
Alosa alabamae   Jordan and Evermann

OHIO SHAD
Alosa ohioensis   Evermann

Not only the nation but two states have had shads named for them, but there seems to have been no official expression of gratitude therefor.

The Alabama shad was reported by Jordan and Evermann from the Black Warrior River, and other Alabama and north Florida rivers, in the late nineteenth century. Little is known of its habits, but apparently it is anadromous from the Gulf of Mexico. It seldom exceeds fifteen inches, and is of no value as a game or food fish.

The Ohio shad is a fish comparable to the Alabama in size and general worthlessness as food and game, ranging the lower Mississippi from its confluence with the Ohio River southward to the Gulf. It is listed by the American Fisheries Society as the only strictly fresh-water member of the herring family and therefore may be presumed not anadromous in Gulf coast rivers.

Chapter 10

SMELTS, MOONEYE, GOLDEYE, CENTRAL MUDMINNOW

AMERICAN SMELT
Osmerus Mordax (Mitchill)

On the early-spring nights of the past, a thousand little rivers and creeks from New England to the Great Lakes became suddenly alive with a multitude of small silvery fish, heading upstream to spawn.

Gleaming in the moonlight as they passed over a shallow bar—so closely massed that often they touched each other—they attracted small armies of rural people to the streams. Sometimes entire families, armed with lanterns, flashlights, and dip nets, waded the icy shallows and scooped out the migrants as they went by. For a few days, while the run lasted, these fishermen feasted on one of the most tender and flavorful of all fishes, the American smelt.

Such sensational runs of smelt are not so common now as in the early 1900's, but they still occur in some tributaries of the Great Lakes and the Finger Lakes of New York.

The smelt is a small prize but collectively of great importance to man. Because of its excellence as food and its still abundant populations it supports an extensive commercial fishery. Winter anglers by the tens of thousands seek it annually in the deep waters under the ice of Lake Champlain, New York's Finger Lakes, Lake Erie, and scores of inland bodies in the Great Lakes region. Inhabiting chiefly the deeper coldwater lakes and traveling in huge compact schools, the smelt is an important forage fish for many game species, especially the lake trout and the landlocked salmon.

Other than the American smelt, which is strictly of Atlantic origin, six species of anadromous smelt and two purely marine species are recognized in Pacific waters. With one exception, these are of little importance commercially and of virtually no interest to anglers. Still another, the capelin, is a marine fish of both oceans. The American smelt, known also as the common smelt, and as frostfish and icefish in some localities, is the most important species.

Its original home was along the Atlantic coast, from Labrador to Virginia. Captain John Smith wrote, in 1622, "Of smelts there is such abundance that the Salvages doe take them up in the rivers, with baskets like sives." An anadromous fish, the smelt lived most of its life and attained most of its growth in the sea or the tidal estuaries, entering fresh water only to spawn. Today it is known on the Atlantic seaboard from the Gulf of St. Lawrence to Virginia. At some long-ago time, beyond the earliest recordings of man, the American smelt migrated up the St. Lawrence River, finding its way eventually to Lake Ontario and Lake Champlain, and there adapting itself to a permanent freshwater life.

Today's great abundance of smelt in the upper Great Lakes drainage stem from comparatively recent introductions. Dr. John Van Oosten, U.S. Fish and Wildlife Service, Ann Arbor, Michigan, notes[1] that smelt were first introduced into the Great Lakes region in 1906, in Michigan's St. Marys River, and that other plantings were made here and elsewhere in later years. The only successful introductions of smelt in that drainage, however, were in Crystal Lake, Howe Lake, and Trout Lake, all in Michigan. "It is believed," Van Oosten writes, "that only the Crystal Lake population, which originated from eggs obtained in 1912 from Green Lake, Maine, is the source of the smelt now found in all of the Great Lakes except Ontario, and in the inland lakes of Michigan."

Dr. Robert M. Roecker, New York State conservation biologist,[2] states that smelt were first reported in Lake Erie, at Vermilion, Ohio, in 1936. The first recorded spawning run out of Lake Erie was reported from a small stream in Norfolk County, Ontario, in April 1942. The six-year gap may be attributed to the fact that smelt of Lake Erie (and some other lakes as well) are prone to spawn along the lake shoreline rather than enter tributaries.

The smelt in New York's Finger Lakes have multiplied from Conservation Department plantings started in 1917 and continued through 1930. In Cayuga Lake smelt were sufficiently abundant by 1941 to permit their harvest as bait for angling, Dr. Roecker writes.

Through other introductions and its own natural adaptation to fresh water, the American smelt is present today in hundreds of lakes in the Maritime Provinces, Maine, New Hampshire, Vermont, New York, Quebec, Ontario, and Michigan. Most of these lakes have cold water in summer at depths of fifty feet or more. Contrary to previous assumptions, however, depth and cold water seem not to be ecological imperatives for the smelt. Robert S. Rupp, of the Maine Department of Inland Fisheries and Game, reports that recent findings of the Maine Lake Survey have shown that smelt "are quite often found in many of our small, unstratified, warmwater ponds which are inhabited mainly by warmwater species."[3]

[1] *The Smelt* (Michigan Department of Conservation, Lansing, Fish Division Pamphlet No. 8, March 1953).

[2] *"Osmerus Mordax*—the Smelt," reprinted from *New York State Conservationist*, April–May 1961.

[3] *Fishes of Maine* (1961).

Mature smelt may be anywhere from six to fourteen inches long. The average is about eight inches, but sizes vary considerably from one water to another, even within the same state. Mr. Rupp reports striking differences: mature fish no longer than four or five inches in some Maine lakes, twelve to fourteen in others. Temperature, food supply, and the competition of other fishes are the influencing factors.

The larger fish in any lake are predominantly females. Smelt are sexually mature usually at the age of two. The maximum life span for males is four or five years, for females six. In a given population, including all ages, females usually outnumber males by a ratio of about three to two.

The smelt is of the family Osmeridae, and though it possesses an adipose fin it can hardly be considered a relative of the salmonid family to which the trouts, chars, and salmons belong. Its scales are larger, numbering not more than seventy-five in a lengthwise row. A slender, handsome little fish, the smelt is olive-green on the back, silvery on the sides and underbody. Numerous small dark spots are sometimes evident on the sides and fins. The gill covers and cheeks are pearly; the dorsal fin is high and short, the forked tail brownish in both lobes; all other fins are pale. The head and mouth are large; well-developed teeth are present on both jaws and the tongue. An odor suggesting that of the cucumber has been detected on spawning fish and also on winter smelt taken by ice-fishermen, but apparently this is not so pronounced as the grayling's odor of thyme.

At spawning time the males can be distinguished from the females by sight and touch. The males' backs are darker, and because of minute tubercles on the body they have a sandpaper roughness that can be seen and felt, while the females' scales are smooth.

The freshwater smelt's preference for depth seems not to be shared at all by the same species in the sea. Along its coastal range the smelt remains close to shore and usually in shallow water. Great schools enter the tidal bays in the fall, stay there throughout the winter, and ascend to fresh water in the spring to spawn. They return to the estuary or the inshore areas of the sea soon after spawning. Smelt are never long-distance migrants either from the sea or from a lake, seldom penetrating more than a quarter mile above tidewater or inland from the lake shore.

Spawning migrations into lake tributaries occur almost always at night and usually at the time of the breakup of ice. Occasionally there are exceptions: Robert S. Rupp of Maine reports that the run from one lake takes place in late February under heavy ice cover on both the lake and the tributary brook. He also reports daytime spawning migrations and, in some lakes, spawning along the lake shore or over sandbars, even though suitable tributaries are accessible.

The upstream run is of brief duration, often lasting only a few days from the first arrivals on the spawning grounds to the last departures. Fish of ages two and three, seven to nine inches long, are predominant in any given spawning run. Males are more numerous in the early run; toward the end the females outnumber the males. An individual female spawns in a single night and returns before daylight to the lake. Some females are not spawned out in a single night; these may re-enter the stream more than once before their eggs are fully shed. Preferred breeding areas are fast shallow riffles. No attempt at nest-building is made, and apparently there is no pairing of any one female with a single male. Males and females are together in little clutches of six or eight individuals, and many such groupings may congregate in the shallow riffles. With the eggs drifting free in the water, survival is certainly not as high as with eggs of the nest-building trouts and salmons. The eggs, however, number 20,000 to 50,000 per female, and are heavier than water. Being strongly adhesive, they stick to whatever they settle on—stones, sand, vegetation, sometimes the spawning fish themselves.

Spent smelt do not necessarily die, yet a tremendous post-spawning mortality, chiefly among the males, occurs annually. At various points along the Lake Erie shore, from June to late August, huge quantities of dead smelt constitute an annoyance to summer residents.

The incubation period for the eggs is fifteen to forty days. The newly hatched larvae, transparent and about a quarter of an inch long, drift downstream.

Young smelt—still transparent up to the length of two inches—feed on insect larvae, Mayflies, small freshwater shrimp, and other minute forms of aquatic life. Adults are primarily fish-eaters, their diet including the young of their own species.

The smelt has a reputation in some quarters as a serious predator upon small trout and other game fish. Probably this charge is exaggerated. Dr. Van Oosten writes that "nowhere have investigations found such species [young game fish] present in stomachs of smelt in any significant quantities." Stomach contents of 210 smelt examined in Michigan revealed that all recognizable fish were minnows. In lakes where the smelt has long coexisted with lake trout, landlocked salmon, and northern pike, the smelt is certainly more preyed upon than preying. Yet biologists, to play it safe, advise against the introduction of smelt into waters being managed for game species.

This little fish is of tremendous economic value, from the commercial-fishery standpoint and as a sport species. A well-organized commercial fishery operates in the Great Lakes with gill nets and trawls. Vessels towing trawl nets are equipped with electronic instruments to locate and follow schools. The New York State conservationist Dr. Robert Roecker reports that experimental trawling by an Ontario research vessel in Lake Erie during 1960 yielded daily catches which occasionally reached 5000 to 6000 pounds. Echo-sounder records indicated a layer of smelt approximately six feet thick extending continuously for more than 200 miles, at depths of 50 to 60 feet.

A major die-off of smelt occurred in 1942–43, beginning in Lake Huron in the fall of 1942 and spreading to Lake Michigan and connecting inland lakes. An unknown infectious disease was blamed for this sensational destruction, which eventually represented a loss, for the years 1943–46, estimated at 50 million pounds. The smelt populations recovered, however; by 1952 the total catch in Lake Michigan reached an all-time high of more than four million pounds.

The smelt's economic value is based not only upon the commercial fishery but upon the ice-fishing it affords to many thousands of anglers. Such eastern lakes as Champlain, Memphremagog, Bomoseen, and New York's Finger Lakes, and to the west Lake Erie and countless inland lakes of Michigan and Ontario, are thronged with smelt-seeking ice-fishermen, with or without shanties, once the surface waters become heavily frozen. Ice-fishing experts say they may start with sixty to one hundred feet of line to reach the smelt depths, but can raise the schools gradually nearer the surface by raising the bait. The best bait on Lake Champlain and many other waters is a strip cut from the smelt itself, near the tail. Other baits are bits of smelt skin, perch skin, live minnows, and bright-colored fins. Despite their large mouths and sharp teeth, smelt are notoriously difficult to hook; some veteran ice-fishermen calculate that one hooked fish out of ten or twelve bites is a fair average.

THE PACIFIC SMELTS

On the Pacific side of the continent, six anadromous members of the Osmeridae deserve mention. All are reported to be excellent as food. In color and size they differ but little from the American smelt, though in their spawning habits some are unlike their eastern counterpart. Only one has commercial importance. This is the eulachon, *Thaleichthys pacificus* (Richardson), also called Columbia River smelt, hooligan, oolichon, and candlefish.

The last of these names is appropriate, for the oil of this fish, solid and lardlike at ordinary temperatures, was once used by the Indians to make candles. Indeed, Jordan and Evermann reported, in *American Food and Game Fishes*,[4] that the entire fish was dried and used as a candle, a wick having been run through it. These authors termed the eulachon "an excellent panfish, unsurpassed by any fish whatsoever in the delicacy of the flesh."

The eulachon ranges from Oregon northward to Alaska, entering the Columbia River, several of its tributaries in Oregon and Washington, and the Fraser in British Columbia. The length of its spawning migrations far exceeds that of the eastern American smelt. This species differs from the American smelt, also, in that most of the individuals die after spawning.

A large fish, as smelt go, the eulachon averages ten to twelve inches in length. Its size, abundance, excellence as food, and proximity to consuming centers have given the eulachon commercial importance. The Washington State Department of Fisheries reports, "For as long as commercial statistics have been available, the Columbia River catch has exceeded one million pounds annually, and has been nearly six million pounds in peak years."[5]

[4] Doubleday, Page & Co., New York, 1902.
[5] *Pacific Northwest Marine Fishes* (Olympia, 1961).

Mooneye with Smelts

The Arctic smelt, *Osmerus dentex* Steindachner, is well called the rainbow herring, for it exceeds in its brilliance all others of the Osmeridae. This species is pale olive on the back; its scales are dark-edged; its sides above the lateral line are purplish, fading below to bluish and finally to a violet and golden iridescence. The silvery white underbody has a rosy sheen, and the fins are pale gold. A northern fish, it inhabits both shores of the Bering Sea, and ranges southward on the

Asian side to northern China. The people of Alaska's Bristol Bay area rate it an important food.

Among the other western species is the Sacramento smelt or Pacific smelt, *Spirinchus thaleichthys* (Ayres); the surf smelt, *Hypomesus pretiosus* (Girard); the pond smelt, *Hypomesus olidus* (Pallas), so called because it spawns in freshwater ponds accessible from the sea; and the longfin smelt, *Spirinchus dilatus* Schultz and Chapman. The surf smelt is a minor bone of contention: many authorities hold that it spawns in the ocean surf, but the American Fisheries Society gives it a Pacific-freshwater listing, indicating that it ascends above tidewater.

MOONEYE
Hiodon tergisus   LeSueur

GOLDEYE
Hiodon alosoides (Rafinesque)

The mooneye and goldeye are unique as the only members of the family Hiodontidae. Though abundant throughout their natural range, they are little-known fishes. Anglers seldom seek them purposely, though frequently take them while fishing for other species and are often unable to identify their catch. Commercially the mooneye is of slight importance anywhere; its flesh is edible but of negative quality. The goldeye, however, is a much esteemed fish when properly smoked.

Both of these fishes, averaging ten to fourteen inches in length, are deep-bodied and laterally thin. The dorsal-surface color varies in different waters from olive to pale green, steel-blue or blue-green. The sides are bright silver, usually with a marked iridescence which, in the goldeye, may have a golden tint. The eyes are large and set well forward over the small mouth. The fins are pale, the dorsal set far back, the anal exceptionally long, bearing thirty or more rays. The scales are large, numbering 56 to 58 from gill cover to the deeply forked tail.

The mooneye and goldeye resemble the shads, freshwater herrings, and whitefishes. This resemblance has earned for the mooneye (and for the goldeye, too, in some areas) such names as toothed herring, white shad, big-eyed shad, river herring, and river whitefish. Both the mooneye and the goldeye can be distinguished from the white-fishes and ciscoes by the absence of an adipose fin and by the presence of well-developed teeth on the jaws and tongue. The latter property of mooneye and goldeye also serves to distinguish these fish from the shads and alewives. Still another difference is the rearward location of the mooneye's and goldeye's dorsal fin, and the absence of scutes, the sharp sawlike ridge of scales on the belly, which characterizes the shad. Both mooneye and goldeye do possess a fleshy keel on the belly, however, and this feature is useful in differentiating one from the other: in the goldeye it extends forward of the ventral fins, but on the mooneye it does not. Perhaps the most obvious differences between the two are the yellow or gold eyes which give the goldeye its name, and the placement of the dorsal fin. On the goldeye this fin's forward edge is farther back on the body than the front of the anal fin; on the mooneye it is slightly forward of the anal.

The northerly range of the mooneye extends from the upper St. Lawrence River westward and north to the Hudson Bay drainages and Manitoba. In the United States this fish occurs from the Lake Champlain system westward to the Great Lakes (chiefly Lake Erie and Lake Ontario). It is present in the Mississippi drainage as far south as Arkansas. The goldeye is scarce in, or absent from, the St. Lawrence River and Hudson Bay tributaries and the Great Lakes, but is abundant in Manitoba and Saskatchewan, and in the Missouri River system as far west as Montana. Its U.S. range does not extend as far east as the mooneye's.

Both fish favor the broad, shallower waters of large lakes or rivers, though they seek greater depths in the summer. Small schools may occasionally move shoreward in the lakes or enter small tributaries, particularly at night. The goldeye spawns in the early spring throughout the southerly range, and shortly after the ice breaks in northerly waters. Lake populations are believed to ascend tributary streams to spawn; river fish may spawn in shallow marshy backwaters. The eggs, averaging 10,000 to 15,000 per female, hatch in about two weeks. The young remain where born through the summer, then descend to the lake or the main river. Little is known of the mooneyes' spawning.

The food of both species consists largely of insects, though mollusks and minnows are readily eaten by the larger individuals. Neither the mooneye nor the goldeye is considered a game fish, but each can give an active fight on light tackle. They are receptive to artificial flies, small spinners, and natural baits such as earthworms and minnows.

These species have considerable value, when small, as forage for game fish, but this asset may be canceled out by their competition when mature.

A so-called southern mooneye, *Hiodon selenops*, was formerly considered a separate species, but most scientists now believe it to be identical with the common mooneye.

CENTRAL MUDMINNOW
Umbra limi (Kirtland)

Among the fishes of the order Clupeiformes, this little species and a couple of its close kin are the only ones known as minnows. This is a curious error—possibly based upon the popular assumption that all small fish are minnows.

The so-called central mudminnow is a hardy little fellow, a good aquarium fish, and distinguished, among anglers, for its lasting quality in the bait can or on the hook.

Commonly three to four inches long, but sometimes reaching six or seven, the central mudminnow occurs throughout a broad but ill-defined range which includes most of the north-central United States and a Canadian area reaching from southern Quebec to Manitoba.

If the "minnow" part of this fish's name is ill-chosen, the first syllable is apt, for the species thrives in the muddy or mucky bottoms of heavily vegetated, sluggish rivers, overflow sloughs and ponds, pot-holes, and even ditches.

In its color the central mudminnow nicely matches its environment, and probably is well protected from predators thereby. Its body is brown or olive, lighter on the underparts, with twelve to fifteen dark vertical bars of irregular widths along the sides, and a black vertical stripe at the base of the tail. Over its fundamental dullness this little fish sometimes shows a surprising bluish green iridescence. The muddy-colored dorsal fin is set almost as far aft as a pike's; the tail is rounded and dark; the lower fins are a yellowish putty color.

The mudminnow is a springtime spawner, dropping its eggs on the vegetation of the muck bottoms. Its food is primarily minute forms of plankton, small aquatic insects, and occasionally tiny fish.

The eastern mudminnow, *Umbra pygmaea* (DeKay), is a similar fish, occurring in sluggish waters of the East. Far less abundant than its central cousin, it is confined to the Atlantic coastal regions from the Carolinas north to the Maritime Provinces of Canada.

Chapter 11

PICKERELS,
NORTHERN PIKE,
MUSKELLUNGE

The pike family, or Esocidae, is now taxonomically simplified to five species in North America—three pickerels, one pike, and one muskellunge. The three pickerels and the muskellunge are native to North America only, but the pike ranges over northern Asia and Europe.

Probably the most voracious tribe inhabiting fresh water, its members are all slender for their length, and arrowlike in their sudden short darts upon their prey. Their jaws are large and strongly toothed; their single dorsal fin, far back near the tail, matches the anal fin directly opposite. From the little grass pickerel, barely a foot long at its maximum, to the muskellunge giants which sometimes attain weights upwards of sixty pounds and lengths above five feet, all of them are silent and solitary, liers in ambush, lurkers in weeds, waiting and concealed to deliver their lightning death-strokes to any passerby. Their prey is anything that lives and moves, from the smallest minnows and crustaceans to large fish, waterfowl, snakes, and muskrats. Their usual waters are shallow and vegetated, but clear, for they hunt by sight.

Thoreau, in *A Week on the Concord and Merrimack Rivers*, saw the pickerel as "a solemn, stately, ruminant fish, lurking under the shadow of a pad at noon, with still, circumspect, voracious eye, motionless as a jewel set in water, or moving slowly along to take up its position, darting from time to time at such unlucky fish or frog or insect as comes within its range, and swallowing it at a gulp." Thoreau recalled catching one which "had swallowed a brother pickerel half as large as itself, with the tail still visible in its mouth, while the head was already digested in its stomach."

Thoreau's pickerel was probably eighteen inches long. But his description would have served admirably for the northern pike or musky, which did not haunt the Concord and Merrimack rivers.

These fishes have a kinship in savagery; they all look alike and are frequently mistaken for one another by laymen and anglers. Small pickerel captured in certain waters have a unique protection: they are often released in the belief that they are under-legal-size pike or muskies.

There are good ways of distinguishing them, however. The best known and most frequently recommended is to note the scale arrangement on the cheeks and gill covers. The rule: The pickerels are scaled on the whole of the gill cover and the whole cheek. The northern pike is scaled on the upper half of the gill cover and the whole cheek. The muskellunge is scaled on the upper half of the gill cover and the upper half of the cheek. The rule is not infallible but it should work in 999 cases of a thousand.

CHAIN PICKEREL
Esox niger LeSueur

The chain pickerel's nomenclature is badly confused. An eastern and southern species, it is correctly called the eastern pickerel, incorrectly called by a number of local aliases, such as eastern pike, pond pickerel, green pike, grass pickerel, grass pike, and jack.

The chain pickerel gets its name from the pattern of dark chainlike markings running the length of its sides, from cheek to the base of the tail. These marks are horizontal stripes or bars, connected at irregular intervals by vertical bars of the same dusky color, giving the general effect of chains. The color and pattern varies widely. Usually the back and the horizontal and vertical stripes are dark bronze-green; the sides vary from dull to bright yellowish green. On some fish the vertical connections are spaced far apart; on others they may be so close as to give an effect of spots, or of light yellow-green bricks mortared with dark dull-green cement. The belly is white to yellowish cream; the dorsal, anal, and caudal fins are greenish, and small dark spots may be on the caudal. The lower fins are pale. A distinguishing mark is a dark vertical bar directly below the eye; another dark bar, usually less distinct, extends forward of the eye. The tail is quite deeply forked. The scales number about 125 on an extreme lengthwise row.

Largest of the pickerels but rarely exceeding three pounds, the chain is subject to exaggerated reports of its size. Most specimens taken by anglers are in the range of fifteen to twenty-two inches, or one to two pounds. A twenty-inch pickerel is about six years old, a two-foot pickerel about seven; and these ages are well above the average for this fish. "Pickerel" above five pounds may well prove to be northern pike or muskellunge upon proper identification.

The record chain pickerel on sporting tackle, however, is one reported as 9 pounds 6 ounces, 31 inches long, taken near Homerville, Georgia, on February 17, 1961, by Baxley McQuaig, Jr.

The chain pickerel occurs in clear quiet waters of shallow weedy streams, ponds and lakes, in a range extending from the Maritime Provinces and southern Quebec to Florida, thence westward to Louisiana and Texas, with occurrences in Tennessee and Arkansas. In its northerly range this fish is abundant east of the Alleghenies.

Rarely living beyond six years, and having a maximum life expectancy of nine, the chain pickerel is sexually mature at the age of two or three, and eleven or twelve inches long at this time. It is one of the earliest spawners in the spring, entering its shallow breeding areas as soon as the surface is free of ice. It is reported occasionally to spawn again in the fall. Spawning takes place in marshy, vegetated backwaters of streams or overflow areas; in lakes and ponds the breeding ground may be in shallows close to shore or at the mouth of an inlet. A female is attended by two or three males; in water perhaps no more than a foot deep the business of reproduction can create a splashing and commotion visible and audible at some distance. No nest is made. The eggs, cast indiscriminately and numbering 8000 to 30,000 per female, sink to the bottom and adhere to vegetation and detritus. The young hatch in a week or two and almost at once begin to look for food. All members of the pike family are said to be born hungry, live hungry, and die hungry.

The first food of the fry is among the minute plankton organisms. Later, as growing or adult fish, pickerel eat insects, worms, crawfish, frogs, mice, but chiefly fish, including their own species. A not uncommon angling experience is to hook a trout of eight inches or so, on a fly, and to have it assaulted, while bringing to net, by a pickerel perhaps twice the length of the trout. On such occasions half a trout may be brought in, at best a badly mutilated fish.

Like the northern pike and muskellunge, the pickerel is believed to play a beneficial role in controlling the overpopulation and consequent stunting of yellow perch, bluegills, and sunfish. One seldom sees many pickerel in any given water, but a few in a pond or a quarter-mile stretch of river will help to maintain a balance of other fish.

As a game species, the chain pickerel is a nice fish for growing boys brought up on yellow perch, bluegills, sunnies, and suckers, whose schools inhabit the same water. The lonely, non-schooling pickerel, usually much larger than the familiar panfish, may be unsuspected until the day it strikes.

Anglers who often take pickerel when fishing for bass rate *Esox niger* a rather inferior game fish, inclined to fold after its savage strike and first hard rush. Spoons, spinners, large bucktail or streamer flies, trolled or cast, are effective lures. Still-fishing with minnows, frogs, or nightcrawlers, and cane-pole "skittering" with frogs, frog legs, or pieces of perch belly, can be productive.

Even in winter the pickerel ranges constantly for its prey, and ice-fishermen take many, with tip-ups and handlines, often where only two or three feet of water is beneath the ice.

REDFIN PICKEREL
Esox americanus americanus Gmelin

GRASS PICKEREL
Esox americanus vermiculatus LeSueur

These are the miniatures among the pike family. The redfin seldom exceeds thirteen or fourteen inches even when six years old, and averages about eight or ten. The grass pickerel, smallest of the Esocidae, averages six to nine inches and is seldom reported above twelve.

The redfin is known in various localities as the banded pickerel, barred pickerel, brook pickerel, and little pickerel. Any of these names would be more appropriate than its official one, for it does not possess red fins.

The redfin's range approximately follows that of the chain pickerel —from Quebec and the St. Lawrence River southward to Florida, in regions east of the Alleghenies. The grass pickerel, called little pickerel and grass pike, occurs from Iowa and Missouri to Wisconsin, Michigan, and tributaries of Lake Erie south to the Ohio River and lower Mississippi drainages. In Canada it is known in the St. Lawrence River basin from Montreal westward to Lake Huron.

In appearance these small fishes differ somewhat from the larger chain pickerel but closely resemble each other. The back of each is a dusky olive to brighter green, sometimes brassy bluish, fading lighter on the sides, which are striped with dark, vertical to slantwise bars. A black bar below the eye is prominent on each. The redfin has a shorter snout, proportionally, than either the chain or the grass pickerel. The scales on each of the small species number about 105 along the lateral line.

The redfin and grass varieties inhabit the typical pickerel waters: flat lowland streams, weedy ponds and lakes, and sometimes far up small brooks. The grass pickerel is often stranded in landlocked pools of summer-dried streams. Both spawn in early spring in very shallow water. The eggs are amazingly numerous: the Missouri Conservation Department reports that a grass pickerel female 6.2 inches long contained 15,700 eggs. This species may spawn more than once in the spring and is known to spawn in the fall, too, if warm weather continues into the autumn months.

In their small way both the redfin and the grass pickerel exhibit the voracity of all the pikes, feeding on insects, worms, small crustacea, frogs, minnows and other fish. They are ready takers of baits and small lures, usually those cast or trolled for other species. Because of their minor dimensions they have no standing as game fish.

Hybridization of the redfin and chain pickerels is reported. Both occur in the same general range and spawn at the same time.

NORTHERN PIKE
Esox lucius Linnaeus

The northern pike is a solitary marauder, the lone wolf of the fresh waters, preying on anything and everything that moves, capable of growing to tremendous size, and ranging much of the Northern Hemisphere above the 40th parallel. Such a background is the fabric of legend, and the northern pike's history is studded with tall tales and hints of the occult.

By any of its forty-odd names (American pike, common pike, great northern pike, Great Lakes pike, and jackfish are a few) it strikes terror in all other life inhabiting its waters, and occasionally in man. Frank Dufresne says[1] that along the Yukon some Eskimos tell of certain remote "devil lakes" where lurk monster pike able to swallow not only a man but his canoe as well. Even to approach these lakes is held to be bad medicine.

[1] *Alaska's Animals and Fishes* (A. S. Barnes & Co., New York, 1946).

Top to bottom: Great Northern Pike,
Chain Pickerel, Redfin Pickerel

In *The Compleat Angler*, Izaak Walton suggested that the pickerel weed may be the genesis of the pike. " 'Tis not to be doubted," Walton wrote, "but that they are bred, some by generation, and some not: as namely of a Weed called *Pickerel-weed*, unless learned Gesner[2] be much mistaken, for he says this weed and other glutinous matter, with the help of the Sun's heat in some particular Months, and some Ponds apted for it by nature, do become Pikes." Walton further cited Gesner as ascribing an age of two hundred years to at least one pike.

The northern pike certainly achieves no such legendary size or age, but it can be big enough, old enough, and savage enough in its own right to satisfy the most imaginative angler. It has been known to reach the age of fourteen years. In its average sizes—two to ten pounds in many waters, with twenty-pounders not extremely rare—it probably equals the more-publicized muskellunge, though the record rod-and-reel musky is well ahead of the record pike. The latter, taken in Sacandaga Reservoir, New York, by Peter Dubuc on September 15, 1940, weighed 46 pounds 2 ounces, and was 52½ inches long. The record musky, also a New York fish, outweighed this pike by nearly 24 pounds.

The pike's lean body is dusky green to olive- or gray-green on top, fading to lighter on the sides and to white or yellowish on the belly. Dark spots may be evident on the fins. The fish is frequently mistaken for the muskellunge despite distinct and obvious differences. The adult pike has light yellowish spots, bean-shaped or rectangular, against a dark background; the musky has dark bars against a light background. The light vertical bars on young pike later become broken to form spots. The difference in the scales of cheek and gill cover was previously noted. Still another distinction, held reliable by ichthyologists, is the number of sensory pores or holes on the underside of the jaws. The pike never has more than five on each side; the musky has six to eight. Further, the corners of a musky's tail are sharply pointed; on the pike these corners are rounded. The lengthwise scale count on the pike is about 125, on the musky 130 to 157.

The pike's basic color varies widely in different parts of the range. Lake Michigan pike have a decided reddish flush. A so-called "blue

[2] Konrad von Gesner (1516–65), a German historian, zoologist, and botanist. His *Historia Animalium* has been regarded as the foundation of zoology.

pike," unspotted, with light silvery blue and a darker blue back, has been reported, but is believed to be a cross between the northern pike and the muskellunge.

The range of the northern pike is probably more extensive than that of any other freshwater game fish. In the United States it runs from New England and northern New York to the Great Lakes, Minnesota, Iowa, South Dakota, and Nebraska. The pike is reported as far south as the Ohio Valley, and has been introduced into several western states. Canada has the northern pike from Labrador, Quebec, and New Brunswick (but not Nova Scotia) westward through Ontario to Alberta (it is rare in British Columbia), and north to Yukon and Northwest Territories. The pike is the only member of the Esocidae in Alaska, where it thrives from Bristol Bay north, throughout the Yukon River and in extreme northerly lakes, but not in the southeast or the Aleutians. Across Siberia, and in much of Europe including the British Isles, the pike is an historic fish.

Typical pike waters are the shallows over weed beds, sandbars that drop off into channels, bays, coves, shoals around headlands, short channels between lakes, and wherever stumps and other obstructions afford cover. If the surface water is too warm the pike moves into deeper areas, but it is never a deepwater fish. Twenty feet is about its limit. The lake whitefish, ciscoes, and deepwater chubs may be thankful therefor. The pike seems most at home in larger rivers and middle-sized lakes, rather than in small rivers or very large lakes. In the Great Lakes, the pike keeps to the bays and connecting straits and is rare in the broad areas far offshore.

The pike is primed for its springtime spawning even before the ice is out, and starts then to move into the shallows for the annual reproduction ceremonies which are enacted just after the ice breaks. River pike seek shoals or backwater marshlands. The protection of such spawning marshes is a major concern of conservationists. Unhappily, however, these breeding grounds are often destroyed by lakeshore developments.

Lake pike enter inlets or extreme shallows along shore. Spawning runs may cover considerable distance. W. F. Carbine reports[3] that

[3] *The Pike—A Prized and Spurned Fish* (Michigan Department of Conservation, Lansing; revised April 1947). The author is now Director, Regional Office of the Bureau of Commercial Fisheries, U.S. Fish and Wildlife Service, Ann Arbor, Michigan.

two pike tagged in the Pine River (part of the Saginaw Bay–Lake Huron drainage) were recovered by fishermen thirty-eight days later, 25 miles upstream.

A female pike, generally with several smaller males tagging along, broadcasts her eggs—perhaps 7500 if she is a 15-inch fish, 250,000 or more if she weighs thirty pounds. The adhesive eggs stick to whatever they fall on, and are immediately deserted by the adults. Incubation may take only twelve days at warmer temperatures, three weeks in colder water. The fry remain close to bottom for a week or so, and do not migrate from their natal shallows to the lake or main river current for a month or more. In this period many river pike fry can be lost by receding waters.

The little pike begin to feed at once on minute aquatic life. As they grow to adulthood they will prefer fish to any other food, but will come to know the heady tastes of all manner of insects and crustacea, minnows, perch, bluegills, suckers, trout, small muskellunge, and their own species, worms, frogs, mice, snakes, ducklings. Attaining the twenty-pound class they will occasionally dine on a full-grown waterfowl or a muskrat.

The piscivorous rapacity of the pike is extraordinary. The stomach of one specimen from West Okoboji Lake, Iowa, contained twenty-seven young yellow perch. It is estimated that a northern pike daily consumes one-fifth of its own weight in food, mostly fish. If this is true, a twenty-pound pike, perhaps eight or ten years old, is eating 1400 pounds of fish a year, has eaten several tons to achieve its present weight, and may well eat a ton or two more before it falls to some angler as it assaults what it believes to be another fish.

Such statistics show the pike to be harmful in waters containing trout, bass, and other game fish, even muskellunge. The pike matures at the age of three years, earlier than the musky, and it spawns earlier in the spring. Wisconsin reports that northern pike raise havoc with musky populations. This state raised its creel limit on pike, in 1958, to twenty-five a day, and its conservationists say this measure has benefited muskellunge populations.

The pike, however, is considered useful in controlling overpopulations of the panfish and sucker species.

This great predator is in turn preyed upon, chiefly by man. In its shallow-water habitat it is not bothered by the sea lamprey. But others, such as herons, mergansers, loons, larger fish, and snapping turtles take their toll of young and growing pike.

To many anglers the large pike is a trophy hardly less desirable than the muskellunge. Other fishermen sneer at the pike, regarding it as easy game, greedy for almost any bait or lure that is tossed its way. Anglers take it by casting or trolling large spoons, spinners, spinner-fly combinations, and plugs, by still-fishing with suckers up to ten inches long, and by ice-fishing. The winter fishermen employ handlines, tip-ups, or spears. Spearing is usually accomplished in a shanty or "dark-house" over the ice hole. It is dark inside but the fisherman can see into the pale-green ghostly luminescence below the ice. He lowers a decoy—a live sucker or chub, or an artificial lure that can be worked to simulate a fish's action—just below the surface, and when the decoyed pike approaches the spear does the rest. So caught, the pike has little chance to display the strength and vigor and spectacular surface tactics it can muster when hung on a rod.

The oft-noted reluctance of pike to take bait or lure during the heat of summer has been attributed by some anglers to sore gums, believed to be caused by the shedding of teeth at this time of year. C. L. Hubbs and Milton Trautman, of the University of Michigan, found in 1935 that the teeth of pike are broken off or shed, and constantly replaced, throughout the year. (The same is true of the musky.) Stomach examinations of summer-caught pike proved they were not "off feed." Light catches of pike and muskellunge during hot weather are attributed to an abundance of the young of other fish at this time, or to retirement of the pike to deeper waters, or to general sluggishness because of higher water temperatures.[4]

Although there is not a large commercial fishery for the northern pike, millions of pounds are caught annually, chiefly in gill nets and seines set for other species. The meat is white, flaky, and palatable.

MUSKELLUNGE
Esox masquinongy Mitchill

The muskellunge is one of the giants among fishes in freshwater, exceeded in American angling annals only by some of the sturgeons,

---

[4] Reported by W. F. Carbine in *The Pike—A Prized and Spurned Fish* (see footnote 3).

Muskellunge
Esox masquinongy

gars, blue catfish, and chinook salmon. The musky's great size and fighting qualities, and the fact that some of its habitats are relatively small waters, have given this fish a tremendous appeal to anglers. Though average musky weights are probably six to ten or fifteen pounds, many of twenty to thirty pounds are taken annually, and several above sixty have been subdued on rod and line. The angling record belongs to a St. Lawrence River, New York, fish that lacked one ounce of weighing 70 pounds, and was five feet 4½ inches long. Mr. Arthur Lawton landed this giant on September 22, 1957.

The range of the muskellunge is greatly circumscribed by comparison to that of the northern pike. It is native only to North America, from the St. Lawrence River drainages of New York and Quebec westward across Ontario and the Great Lakes region to the Mississippi Valley. It is plentiful in Minnesota and particularly abundant in Wisconsin, where it is found in more than six hundred lakes and fifty streams. It was named the state fish by the Wisconsin legislature in 1955. The musky's range also includes Chautauqua Lake in western New York, at the head of the Ohio River system.

Many names, including a dozen variations in the spelling of "muskellunge," designate the fish. Others are musky, lunge, longe, tiger musky, and great pike. Maskinonge is the official name in Canada, as used in the statutes of Ontario and Quebec.

The entire muskellunge population, now considered one species, was formerly divided into three: the Great Lakes muskellunge, *Esox masquinongy masquinongy*; the northern, Wisconsin, or tiger muskellunge, *E. masquinongy immaculatus*; and the Chautauqua or Ohio muskellunge, *E. masquinongy ohiensis*.

Specimens of muskellunge-pike hybrids appeared to be infertile, according to Alan S. Hourston,[5] in *The Food and Growth of the Maskinonge in Canadian Waters*. These fish approximated the length-weight relationships of their muskellunge parents but made faster growth, which could be attributed to hybrid vigor.

Like the pickerels and the northern pike, the musky is a solitary, non-schooling fish. It frequents the clear, shallow, weedy areas of lakes and the slow-flowing reaches of rivers, but is sometimes found in clear, sterile, almost weedless lakes. The muskellunge prefers medium-sized lakes and larger rivers; it is rarely found in the smaller lakes and

[5] Fisheries Research Board of Canada, 1952.

ponds, or in the vast open waters of the Great Lakes. Usually it goes no deeper than 15 feet, but is occasionally in 40-foot depths.

Spawning time for the musky may be April or May. Lake muskies spawn in the shallow weedy bays, in one to three feet of water over muck bottoms covered with detritus. They are not reported to migrate up tributaries to spawn, but the river muskies may undertake an upstream migration at spawning time. Scientists Oehmcke, Johnson, Klingbiel, and Wistrom[6] state that spawning-water temperatures range from 49° to 60° F., with an optimum of 55°. Females are sexually mature at four to six years. Fish 25 to 53 inches in length produce 22,000 to 180,000 eggs; a specimen weighing forty pounds was known to produce 225,000. The eggs are cast haphazardly, sometimes along several hundred yards of shoreline, in water 6 to 30 inches deep. The young hatch in eight to fourteen days in water temperatures of 54° to 62° F.

Muskellunge fry suffer losses from various species of fish, including minnows, and from insects such as water beetles and dragonfly nymphs. The survivors feed heavily for a short period on plankton, but fish is an essential food from the fingerling stage on. The species is primarily piscivorous, though its food, like the pike's, includes virtually all animal life that comes its way. Heavy catches of muskellunge from a given water are invariably followed by increased and perhaps stunted populations of yellow perch and other panfish.

Many studies of the age-length-weight relationships of muskellunge have been made. These vary somewhat from one water to another. Wisconsin averages follow:[7]

Age	Length	Weight
1 year	8 inches	½ pound (or less)
2 "	16 "	1 "
3 "	23 "	3 "
5 "	30 "	8 "
7 "	35 "	12 "
10 "	43 "	19 "
12 "	46 "	25 "
20 "	59 "	33 "

[6] *The Wisconsin Muskellunge—Its Life History, Ecology, and Management* (Wisconsin Conservation Department, Publication 225, 1958).

[7] Reported in *The Pike—A Prized and Spurned Fish* (see footnote 3).

In the upper brackets, length-weight relationships may vary extremely. Several prize-winning muskies in the five-foot class have weighed sixty pounds or more. Such specimens are invariably females, and may be eighteen or twenty years old. Age can be determined by counting the rings in the scales, in cross sections of the pelvic- or ventral-fin bones, and on the ends of vertebrae. Since all these methods are difficult or impossible with old fish, many muskies of five or six years are scale-read, then marked with dated tags or by fin-clipping, and released. If they are recaptured years later their ages can then be determined.

Anglers employ more or less the same methods and lures for muskies as for large pike. Veteran musky fishermen say their quarry is apt to lurk near rock shoals or sand bars that slope into deeper water, over weed beds, in small weedy bays, and sometimes close inshore where trees overhang the water.

Large muskies confine themselves quite strictly to given areas, seldom roaming unless food is short. Hence the sort of knowledge possessed by local fishermen and guides is of first importance. It is no guarantee of a fish, however. Many a good angler has spent every day of a two-weeks' vacation over high-potential musky water, without a strike.

Hatcheries today are changing to the concept of raising and stocking fewer numbers of larger fish rather than tremendous numbers of fingerlings. With muskellunge this plan is producing better fishing but presents certain unique difficulties—for example, the need for more rearing space, and the occasional shortages of forage fish. The muskellunge will become cannibalistic unless plenty of live food is provided; and unlike the trouts, it cannot be fed prepared diets. Despite these difficulties, conservation departments of Wisconsin, New York, and other musky states have done much to maintain the sports fishery and its consequent revenue at high levels.

Chapter 12

SUCKERS

At the opposite pole from the predacious pike family is the tribe of suckers. A quiet breed this, at peace with other fishes, content to feed on or near the bottom. It adapts itself easily to many fresh waters, from northern Canada and Alaska to the deep South of the United States, and from the eastern seaboard to the Pacific slopes.

Never anadromous, the suckers are dwellers in large and small lakes and rivers. Their family, the Catostomidae, numbers twelve recognized genera and sixty-five species in the United States, and at least one species in Mexico and Central America.

The sucker is a vacuum cleaner among fishes. Its mouth is a true suction cup with protrusile lips, situated on the underside of the head. This is an ideal organ for siphoning small mollusks, worms, aquatic insect larvae, and vegetable material from the bottom stones and gravel. A few suckers, however, do not possess it.

Seemingly in keeping with its quiet, industrious character, the sucker's color is inconspicuous, inclined to dullness. Viewed from above, even large specimens in clear streams may be almost invisible as they work over the bottom terrain. The back and upper sides vary in different waters but always they are of somber hue: olive-green, dark gray, bronze, sometimes mottled. The lower sides are silvery, and occasionally gleam like metal on the floor of the stream as a feeding sucker rolls sideways.

On all the suckers the dorsal and lower fins are soft-rayed, and the tail quite deeply forked. There is no adipose fin. The head is completely unscaled, but the body scales are large. Teeth are absent from the mouth, but those in the throat are useful tools for crushing the shells of small mollusks.

Closely resembling the minnow family, the sucker is often mistaken for one of the larger minnows such as the fallfish. The inferior mouth, typical of all suckers except the buffalos, is the best mark of distinction between suckers and minnows. Another rule was recommended by Hubbs and Lagler, of Michigan, years ago: Measure the space from the front of the anal fin to the base of the tail fin. Then measure from the front of the anal to the tip of the snout. If the latter measurement contains the former more than two and a half times, the fish is a sucker; if less than two and a half times, it is a minnow. The carp and goldfish, both minnows, are exceptions to this rule, but each has a stiff, serrated spine in the dorsal and anal, and the carp has barbels on each side of its mouth.

Suckers in the smaller streams seldom exceed eighteen inches. In the larger rivers and lakes greater sizes are attained, especially by the buffalos, the largest of the suckers.

Unlike many other fishes, the sucker can find its food by the senses of taste and touch, and hence is not hampered by roiled or turbid water. Despite this faculty, most of the stream suckers frequent clear, moving water, riffles, or flowing pools over stony, gravelly, or sandy bottoms. The buffalos, carpsuckers, and blue sucker are often found in a turbid habitat. In lakes the suckers are largely shallow-water fish, though in summer they may descend to depths of 40 or 50 feet. At least one species, the longnose, has been taken from Lake Superior at extreme depths.

A springtime spawner, the sucker seeks its breeding sites on gravelly bottoms in comparatively shallow water. Lake suckers may spawn in the shoals along shore, but often migrate up tributaries in huge schools, mostly at night. At this time they are killed in great numbers by men and boys who spear the fish as they swarm over shallows. Old-timers recall sucker-spearing by night before the advent of the flashlight. A common device was a large round galvanized tub with a kerosene lantern lashed inside. One man in a spearing team held the light-reflecting tub edgewise, and in this illumination of the shallows the others went to work with their spears.

The male sucker at spawning time develops tubercles or "pearl organs" on the snout, tail, anal fin, and sometimes the body. At least two males accompany the female, pressing against her as eggs and milt are simultaneously shed. The female is prolific of eggs: a twenty-inch fish may broadcast 100,000 or more, which are scattered at random over the bottom. The suckers are not nest-builders, and desert their eggs as soon as spawned. Great swarms of fry, often remaining in the shallows for several weeks after hatching, offer food for many game species.

Though not classed as a game fish, some of the suckers afford rod-and-reel sport, and the larger ones represent a commercial fishery of considerable value. The white flesh, somewhat bony but sweet, is esteemed by many, especially when cooked shortly after the fish is caught.

The sucker is frequently charged with being a great predator upon the eggs of game fish, but evidence is scanty. On the other side of the ledger, the sucker has a positive value as food for many game species, and is one of the best of baits for the pike and muskellunge.

WHITE SUCKER
Catostomus commersoni   (Lacépède)

LONGNOSE SUCKER
Catostomus catostomus (Forster)

The white sucker is probably the best known and most widely occurring of all the family. Called common sucker, mullet, slender sucker, and black sucker—the last because of the very dark back of the male at spawning time—this member of the tribe ranges from the Mackenzie River across Canada to Labrador, south to the Gulf states and Mexico. In this tremendous range it frequents large and small streams and lakes, and is plentiful in smaller clear water streams.

Capable of attaining large size when its environment permits, the white sucker reaches weights above six pounds in some larger lakes. It averages far less than that, however: twelve to sixteen inches is the rule for many of the smaller streams.

The male white sucker is marked at spawning time by a lengthwise stripe which is black above and pink below. The young of this species, up to three inches, show three black spots on each side. Scales of adults are smaller than those of some other sucker species, numbering 60 to 70 along the lateral line.

The white sucker is sought by millions of fishermen with cane poles or light rods, small hooks, and baits such as worms, freshwater mussels, and dough balls. On the spawning runs, nets and spears are used, though spears have now been outlawed in many areas.

The white sucker is said to be a fish-eater at times, though certainly fish is not a principal item of its diet. It has been accused of eating lake-trout and salmon eggs. Maine conservationists report, however, that examinations of more than one hundred sucker stomachs in salmon-spawning areas revealed no salmon eggs. In lake-trout spawning shoals, captured suckers contained insignificant numbers of trout eggs, and only during the peak of the spawning season.

Large suckers in game-fish waters do compete with the game species for food, however, and can be eliminated only by chemical reclamation.

The longnose sucker, also called the northern sucker, fine-scaled sucker, sturgeon-nosed sucker, and red-sided sucker, is one of the larger of the Catostomidae. It is said to reach a length of thirty inches and a top weight of six pounds, though it averages less than a pound in most waters.

As its name implies, this fish is distinguished by a long head, broad at the base but tapering to a slender snout which overhangs a large mouth. The scales are the smallest possessed by any of the sucker family. The males at spawning time, and well into the summer, exhibit a wide pinkish stripe along the side.

The longnose has an extensive range northward but is absent from the southerly range of the white sucker. It occurs from Alaska south to the Columbia River drainages, and eastward to Laborador. It ranges in the United States from Washington to Maine, throughout the Great Lakes, except Lake Erie, and as far south as the 40th parallel. In the Great Lakes large numbers of the longnose are caught in commercial nets.

Seeking great depths at times, the longnose is in this respect highly exceptional among the suckers. It has been taken commercially in Lake Superior at depths of 600 feet.

White Sucker

Included in the genus *Catostomus* are several suckers more or less well known in the West but rare or absent elsewhere. The flannel-mouth sucker, *C. latipinnis* Baird and Girard, occurs in the Colorado River drainage. The Sacramento sucker, *C. occidentalis* Ayers, is a native of California and was once abundant in the Sacramento and San Joaquin rivers. The largescale or Columbia River sucker, *C. macrocheilus* Girard, ranges through the Columbia River basin and rivers and lakes of Oregon and Washington. The Utah sucker, *C. ardens* Jordan and Gilbert, lives in the Snake River system and in lakes and streams of Yellowstone Park and the Great Salt Lake basin. It was reported by Jordan and Evermann, at the turn of the century, as "swarming in myriads in Utah Lake, the greatest sucker pond in the world."

QUILLBACK
Carpiodes cyprinus (LeSueur)

The quillback, known in various quarters as the quillback carp-sucker, broad mullet, white carp, and silver carp, resembles two other carpsuckers which are of its genus, and the buffalos which are not. Superficially, it also resembles the carp. All of these fish are deep-bodied and more or less laterally compressed. The carpsuckers are generally smaller and paler than the buffalos, and possess a dorsal fin with higher anterior rays. The long dorsal fin of the quillback, with its greatly extended forward rays, gives this fish its name.

The northerly range of the quillback extends from the St. Lawrence River system across Ontario to Lake of the Woods, with abundance in Lake Erie. Southward this fish occurs from Minnesota, Iowa, and Missouri to the Tennessee River valley and eastward to Chesapeake Bay drainages.

In some of the midwestern lakes the quillback attains a weight of five pounds in exceptional instances. Fish of such heft are perhaps fifteen years old. Quillbacks about a foot long represent the average size.

Catholic in its choice of habitats, the quillback is at home in clear or muddy streams and lakes. In turbid rivers the flesh has a muddy taste; elsewhere it is palatable, and some commercial fishing is carried on in the Midwest, where the quillback is marketed as "white buffalo" or "carp." Rarely taking the hook, the quillback is of little or no importance to anglers.

Closely related to the quillback and similar in appearance are the highfin carpsucker, *Carpiodes velifer* (Rafinesque), and the river carpsucker, *C. carpio* (Rafinesque). Both are more southerly fish than the quillback. The river carpsucker has a broad range from Montana to Oklahoma and Texas, and eastward to the Tennessee and Ohio river valleys.

NORTHERN REDHORSE
Moxostoma macrolepidotum (LeSueur)

The thick-set and large-scaled redhorses are easily distinguished from other suckers. All of them have reddish fins. On the northern redhorse the lower fins and the caudal may be bright orange or blood red. The top and side coloration is similar to that of other suckers. The scales number 40 to 48 in a lengthwise row.

The best known and most widely distributed of the redhorse suckers, the northern occurs in lakes and the swifter rivers from the upper St. Lawrence and Lake Champlain to the Great Lakes, where it is abundant in Lake Ontario and Lake Erie. The range extends westward to Montana and the Canadian prairie provinces, and southward as far as a line between Kansas and Virginia. The northern is said to be the most common sucker in the upper Mississippi River.

This fish attains a length of two feet at its maximum, but in most waters averages about twelve to fourteen inches.

The flesh of the redhorse is perhaps more highly rated than that of any of its sucker cousins, and the fish has commercial importance. As a sport fish, it is caught by bait fishermen using worms, crickets, grasshoppers, mussels, and small pieces of meat.

Closely related to the northern but less abundant are the golden redhorse, *Moxostoma erythrurum* (Rafinesque); the river redhorse, *M. carinatum* (Cope); and the shorthead redhorse, *M. breviceps* (Cope). These have the characteristic reddish fins, and are generally smaller than the northern. Also of the genus *Moxostoma* are several smaller species called "jumprocks."

BIGMOUTH BUFFALO
Ictiobus cyprinellus (Valenciennes)

Greatly resembling the carp and competing with it in many waters, the bigmouth buffalo is the largest of all suckers. Though the average is probably about three pounds, specimens of 30 pounds are not uncommon in the Mississippi River and some lakes of the Midwest. Missouri reports 60-pounders. One of 80 pounds, taken from Spirit Lake, Iowa, is the record for the species. Large females have been known to shed more than 400,000 eggs.

All the buffalos are wide, coarse, large-scaled fish, and distinct from others of the sucker family in more respects than their extraordinary size. The mouth, unique among the suckers, is terminal rather than inferior. The color is dull brownish olive to blue-green on the top, somewhat lighter below but without the silveriness of other suckers. The general shape is elliptical, with the upper outline more curved than the belly. The dorsal fin is long, with 24 to 28 rays, and is elevated at the anterior end. The scales number 38 to 40 on the lateral line.

The food of the buffalos includes some items not common to most suckers' diets. Small fish seem frequently to be taken, and the seeds of aquatic and terrestrial plants bulk large among the buffalos' stomach contents. Iowa reports spring-caught buffalo stomachs packed with the "cotton" from cottonwood trees.

Though abundant in the Mississippi and Missouri river drainages as far west as Montana, the buffalos are seldom seen by anglers except in the fish markets. These fish rarely take a hook but occasionally are caught on set lines or by bait fishermen with worms or dough balls. The commercial catch on the Mississippi and Missouri rivers averages about a million pounds annually.

In lakes, buffalos can build up a tremendous population, as measured in pounds of fish per acre. The Missouri Conservation Department reports that 35-acre Slater Lake, when drained for reno-

Top to bottom: Quillback, Carp,
Bigmouth Buffalofish

vation, yielded 5000 pounds of bigmouth buffalo, with twenty- to
thirty-pound fish common. Perco Lake, seven acres, yielded 275 bigmouth buffalo, averaging eighteen pounds each—a total of about 5000
pounds, or 700 pounds per acre. The Missouri bulletin adds that
anglers never caught buffalo in Perco Lake and rarely in Slater Lake.

The smallmouth or white buffalo, *Ictiobus bubalus* (Rafinesque),
has much the same range as the bigmouth. The black buffalo,

Ictiobus niger (Rafinesque), darker than the bigmouth, occurs throughout the Mississippi Valley, with greater abundance in the South. Both species are large fish but do not equal the bigmouth buffalo's maximum size.

NORTHERN HOG SUCKER
Hypentelium nigricans (LeSueur)

The northern hog sucker is a fish of small, clear, rocky, swift-flowing streams. It differs somewhat in general shape and coloring from the white sucker, and markedly in its habits from most of the family.

Its head is usually wider than the body, which is larger forward and tapering to slenderness near the tail. This feature, and the fish's habit of dislodging stones with its big armor-plated head to get at insect larvae and mollusks, have given it the names of riffle sucker, big-headed sucker, and stone roller. The hog sucker's coarsely mottled colors on the upper sides make the fish almost invisible against stony bottoms.

The hog sucker is a friend of other fishes, including trout, which often follow it and gather up nymphs dislodged by its habit of leaving few stones unturned.

This member of the family averages less than a foot long, and rarely grows to two pounds. It occurs from New York across the Great Lakes region, and the Mississippi-Missouri system westward to Montana.

More southerly species are the Alabama hog sucker, *Hypentelium etowanum* (Jordan), and the Roanoke hog sucker, *H. roanokense* Raney and Lachner.

Among other sucker genera, a few fish are worth noting. The blue sucker, *Cycleptus elongatus* (LeSueur), with a dark gray-blue to slate-blue back and a dorsal fin similar to that of the carpsuckers, is the only species of *Cycleptus*. A fish frequenting the channels of large midwestern rivers, it is reported as quite common in the Missouri, less so in the Mississippi, and nowhere abundant. It averages perhaps a pound in weight but occasionally reaches four or five pounds. Though regarded by some as superior in food value to any other sucker, it is relatively little known to sports fishermen and has no significant commercial value.

The genus *Xyrauchen* also includes but one species, the humpback sucker, *X. texanus* (Abbott). A southwestern species, it occurs from the Colorado River basin to Texas. Its distinctive hump—an abrupt rise of the back line just behind the head—gives it its name.

Among the three species of the genus *Erimyzon,* two are fairly well known: the creek chubsucker, *E. oblongus* (Mitchill), and the lake chubsucker, *E. sucetta* (Lacépède). Both are small fish, rarely exceeding twelve inches, and of little value.

Chapter 13

MINNOWS

In the entire lexicon of fishes, probably no word is more loosely or incorrectly used than "minnow." For a minnow is emphatically not any small fish, as many people believe. It is not the fry or fingerling stage of the trout, bass, pike, or any other non-minnow species. Although most true minnows are small, the fallfish grows to be eighteen inches long; others, such as the squawfish and carp, may grow to be four feet long and fifty pounds heavy.

Specifically a minnow is any member of the family Cyprinidae. This is a tremendous clan; currently numbering, according to the American Fisheries Society, 41 genera and 193 species in the United States and Canada. Other species are found in Europe, Asia, and Africa. No true minnow is native to South America, but that continent does have a large and similar group, the charatins, occupying a similar biological niche and performing the same important function in the food chain.

The cyprinid family includes the dace, several chubs, shiners, squawfish, roach, carp, and goldfish. It does not include the killifishes and the darters. All minnows are freshwater fishes, non-anadromous, though rare strays among the golden shiner have been reported from brackish rivers, and the carp has been found occasionally out of its element in the salt water of Chesapeake and New York bays.

Among the very numerous minnows, identification is often impossible to laymen and difficult even for ichthyologists. Not many years ago, well over two hundred separate species were recognized; today many of these are classed as subspecies or variants.

In general, the Cyprinidae have certain obvious features common to all species. They are inclined to be deep and laterally compressed, have large scales on the body but none on the head; teeth in the throat but none in the mouth; a stomach that is simply an enlargement of the intestine; a centrally located, single short dorsal fin; no adipose fin; and a deeply forked tail. The carp and goldfish are exceptional in having long dorsal fins and a serrated spine on the front edge of the dorsal and anal. All other minnows have soft-rayed fins. Many have barbels at the mouth, but in some species these are so small as to be almost invisible.

The range is tremendous. Minnows of one kind or another are found virtually everywhere in the North American continent, from Alaska and northern Canada to Mexico, and from the Atlantic to the Pacific. They inhabit ponds, large lakes, brooks, creeks, and big rivers; clear and turbid water; cold streams at altitudes of several thousand feet; muddy warm rivers, and bayous close to sea level.

All are spring or summer spawners; some have prolonged spawning periods, shedding their eggs at any time from May to August, and several species spawn more than once in a season. The males of some minnows take on brilliant colors in the breeding season and develop horny tubercles on the head. Some are accomplished nest-builders; some spawn in the nests of other species; still others shed their eggs at random.

The minnows are of crucial importance in nature's grand design of fish populations and in man's schemes of fisheries management. Some of the smaller minnow species have a sacrificial role. They die that larger fishes may live, thus keeping the food chain intact in one of its vital links. Feeding chiefly on small invertebrate animals and vegetable plankton, they convert this material into protein food for the many larger fishes which prey upon them. In this sense, their commercial worth is incalculable. Where the minnows are abundant, the larger game and food fishes thrive and prosper. Where the minnows are thinned out by seining for bait or by other causes, the game fish assert their instinctive cannibalism and depopulate their own kind. Other predators such as herons, mergansers, and turtles, will also turn to the game species for food if their natural prey, the minnow, is absent.

Minnow depletion in many waters has led conservationists to promote the artificial propagation of bait minnows in ponds, and legislators to pass laws against the seining of wild minnows. Minnow-raising has become big business in some areas. In the Midwest some of the larger bait-raising firms are managing two or three hundred acres of water.

The cyprinids most sought by anglers are the common shiner, golden shiner, fallfish, horned dace or creek chub, squawfish, and carp.

COMMON SHINER
Notropis cornutus (Mitchill)

This member of the minnow family grows large enough—six to eight or, rarely, ten inches—to have interested generations of boys. These youthful anglers knew the shiner in the home brooks usually before they learned of the brook trout which in many instances inhabited the same water. The past tense is used here because in the little brooks and creeks close to the larger cities the common shiner has all but disappeared. Half a century ago, within fifteen miles of New York City, we went after it with a pole cut from a straight small sapling, a short length of line, an eyed small Sproat hook *sans* leader, a can of worms or a chunk of dough mixed with absorbent cotton so that it would stay on the hook. Sometimes we would essay a float or dobber—a cork slit halfway through, with the line wedged into the slit. In an afternoon after school, under a railroad bridge where our creek widened into a considerable pool, a catch of twenty-five was routine. It is this writer's sad suspicion that he could employ the same gear and tactics in the same place, now in the 1960's, all day long, and never once see his cork move downward with the little tug of the shiner.

This fish was known to us simply as the shiner. Elsewhere, in a range extending from Nova Scotia to Saskatchewan and south to the Gulf coast, it is variously called the redfish shiner, creek shiner, and silver shiner. In color it is dusky to olive on the back, with a dark stripe along the dorsal surface. The scales are high and narrow, large in proportion to the fish, and some of them are dusky, giving a mottled appearance to the otherwise silvery sides. Spawning males become reddish on their bodies and lower fins.

During May and June the mature females, two to three years old, deposit their adhesive eggs in shallow riffles over a gravel bottom, often in the excavated nests of other fishes. These pre-empted breeding sites are guarded stoutly by the males. Larger than the females, the cock fish develop hard tubercles, and fight each other in a small, darting, miniaturely savage way at spawning time.

Aquatic insects are the common shiner's principal food, varied upon occasion with terrestrial bugs and small fish. Trout fishermen are frequently surprised by the quick strike of a shiner on a wet fly.

GOLDEN SHINER
Notemigonus crysoleucas (Mitchill)

The golden shiner is also called the butterfish, bream, roach, bitterhead, chub, gudgeon, and windfish. Some of these names are narrowly localized and confusing, since they apply to other species. This fish resembles the common shiner, and attains about the same size, but in some respects is quite different.

The golden's native range stretches from Nova Scotia, where it is said to be the most common minnow, westward to Manitoba and the Dakotas, including the James Bay drainages in northern Ontario, and southward to the Gulf. At least three subspecies were formerly recognized, the most common being the western golden shiner, *N.c. auratus*. This fish, now held to be a variety of the golden, is present in the far West, through introductions, on both sides of the continental divide.

Unlike its common kin, the golden shiner is a fish of warm, weedy ponds and lakes, and the shallow, vegetated areas of large rivers and bayous.

The golden has the deep, laterally compressed body of the common shiner, a smaller mouth without barbels, and a pointed head. It possesses a fleshy, unscaled keel between the ventral fins and the unusually long anal. Adult goldens are dark brown to olive-green on the dorsal area, with a golden flush on the sides which becomes brilliant at spawning time. The lower fins may be amber-colored or pinkish. A black lateral band on the young fish disappears with maturity.

Female goldens grow faster and attain a larger size than the males, and if they elude their multitude of predators may live to be eight years old. Maturing usually at the age of two, the golden spawns from May to August, sometimes twice in a season, building no nest but scattering its adhesive eggs in shallow water and deserting them at once.

Though an omnivorous fish, the golden in some areas consumes plant food as 90 per cent of its diet. But in most waters it feeds largely on insects and plankton, varied with small fishes, crustaceans such as water fleas, and mollusks. Like the common shiner, the golden will take an artificial fly and is a traditional quarry of small boys fishing with worms and dough balls.

It is one of the best of the forage fishes for game species, widely propagated for bait and cultivated in state hatcheries as food for bass.

FALLFISH
Semotilus corporalis (Mitchill)

One of the large minnows, the fallfish attains a weight of three pounds in certain eastern lakes. In the clearwater streams it is smaller but commonly runs from ten to fourteen inches. In such sizes the fallfish may be classed as a game species, for it inhabits many trout streams, feeds largely on insects, and hits wet and dry flies with abandon. Once hooked, however, the fallfish in this writer's experience have very quickly identified themselves, even if unseen for a moment, by giving in after one or two hard rushes. Despite Thoreau's appraisal of the fallfish as tasting "like brown paper, salted," it can be quite palatable, pan-fried, if taken from cold swift water.

The fallfish is known to many anglers as chub, silver chub, chivin, windfish, and corporal. The name fallfish is derived from this species' frequence in pools at the foot of falls, though it is by no means confined to such water.

It is less rounded, more laterally compressed than its close relative the creek chub or horned dace. Its mouth is larger and somewhat inferior, giving the fallfish an almost suckerlike appearance and causing it sometimes to be mistaken for a white sucker. A small barbel is present, almost concealed in a groove near each corner of the upper jaw. The back color is bluish to olive-brown; the sides are silvery, sometimes with a rosy iridescence. The lower fins become reddish on spawning males. Black bars at the base of each scale on the sides give a kind of checkered effect.

The fallfish's range is somewhat restricted, by comparison with that of the common and golden shiner. It extends from the Maritime Provinces westward across Ontario, and south to Virginia.

A springtime spawner, the fallfish male is a nest-builder of great distinction, sharing this talent with the creek chub. After excavating a nest and fertilizing the eggs deposited therein by the female, the male fallfish covers the eggs with stones up to two inches in diameter, piling them in large mounds.

CREEK CHUB OR HORNED DACE
Semotilus atromaculatus (Mitchill)

Similar to the fallfish in its nest-building, the creek chub is in other ways a very different fish. Though large for a minnow, it seldom reaches more than twelve inches and averages about eight. Males are considerably larger than females of the same age. This fish is essentially a clearwater, small-stream inhabitant, seldom found in lakes or large rivers. Its range is much broader than the fallfish's, running from the Maritime Provinces to Alberta and Montana and reaching south and west to the Gulf states and New Mexico.

The creek chub is readily identified by a black mark at the base of the first three rays of the dorsal fin. Its general color is similar to the fallfish's, but it often has a purplish sheen along its flanks. A small barbel is present at each angle of the upper jaw. Spawning males are well equipped with six to eight hard tubercles on the head and snout.

Spawning in April in the South to June in the North, the creek chub seeks its breeding sites in shallow riffles or rapids over gravel bottoms. The female may deposit only thirty to forty eggs at a time in pits excavated by the male; these are covered by the male, who then awaits the subsequent depositions, covering all until the female is spawned out. In burying the eggs, the male does not wrestle with such large stones as those tackled by the fallfish, but often makes a larger mound with its smaller material. Eggs are guarded by the male until incubation is complete.

The creek chub is a carnivorous minnow. Stomach contents of specimens examined by U.S. Fish and Wildlife Service workers consisted of 51 per cent insects and 26 per cent surface drift; the rest included mollusks, crustaceans, algae, and plant seeds. A fish so fond of insects may be expected to take artificial flies, and it does.

The creek chub is distinguished also for its tenacity as a bait minnow, on the hook or in the bait bucket; its ability to survive handling and transporting; and its tolerance of sudden changes in water temperature.

BLACKNOSE DACE
Rhinichthys atratulus (Hermann)

This fish is a small (usually under three inches) denizen of clear-water brooks and creeks, ranging from Nova Scotia westward to southern Ontario and North Dakota, and south to the lower Mississippi drainages. It is rare in lakes or ponds.

The blacknose dace's color scheme varies widely in different waters. Its back may be black or dark blue or olive-green; its body is silvery but has a kind of mottled pattern owing to darkened scales here and there. A black stripe on the side extends from the snout the full length of the fish, and gives the blacknose dace its name. Spawning males are suffused with a reddish flush on their sides and have a deep-red lateral line. The scales number 62 to 71 in a lengthwise row. A barbel is visible at each corner of the mouth. The dorsal fin is set rather far back, slightly forward of the anal.

This little fish spawns in April or May, usually at the head of riffles, and its mating techniques are courtly and picturesque. T. H. Langlois[1] describes them thus: "Each male occupies a 'holding' though shifting around considerably. When a female enters a 'holding' the male goes to her and sometimes passes several times around her before coming to a lateral parallel position for spawning. When side by side, the female vibrates her tail, sometimes nearly burying it while doing so, and at the same time the male's tail starts vibrating and curling up over the female's tail to her dorsal fin, when vibrations cease. Occasionally the pair remains in place and spawns again immediately, but usually they separate, the male darting forward while the female relaxes limply onto one side, remaining there for several seconds."

The blacknose dace is an excellent bait for bass and other game fish. As trout fishermen know, one of the famous and effective streamer flies is patterned upon and named for this minnow.

BLUNTNOSE MINNOW
Pimephales notatus (Rafinesque)

The bluntnose is as small as most people think minnows should be: two to three inches, rarely reaching four. Inhabiting many waters containing large game fish, the bluntnose is an outstanding forage fish for game species. It is widely propagated by commercial bait suppliers. In rearing ponds containing an abundance of its preferred foods —plant plankton and insect larvae—the bluntnose has been produced at the rate of more than 400,000 per acre per year. As a bait minnow it has, however, the disadvantage of dying quickly in a crowded minnow bucket.

[1] "Observations on Bait Culture," *Ohio Conservation Bulletin*, 1941.

Top to bottom:
Common Shiner, Blacknose Daces, Fallfish

A fish equally at home in lakes, small creeks, and large rivers, the bluntnose ranges from southern Quebec to Manitoba and Minnesota, and south to Iowa and Missouri. East of the Mississippi it is present as far south as Tennessee, Kentucky, and Virginia. It has been introduced into the Rocky Mountain area.

The bluntnose is a round-bodied minnow with a small mouth overhung by a blunt, rounded snout which gives the fish its name. The back is a pale olive-green, the sides bluish-silvery. A dark band runs the length of the fish, terminating in a distinct black spot at the base of the tail.

An unusual if not unique habit distinguishes the bluntnose's spawning. The eggs are invariably laid on the underside of flat rocks, submerged logs, or any object affording the male protection while he stands guard during the eight- to twelve-day incubation period. Those who raise the bluntnose for bait must supply such objects for breeding fish. The spawning period is prolonged—late May to August. Small as they are, the females cast 500 to 2000 eggs.

SQUAWFISH

These are among the largest of the minnow family, exceeded only by the carp. There are four recognized species of squawfish in the United States and Canada, all native to the far West. The total range is from British Columbia to California, including the Columbia River basin to Idaho and Montana, and rivers and lakes of Colorado, Wyoming, Nevada, Utah, and Arizona. Indians esteemed the squawfish as food, hence its name.

Jordan and Evermann[2] reported squawfish reaching a length of four feet. Recent records do not include any such giants, but squawfish two feet long are not uncommon. Anglers are of two schools concerning this fish. Some disdain it as a game species and as food; others assert that it is a strong fighter on light tackle and good eating when properly cooked.

All the squawfish are springtime spawners, the lake fish migrating a short distance up tributaries at spawning time. Though the squawfish feed largely on insects and mollusks, they are accused of preying upon the young of game species. The charge may be just, but certainly it has been made with equal fairness against many other fishes.

Perhaps the best known of the four species is the northern squawfish, *Ptychocheilus oregonensis* (Richardson), occurring from British Columbia to the Oregon, Washington, Idaho, and Montana drainages

[2] *American Food and Game Fishes* (Doubleday, Page & Co., New York, 1902).

of the Columbia River. This fish is known by other names such as Columbia River squawfish, chappaul, bigmouth, and yellowbelly.

It has a large head, a large toothless mouth, a short spineless dorsal situated somewhat back of the middle, and a deeply forked tail —all characteristic of minnows. The back and upper sides are olive-green, fading to yellowish below. A number of dark spots are evident on some fish.

The Sacramento squawfish, *Ptychocheilus grandis* (Ayres), is native to the Pacific drainages of northern California and southern Oregon. Known as the Sacramento pike, it closely resembles the northern squawfish and attains a comparable size. This species sometimes enters tidal bays but is not anadromous.

Others are the Colorado squawfish, *Ptychocheilus lucius* Girard, native to the Colorado River system; and the Umpqua squawfish, *P. umpquae* Snyder, of the Umpqua River in Oregon. The Colorado squawfish, largest native American minnow, is threatened since its major population was destroyed by poisonous chemicals in September 1962.

CARP
Cyprinus carpio Linnaeus

In many ways, not all of them flattering, the carp is the most distinguished of the entire minnow family. From the recorded data on a few outsize specimens, this species is the largest of the minnows, and its annals and legends date back to antiquity.

The carp's range in North America (none of it native) embraces southern Canada from east to west, the entire continental United States, and Mexico. Its habitat includes ponds, small and large lakes, and rivers—preferably the warmer muddy waters, and if they are not muddy the carp may make them so.

The carp is recorded in China as far back as 500 B.C., and for centuries has been a symbol of fertility in Japan. It was imported to Europe at an unknown date. F. E. Zeuner, in *A History of Domesticated Animals*,[3] writes, "The earliest record is probably that of the

[3] Harper & Row, New York, 1964.

Ostrogoth king Theodoric (A.D. 475-526), whose secretary Cassiodorus was compelled to issue a circular to the provincial governors to improve the supply [of carp] for the king's table."

Culture of the carp in well-managed ponds has made this fish an important source of food in Europe and Asia for centuries. Fancy strains of carp have long been bred in central Europe for gourmet markets.

The first carp were imported to the United States as early as 1830 but failed to establish a permanent population. Today's vast numbers of carp stem from importations beginning in the 1870's, from Germany via California.

The carp's history in this country is an extraordinary reversal of that of the imported German brown trout and the transplanted rainbow. Both of these fish were unwelcome at first but later came to be valued. The carp, originally received with enthusiasm as a new source of food, became hated later by anglers and conservationists who saw it competing with game species for food and space, muddying their clear waters, disturbing their spawning grounds, eating their young, and spreading new parasites and diseases. Today several midwestern states are spending large amounts of money in the effort to eliminate carp to make room for game fish. Iowa alone is currently removing half a million pounds of carp annually from its waters.

Other names for this fish are German carp and European carp. The names mirror carp, and leather carp or leatherback denote not subspecies but merely phases or types of the one and only species of the genus *Cyprinus*. Normally the carp is fully scaled; the mirror carp has patches of scales on the back and sides; the leather carp or leatherback is totally or almost devoid of scales. The progeny of these oddities apparently are born and grow fully scaled. In 1887, the U.S. Fish Commission arranged the first government-sanctioned importation of carp. Of 345 fish imported as brood stock, 227 were mirror and leather carp, 118 were scaled carp, but nearly all the offspring were fully scaled. Mirror and leather carp are quite rare today, probably constituting less than 2 per cent of all wild carp.[4]

The carp is a deep, laterally compressed fish. Its scales are large and thick, numbering 35 to 37 along the middle row. Two pairs of

[4] Gilbert Weiss, Missouri Conservation Commission, Jefferson City, Mo.

barbels, one pair conspicuous, are present at the mouth. The color varies widely: in some waters carp are very dark, in others silvery to yellowish below the dorsal surface, which may be black, brownish, or olive-green.

Throughout its range the carp taken by commercial and sport fishermen average probably one to three pounds. Fish of five, ten, and fifteen pounds are not uncommon; thirty-pounders are taken in such large waters as Lake Erie. The record rod-and-reel carp from U.S. waters was a 55-pound 5-ounce specimen, 42 inches long, taken from Clearwater Lake, Minnesota by F. J. Ledwein on July 10, 1952. Much heavier carp have been reported from abroad, including one of 83½ pounds from Pretoria, South Africa.

From south to north, carp spawn from May to mid-July. Breeding sites are shallow weedy bays or tributaries of lakes, or backwaters of rivers, sometimes in water only inches deep. Females become sexually mature at two or three years of age, when weighing between one and two pounds. A large female may shed more than a million adhesive eggs, broadcasting them indiscriminately over vegetated muck bottoms. Once shed, the eggs are deserted by both parents, and hatch in six days to two weeks.

The carp's food includes almost everything: aquatic vegetation, insects, crustaceans, mollusks, domestic waste, small fish, and fish eggs. Its habit of uprooting vegetation—whether for the tender roots and stems of the plants themselves or in a search for bottom invertebrates —has earned the carp an unsavory reputation as a muddier and befouler of game-fish waters.

Defenders of the carp, however, point out that it inhabits many waters already muddied and polluted by man, where other fish could not survive, and that its bottom-rooting habits are actually beneficial in areas where the water would otherwise become too weed-choked for any fish.

Some anglers defend the carp, too, as a provider of sport where other fish are lacking. A preferred bait is a dough ball made of corn meal. The ubiquitous earthworm also catches carp, as does—in this writer's experience—a half-inch cube of raw potato.

Commercially, the carp is the major species of fish in many midwestern areas. Statistics of the commercial catch are not available, but probably ten million pounds of carp are marketed annually in the United States, and a million pounds in Canada.

The goldfish, *Carassius auratus* (Linnaeus), is very similar to the carp. It differs, however, not only in its familiar aquarium colors but in the absence of barbels. It is another import, and is primarily an ornamental fish for tanks and city-park ponds. If placed in the semi-wild environment of a natural lake or large pond it loses its bright domestic colors and takes on the duller hues of the carp.

Chapter 14

CATFISHES

The Ictaluridae family of catfishes numbers five recognized genera and twenty-four species in the United States and Canada. These include the catfishes, bullheads, madtoms, stonecat, and blindcats.

Collectively, their range extends from Canada to Mexico. None is native to the Pacific slopes north of Mexico,[1] but several species have been introduced into Pacific drainages and have established permanent populations, most abundantly in California. Through introductions

---

[1] Jordan and Evermann, in *American Food and Game Fishes*, 1902, reported a native catfish, *Ameiurus pricei*, in San Bernardino Creek, a Gulf of California tributary in southern Arizona. This fish is the Yaqui catfish, now with the scientific name *Ictalurus pricei* (Rutter).

beginning in the West in the late 1800's and continuing elsewhere, various catfishes and bullheads have taken permanent residence in the waters of every state except Alaska. Some of the freshwater catfishes occasionally stray for brief periods into brackish estuaries and tidal rivers, but none is anadromous.

Essentially warmwater fishes, most of the cats are at home in mud-bottomed, sluggish rivers and creeks, weedy ponds and lakes. They are tolerant of degrees of pollution and oxygen depletion which few other fish could survive. Some of the catfish species are found, however, in swifter, cooler rivers, even coexisting with trout in the clean, cold, rock-bottomed streams of the North.

Nocturnal in their habits, the catfishes and bullheads are inclined to hole up by day and make feeding forays into the shallows by night. But like the pike, they seem eternally hungry, and even at high noon will go for any bait that comes along. They are omnivorous: anything and everything is on their menu. Their natural food includes aquatic and terrestrial insects and insect larvae, crayfish and other crustaceans, mollusks, small fishes, fish eggs, worms, aquatic vegetation, wild grapes, windborne arboreal driftage such as elm seeds and the "cotton" of cottonwood trees. Feeding upon dead animals and fishes too, the catfish are the great scavengers and cleaners of the lakes and rivers. Baits include nightcrawlers, chunks of meat, chicken entrails, dough concoctions of flour and cottonseed meal, "stink baits" of putrid fish, meat, or mussels, secret home-formulated compounds, and various manufactured preparations which are big business in the Midwest. Even metal jigs bumped off the bottom, and spoons trolled slowly along the mud, will often draw the lunker cat from its lair.

The Ictaluridae includes species of all sizes, from small to great. The tadpole madtom averages two to four inches at full growth; the blue catfish has been reported at 150 pounds.

Despite these wide dimensional variations the catfishes are alike in many respects. All in the United States and Canada are without scales (South America has some scaled species); all possess eight distinct barbels or "whiskers"—a long one trailing from each corner of the mouth, a shorter pair arising near the nostrils, and four under the chin. It is interesting to note that the catfish's "whiskers" or barbels carry taste buds and are sensitive to touch. Extending the fish's sensory field, they help it to find food at night or in turbid water. A distinguishing feature of the catfishes is a defensive armor consisting of three sharp, stiff spines, one at the forward end of the dorsal and of each pectoral fin. These spines are sharp enough to puncture a careless hand, and the pectoral spines carry the added menace of poison. No hypodermic action, such as the rattlesnake practices, is involved. Secretions from the pectoral poison gland exude from its pore and are washed over the side of the fish. Folded back against the body, the pectoral spine is bathed in the poison. Probably the venom is far less toxic than that of the vipers; at any rate, its dilution by water renders it harmless enough, though its effect may approximate the sting of a wasp. The tadpole madtom has a poison gland at the dorsal spine as well as the pectorals. Formerly scientists attributed this venomous feature only to the madtoms; now it is known that all catfishes are so equipped. The poison glands do not affect the flesh for eating purposes and do not seem to bother the predator trout whose powerful digestive juices dissolve any madtom or small stonecat in short order. In netting an obviously healthy brown trout of fifteen inches, this writer found a four-inch, partly digested stonecat in the trout's mouth, disgorged in the trout's struggle to free itself.

Other marks of the catfish tribe are an adipose fin, a short, high dorsal fin, well forward in most species, a long anal fin, and a large air bladder.

The catfishes spawn from April to early July, south to north. In their parental solicitude they are exemplary, being accomplished nest builders and stout guardians of the eggs.

Yet human prejudice has long contrived to despise the catfishes. Perhaps their barbels, their spines, large heads, large mouths, muddy habits and indiscriminate feeding, and their alleged dull color (not really dull to the appreciative eye), have combined to evoke human revulsion.

People who truly know the catfish, however, appreciate its virtues. In the Northeast the bullhead is one of the classic fishes of boyhood, but there its reputation ends. For true justice to the Ictaluridae, look to the Midwest and South, where the big channel cats, blues, and flatheads have challenged generations of anglers, and most people have a decent appreciation of catfish meat. Easterners, lacking conviction that a catfish can be a supreme thing on the table, should try it in one of the better restaurants of almost any middling town in Illinois or Iowa.

The catfish's gustatory virtue has long prospered commercial fishermen who ply their trotlines along the Mississippi and Missouri, the lesser streams and the lakes throughout the Midwest and South, and more recently in California.

CHANNEL CATFISH
Ictalurus punctatus (Rafinesque)

Its tremendous native range, large size, stubborn and often spectacular fight, and excellence as food have made the channel cat one of the accredited game fishes of America.

Originally it swam in the rivers and lakes from the St. Lawrence basin to Montana, Wyoming, and the Prairie Provinces of Canada, and southward from that line to the Gulf states, Texas, and Mexico, with abundance in the Mississippi-Missouri River system. Through introductions, the channel cat is now established in eastern and far western rivers distant from its original range. It is widely stocked and reared in farm ponds, particularly in the South and Midwest. Sac fry of channel cats were air shipped to Hawaii from Oklahoma and Kansas in 1958; as of 1963 the Division of Fish and Game at Honolulu reports that this fish "offers excellent promise for development as a game species in Hawaii." It is present today on four of the Hawaiian islands.

A thoroughgoing cosmopolite, the channel cat is at home in typical catfish environs—large sluggish rivers and warm weedy lakes—but again it will be found in swift, cool, clear-running streams and rock-hemmed lakes.

"Average" sizes, with the channel cat, are meaningless. In big waters the average may be five to twenty pounds; in lesser rivers and lakes it may be one to two pounds. But this fish has a growth potential that lends enchantment to its pursuit. It is capable of becoming huge. The record on sporting tackle is held by a fish of 57 pounds, taken from the Santee-Cooper Reservoir, South Carolina, by C. B. Dennis on March 8, 1960.

Various local names have attached to the channel catfish. One of

these, "spotted cat," is appropriate, for this fish is generally sprinkled
along its side with dark round spots of various sizes. They are not
present on young fish of three or four inches, and tend to disappear
on larger adults. The over-all color varies from one water to another.
Traditionally it is light brownish to slate-gray, darker gray-brown on
top. In some waters, however, the dorsal surface is a very dark brown
to olive-green, sometimes bluish, the sides a lighter yellowish or
grayish green, the underbody a dirty white. Albinos with pink eyes
and creamy bodies occur in some southern waters. The head is pointed
and small, with the upper jaw slightly overhanging the lower. The tail
is deeply forked, the dorsal fin high, short, and well forward of the
middle, the anal long, wide and rounded, containing 25 to 30 rays. The
pectoral spines are serrated on the rear edge. More than others of its
family, the channel cat is inclined to slenderness throughout its length.

Spawning in April to June, it ascends tributaries of lakes and large
rivers, and seeks its breeding site under rock ledges or deeply undercut
banks, in the submerged runs of muskrats, and in hollow logs. (Nail
kegs are commonly provided for channel catfish nests in artificial
rearing). The male cleans the nesting site and guards the eggs during
incubation, fanning them gently, and chasing off any trespassers. A
first-spawning female, mature in her fourth year and at a length of
thirteen to fifteen inches,[2] may lay 4000 eggs. Larger fish spawn 20,000
or more. The adhesive eggs, each half the size of a pea, from a golden-
yellow, gelatinous mass. They hatch in seven to ten days; thereafter
the male parent shepherds the tight-packed school of fry until they
can shift for themselves.

An interesting record of a typical nine-day incubation of channel
catfish eggs, in water at 70° F., is supplied by Harry E. Schafer, Jr.,
Superintendent of the Fisheries Section, Louisiana Wild Life and
Fisheries Commission:

[2] These figures are for northern fish. Channel cats in the deep South mature at
shorter lengths and earlier ages. James T. Davis and Lloyd E. Posey, Jr., of the
Louisiana Wild Life and Fisheries Commission, studying 1097 female and 1125
male channel catfish, found that the majority of females are mature at 10½ to 11
inches, the majority of males at 12 to 12½ inches. There was considerable overlap
in lengths of mature fish. One female was found to be ripe at 7 inches, another
was undeveloped at 15½. A fully developed male was only 8½ inches long, while
one immature specimen was 17 inches.

Similar studies on the upper Mississippi River showed the smallest mature
female to be 12 to 13 inches, and in California some channel cats were reported
immature at 20 inches.

1st day: eggs clear.

2nd day: small hairlike white stripe forms on yolk.

3rd day: white stripe has several small stripes on either side.

4th day: stripes acquire a slight pink color.

5th day: two dark spots, which are eyes, appear.

6th day: stripes are red, eyes very prominent, and close observation will detect slight movement.

7th day: action very noticeable.

8th day: fish appear to turn over in egg; if egg is squeezed until broken, fish will swim out.

9th day: eggs hatched and ready to move to rearing pond.

Anglers fish for the channel cat with all manner of rigs and baits. In the well-known jugging method, the fisherman drops in strategic spots a number of floating gallon jugs, each with line and baited hook attached. Then he rests on his oars to await action, which may be quite strenuous should three or four jugs become simultaneously engaged with channel cats.

During the day the lunkers sulk in the deeper holes and around dams, brush piles, and other current obstructions. At dusk they cruise into the river shallows, sometimes into very fast water, or over the lake sand bars, and begin more active feeding. Large fish have their favorite haunts, and the successful fishermen know where they are. The channel cat can be a traveler, however. Tagged fish in the Colorado River were recovered many miles downstream from the tagging point. The longest journey was 76 miles in 180 days; the fastest, 46 miles in 45 days.[3]

With its white, flaky and flavorful flesh, the channel cat is excellent on the table, and the chief species in commercial fishing.

BLUE CATFISH
Ictalurus furcatus (LeSueur)

Known also as the great forktail cat, chucklehead, and *poisson bleu*, the blue catfish is the giant of the family. A fish of large, slow-

[3] George W. McCammon, "A Tagging Experiment with Channel Catfish in the Lower Colorado River," reprinted from *California Fish and Game*, Vol. 42, No. 4 (October 1956).

coiling, turbid rivers, it has generally a more southerly range than the channel cat. It seems not to occur in Canada, ranging from South Dakota, Minnesota, and Iowa southward through the Mississippi, Missouri, and Ohio river systems to the Gulf, Texas, and Mexico, with its greatest abundance in the lower Mississippi and its tributaries.

The blue cat has attained immense sizes. Jordan and Evermann cited a 150-pound specimen taken from the Mississippi River at St. Louis, many years ago. The current sporting record as reported by *Field & Stream* is a 97-pound leviathan, lacking three inches of being five feet long, taken from the Missouri River in South Dakota by Edward Elliott on September 16, 1959. A still larger blue cat is reported by the Tennessee Game and Fish Commission. This fish, weighing 102 pounds, came from Kentucky Lake, near Savannah, Tennessee, and was landed by Paul Walker on June 28, 1955. Among the blue cats taken by most anglers, 15- and 20-pounders are not rare.

With its protruding upper jaw and deeply forked tail, the blue catfish resembles the channel cat in appearance but can be easily distinguished. It has a blue to blue-gray dorsal-surface color, is without spots; and its anal fin is longer (30 to 35 rays), narrower, and pointed rather than rounded on its trailing edge. The dorsal is very far forward and is higher and more pointed than the channel cat's.

Years ago, before levees were built along some of the rivers draining into the lower Mississippi, spring floods inundated the flatlands far back from the river channels. The blue cats would then leave the river to cruise overland and follow the flood, and fishermen with "brush lines" would follow the blue cats. "Brush lines" were tied to trees in likely spots throughout the flooded area; the trees were marked with white flags or rags so as to be easily found, and the lines—perhaps as many as fifty per fisherman—were attended regularly, as a trapper attends his trapline.

The blue cat is a June-to-July spawner, a nest builder, and a guardian of its eggs. Females are sexually mature at four to five years, and cast about 3000 eggs per pound of adult fish. A huge female blue may deposit upwards of 100,000 eggs.

Excellent as food when taken from reasonably clear water, the blue cat is an important commercial fish throughout its range.

FLATHEAD CATFISH
Pylodictis olivaris (Rafinesque)

This is the third of the very large catfishes; indeed, some authorities say it is the largest of all in its average sizes. Commercially caught flatheads of 100 pounds and over are reported. In Iowa, 60-pounders have been exhibited at the annual state fair. Anglers' catches average perhaps 2 to 5 pounds over the entire range, but 20- to 40-pound flatheads are not uncommon. Fishermen who purposely seek the outsize flatheads arm themselves with stout rods, large bait-casting or light surf-casting reels, 30- to 50-pound-test lines, and large hooks baited

Channel Catfish   Flathead Catfish

with several nightcrawlers or an eight-inch chub. The flathead is big game.

Nocturnal, like others of its family, it frequents deep hideouts by day and enters the shoals at night to feed. More piscivorous than most of the cats, it preys heavily on minnows and other small fishes.

The flathead catfish has acquired several local names, such as mud catfish, goujon, shovelhead, and yellow cat. Its range extends from South Dakota to western Pennsylvania (upper Ohio River system) and south to the Gulf, Texas, and Mexico. Like the blue catfish, the flathead is a fish of large sluggish rivers, and reaches its greatest abundance in the lower Mississippi drainages where it supports a substantial commercial fishery. It frequents large lakes where

Clockwise from top: Brown Bullhead, Stonecat, Tadpole Madtom, Blue Cat, Black Bullheads

rivers have been impounded, and is occasionally found in fast, well-oxygenated water below dams.

Though comparable to the blue and channel cats in size, the flathead is of a different genus and noticeably different appearance. Its long, flat, wide head gives it its name. The under jaw projects beyond the upper; the tail is not forked as the channel's and blue's, but is square or slightly notched. The adipose fin is very large, its base approximately the length of, and directly over, the comparatively short anal fin. The color is olive to brownish-yellow, mottled on the sides and fading to grayish below. Flatheads up to eight or ten pounds are slender, but larger ones tend to become pot-bellied.

Females first become ripe in their fourth or fifth year and may live to be twenty years old. They spawn in the late spring or early summer. The parents are assiduous in their duties, building nests and watching over their eggs.

Large flathead and blue catfish have an unfortunate predilection for submerged hollow cypress logs where sometimes they become permanently lodged, unable to swim through or to turn or back out.

WHITE CATFISH
Ictalurus catus (Linnaeus)

Originally an eastern and southern fish, ranging from the Delaware River southward to the Gulf and Texas, the white catfish has been widely transplanted. Through introductions it is now abundant in California and is well established in southern New England. It has always been plentiful in the Chesapeake Bay drainages, in fact "Potomac cat," or "white cat of the Potomac," is one of its local names. Perhaps more than other freshwater catfishes, it strays from its element into brackish waters.

The white catfish is a forked-tail species, like the blue and channel cats, but does not approach those fishes in size. The average white taken by anglers is probably under a pound; fish of over three pounds are uncommon, and ten or twelve pounds is the very rare maximum.

In color this species is greenish blue to olive on top, silvery to white below. It is unspotted but sometimes mottled or clouded on the sides. The rounded anal fin has 19 to 22 rays. The head and mouth are proportionally large.

THE BULLHEADS

BROWN BULLHEAD
Ictalurus nebulosus (LeSueur)

BLACK BULLHEAD
Ictalurus melas (Rafinesque)

YELLOW BULLHEAD
Ictalurus natalis (LeSueur)

The total native range of these three bullheads includes virtually all of the United States and southern Canada, except the Pacific drainages. Through wide transplantings, one or more species of bullheads now thrive in the rivers and lakes of California, Oregon, and Washington, and other waters west of the continental divide.

The brown bullhead, often called common bullhead, mud cat, and horned pout, is the most numerous of all the catfish tribe in eastern waters, where it lives in a great variety of habitats. These include not only the mud-bottomed creeks and ponds but also many swift, clean, coldwater brooks, and here the trout angler who fishes worms not infrequently hooks a brown bullhead in a pool where a trout ought to be.

The black bullhead, though native to the Northeast, is rare in Canada, more common in the northern Midwest—North Dakota through the Great Lakes country and down to Nebraska, Kansas, Iowa, and Missouri. Called the northern bullhead by many anglers, the black is by preference a pond and lake dweller.

The yellow bullhead, also a species of lakes and ponds, has more or less the same northern range (apparently absent from Lake Superior drainages), plus a southward extension to the Gulf states, including Texas.

These three are sometimes difficult to distinguish, one from another. All are small, averaging less than a foot long, yet all are capable of attaining much greater sizes. There is an official record for the black bullhead on sporting tackle: a fish of eight pounds, 24 inches long, taken from Lake Waccabuc, New York, by Kani Evans on August 1, 1951.

The yellow bullhead is quite easily identified by its lighter, yellowish-amber sides, its chunky body, heavy thick caudal peduncle, large adipose fin, extremely long anal with a distinct dark brown band close to the base, rounded tail, and light chin barbels.

The tails of both the brown and the black bullhead are square or slightly notched, the anal fin of each is shorter and more rounded, and the chin barbels are dark. The black bullhead has a yellowish vertical bar at the base of the tail, not possessed by the brown. The underparts of the black bullhead, except in the pectoral area, are greenish or yellowish, not white, and all of its rayed fins have sharp light and dark demarcations of the rays and membranes. There is a further difference in the pectoral spines. On the brown and yellow bullheads the rear edges of these spines are serrate; on the black they are smooth.

Commonly considered dull-colored, the bullheads in truth have a rich overcast of deep browns, olives, greens, and yellows, often with a fine iridescence when fresh from the water.

From April to June the bullheads make saucer-shaped nests beneath overhanging banks or other protected places. The females, mature at three years, are highly prolific, a nine-inch fish sometimes depositing 6000 to 7000 eggs in gelatinous, yellowish clusters. During the five- to ten-days incubation one or both parents may inhale an egg cluster, move it around like a mouthwash and expel it again. This practice is assumed to clean and aerate the eggs. The newly hatched fry, massed in tight dark little schools, are escorted about by their parents in the first day or two of their swimming life.

Adult bullheads may congregate in deep-cruising schools which can be thinned out in short order by any careful small-boy fisherman with a sapling pole and a can of worms. The omnivorous bullhead, though chiefly a nocturnal feeder, seems ready at all times to take a likely bait.

These little fish are very tenacious of life, capable of surviving in almost solidly frozen ponds and even able to live a considerable time out of water. They are fine panfish, especially when taken from clear running brooks.

STONECAT
Noturus flavus Rafinesque

TADPOLE MADTOM
Noturus gyrinus (Mitchill)

The stonecat and the madtoms are the smallest of the catfishes, the former seldom exceeding eight inches, the latter averaging two to three inches and rarely over four.

Their range is vast, stretching from southern Quebec and northern New England westward to Montana, southward to Florida and Texas. The stonecat is more abundant westward, the tadpole madtom in the Northeast and down the Atlantic seaboard. The latter is more at home in the mud-bottomed, weedy lakes or the still areas of streams. The stonecat frequents flowing, stony brooks, where it finds weedy areas in slack water or lurks under submerged logs or the larger rocks in riffles.

Both are distinguished chiefly by a fleshy adipose fin which is contiguous with the caudal, having no free posterior end. The stonecat has a protruding upper jaw and a slightly notched tail; the tadpole madtom's upper and lower jaws are even, and its tail rounded, the upper caudal lobe meeting the adipose and the lower almost reaching the anal fin.

The thick-skinned, often mucus-coated stonecat is light to dark gray-brown on the back, creamy to yellow on the sides, and white below. Its barbels are pale. The dorsal spine is very short, but the pectoral spines are strong, serrated, and mildly poisonous.

The tadpole madtom is a stocky little fish by contrast to the rather elongate stonecat. It is a somber-colored species in most waters, dark brown on top, gray-brown along the sides, white on the forward underbody. The dorsal and pectoral spines are smooth.

The food of the adults consists of tiny aquatic insects, larvae, and vegetable material. The tadpole madtom, with its fondness for still water, is said to be a good aquarium fish. Otherwise its value, and that of the stonecat, is reckoned only as food for larger species—a not inconsiderable worth.

There is only one stonecat, and probably that is enough. There are other madtoms—and how they earned so waggish a name is unclear—under the stones and sunken logs of a thousand rivers. There are the Carolina, the black, and the orangefin, the least, the margined, and the speckled, the brindled and the freckled. And there are the blindcats too, the widemouth and the toothless. And though few anglers know any of them, they are doubtless a credit, in their diminutive secret ways, to the illustrious family of the Ictaluridae.

Chapter 15

SUNFISHES

Among freshwater fishes the sunfish family is probably the best known to American fishermen and the most sought by the traditional boy with a pole and a can of worms. It is native only to North America; originally all but one of its members swam in the brooks, creeks, rivers, ponds, and lakes east but not west of the Rocky Mountains. The lone far western native is the Sacramento perch, which isn't a perch at all

NOTE: Illustrated are black crappie (*top*) and white crappie (*below*).

but a true sunfish. Today, by virtue of wide introductions, and its own extreme fecundity, the sunfish clan is everywhere from southern Canada to northern Mexico, in all states except Alaska but including Hawaii.

This great family, called the Centrarchidae by scientists, embraces thirty species grouped in ten genera. It includes not only the small, colorful species which are popularly called sunfishes, but also the crappies, rock bass, warmouth, and those eminent game fishes, the smallmouth and largemouth bass. Those commonly called sunfishes closely resemble each other in shape and appearance, and have similar ecological requirements. These factors, plus a widespread hybridization among several of the species, make identification difficult. There are some seventy names—most of them regional or local and hideously incorrect—for the pumpkinseed and its close cousins.

The sunfishes and the crappies are deep-bodied, roundish, the space between the dorsal and ventral surfaces being about half the length of the fish. All are laterally compressed, or thin from one side to the other. The curves of the upper and lower outlines are approximately equal, the body narrowing abruptly, above and below, to the caudal peduncle. All species have a long and continuous dorsal fin, its forward part spiny-rayed, its rear section soft, but lacking the notch between the two that is characteristic of the black basses. This fin proves that a sunfish is not a perch—though it is so called in many places—for the perch's dorsals are distinctly two and definitely separated.

A further mark of the sunfishes is a bony projection, commonly called the "ear flap," at the rear angle of the gill cover. The body is fully scaled, the scales being moderately ctenoid in most species and quite large in proportion to the fish, numbering 34 to 49, depending on the species, along the lateral line. Smaller scales occur on the cheeks and gill covers. The tail is emarginate or notched, with more or less rounded corners, never deeply forked. Teeth are present on the vomer and usually the palatines, and in some species on the lower jaw and the tongue.

Color is not a reliable distinction. In a single species it varies widely from one water to another, and it can be changed by some of the sunfishes, notably the pumpkinseed and the rock bass, almost at will. There are, however, certain identifying cues: minor differences in the ear flap and in the ray counts of the dorsal and anal fins.

All members of the family are spring or summer spawners, and some spawn more than once in a single season. Breeding begins in March, or earlier, in Florida and south Texas, and may not end until late August in the extreme northern range. The males are nest-builders, though some will at times appropriate the nests of other sunfish species. Some of the clan are solitary in their nesting; others spawn in close little colonies which may contain forty nests in an area 60 feet square. The eggs are adhesive. The males of most species closely guard the eggs during the relatively short incubation, and protectively shepherd the schools of tiny fry for a couple of days after hatching.

Growth rates of the sunfishes are highly variable, north to south. A four-year-old Wisconsin bluegill may be six inches long; a Florida bluegill of the same age can be eight inches or more.

A relatively short-lived family, the sunfishes have a normal life span of five or six years, though specimens of ten years and more have been recorded. Most species are sexually mature at ages of one to three, however,[1] and being highly prolific, often populate a pond or lake far beyond the carrying power of its food resource. Stunting is the inevitable consequence—a pond full of three-inch bluegills but with so few large ones that the pond loses its angling appeal. Overpopulation of sunfishes is one of the major problems of American fisheries management. Not only does it stunt the sunfishes themselves, but in competition for food and predation upon eggs it is detrimental to game-fish species inhabiting the same water. Attempting to maintain a healthy balance, state conservationists everywhere are abandoning artificial propagation, removing size and creel limits, instituting year-round open seasons, and urging heavy fishing for the pumpkinseed, bluegill, crappies, and their ilk.

All sunfishes are carnivorous. Though vegetable plankton has a minor role in the diet of adults, the chief food is of animal origin: aquatic and terrestrial insects and their larvae, crustaceans and mollusks, worms, leeches, and small fish.

Voracious in their feeding, the sunfishes go for virtually all baits

[1] The Florida Game and Fresh Water Fish Commission reports that bluegills may spawn at the age of five months.

and such artificial lures as wet and dry flies, small spinners, tiny metal jigs, and bass bugs. These bright little species are the "bread-and-butter" fish of the angling millions across the country—the bank-sitters who doze in the sun with a cane pole propped in a forked stick, the small boys who seek out the deep holes in the farm brooks, and some tens of thousands of mature anglers with tackle fit for trout or bass. Flies, plugs, and spinners are made for trout, bass, and others of the nobility, but the lowly sunfishes take many of them. Fly-fishermen who have known the feel of a one-pound bluegill or crappie on a four-ounce rod will never underrate the gameness of these little brothers to the bass.

BLUEGILL
Lepomis macrochirus Rafinesque

Probably the most widely distributed of all the sunfishes, the bluegill in the South is a bream (pronounced "brim") and a copperhead; elsewhere it is called blue perch, copper-nosed bream, and dollardee.

The bluegill's native range ran across southern Canada from Quebec to Manitoba, thence south to the Gulf states. Plantings have established it in all states except Alaska, though some of the higher-altitude waters of the West are not to its liking. It is a fish primarily of quiet streams, ponds and medium-sized lakes with weeded areas and moderately deep holes. Like most of the sunfishes it is tolerant of high water temperatures but is intolerant of low oxygen, and is among the first fish to perish in "winterkill" lakes. (Winterkill occurs in lakes when heavy snow over ice reduces light penetration and consequently photosynthesis, thus retarding oxygen renewal in the water.)

The color may be dark green, olive-green, or blue-green on the back, fading to yellowish green on the middle sides. The throat is a brilliant orange-red in some waters, yellow-brassy in others. The belly is similarly orange-red to grayish, depending on environment and season. On the males this color is vivid at spawning time. Five to seven darker vertical bars, like shadows, extend downward on each side. The lower jaw and lower margin of the cheek and gill cover are bluish, giving the fish its name. The ear flap is black to deep purplish, broad vertically but narrow horizontally. A series of dark marks, seeming a single blotch, occurs in the last rays of the soft dorsal. The dorsal has ten spines ahead of the soft rays, and the anal three.

One of the larger sunfishes, the bluegill may attain three and even four pounds, but such sizes are rare. The average may be under six inches in overpopulated waters, nine to twelve where bluegill numbers are held in check. The record on sporting tackle was a fish of 4 pounds 12 ounces, only 15 inches long but with a girth of 18¼ inches, taken from Ketona Lake, Alabama by T. S. Hudson on April 9, 1950.

The bluegill may spawn three times in a single season. It nests usually in colonies, though sometimes singly, the males fanning out circular areas on sandy, gravelly, or even mucky bottoms in shallow water. For late spawnings the bluegill may use the nests of the pumpkinseed and rock bass. More than one female may spawn in the nest of a single male. Large female bluegills have been found to contain more than 60,000 eggs.

The bluegill is fished for at all times of the year, including the dead of the northern winters, when it takes baits dangled through the ice. Wisconsin conservationists Howard Snow and Warren Churchill, reporting on the experimental waters at Murphy Flowage, Wisconsin, write, "Bluegills are caught more than twice as fast in winter as in summer."

In its game qualities and frying-pan virtues, the bluegill is generally ranked by anglers near the top of the sunfish family. Perhaps for these reasons the bluegill is stocked in thousands of farm ponds. The bluegill–largemouth bass combination is a favorite one for farm-pond stocking, especially in the South, though farther north the growth of bass may be so slow as to cause severe imbalance. According to the Alabama Agricultural Research Station, this teaming of fishes produces in that state "the best fishing and the most pounds of fish per acre with the least trouble." The bluegills feed on the pond's invertebrates; the bass feed on the bluegills, and all is well if the bluegills are harvested. But if the pond owner and his guests fish for the bass and let the bluegills alone, the end result will be a pond full of small bluegills and virtually empty of large fish of either species.

PUMPKINSEED
Lepomis gibbosus (Linnaeus)

The common sunfish, or pumpkinseed, is perhaps the most colorful of all the family. It has many names—kivvy, kiver, pond perch, robin, ruff, sun bass, and others—but "sunny" is the boy's natural and appropriate contraction. For this fish seems a sun-worshiper at times, daring the open exposed sunshot areas which trout most thoroughly avoid. This writer can recall the small schools of sunnies in a boyhood brook. Seen from above, in some deep-shadowed grotto at a bend of the stream they were dim darkish forms; but suddenly, as if at a command or by some simultaneous impulse of them all, the school would dart into the summertime brilliance of a sand-bottomed shallow and become at once a constellation of small suns.

The pumpkinseed originally swarmed in clear weedy brooks and ponds from the Maritime Provinces and Maine to Minnesota and western Ontario, and southward to the Gulf. Today, through introductions, it is present in virtually every state. Like all its family it is a lowland fish, and does not prosper in the higher altitudes of the West. Occasionally it enters brackish waters along the eastern seaboard.

Sporting a fabulous array of colors, the pumpkinseed is dark greenish olive on its back; its sides are spotted or blotched with orange, red, and blue; its underparts are yellowish to bright orange. Six to eight dark green vertical bars extend from the back to the middle sides. The cheeks and gill covers are crossed horizontally by alternate bands of brown-orange and brilliant blue. The spiny and soft-rayed parts of the dorsal are often profusely dotted with orange or brownish specks. The pumpkinseed's distinguishing mark, serving to identify it among others of its tribe, is a brilliant small scarlet spot on the ear flap. The mouth is small, but strong teeth in the throat serve to crush small mollusks and crustaceans.

Attaining eight to nine inches in large ponds but averaging only four to six in brooks, the pumpkinseed is gamy for its size, and a quick taker of worm baits and artificial flies. Pan-fried, it is a small but sweet morsel.

The pumpkinseed may spawn more than once in a season. The

males build saucer-shaped nests, usually in colonies, in one to five feet of water, and sometimes appropriate the nests of bluegills or rock bass. A single pumpkinseed nest, after the spawning of more than one female therein, may produce 8000 fry. Hybridizing with the bluegill and green sunfish is said to be common.

GREEN SUNFISH
Lepomis cyanellus Rafinesque

This sunfish is duller-hued and more elongate than its close kin, resembling the smallmouth and rock bass in its shape. It is distinguished, too, by a projecting lower jaw and a large mouth, and often surprises bass fishermen by seizing a minnow bait half its own length.

The green sunfish's back is a dull olive, fading to brassy yellow on the sides and paler below. The characteristic vertical dark bars, numbering six or more, extend well down from the back. Bluish flecks on the cheeks have caused it to be called, erroneously, the blue-spotted sunfish. Distinguishing marks are the black round gill-cover spot, covering the bony part of the opercle and edged in white on the rear margin; the rounded lobes of the tail; the short round pectoral fin, and dark blotches on the soft-rayed dorsal and anal.

More abundant west than east, the green sunfish has a native range running from western New York to South Dakota and thence southward to Mexico and the Gulf. It was long ago introduced into the far West. The Canadian occurrence seems limited to a few small lakes in Ontario. The green sunfish is essentially an inhabitant of ponds and small sluggish brooks, rare in large rivers and lakes. It enters tiny rills when moving upstream in the spring. Indeed, there is a legend in Missouri that this fish will forsake the streams for the meadows after a heavy fall of dew.

Seldom spawning more than once a season, the green sunfish nests in colonies and is highly prolific, the females bearing 15,000 to 50,000 eggs.

In its size, gameness, and food quality, the green sunfish is comparable to the pumpkinseed. It is known by many names, among them blue bass, creek sunfish, rubbertail, green perch, and sand bass.

REDEAR SUNFISH
Lepomis microlophus (Günther)

The redear is one of the larger sunfishes and probably the most important species in Florida and other deep-South states. In these regions it is commonly known as the shellcracker, for its throat teeth are used to crush snails and crustaceans.

Formerly occurring from Virginia to the Gulf, the redear sunfish has been introduced farther north. It remains, however, chiefly a southern species, inhabiting bayous, ponds, large warm rivers, and clear sand-bottomed lakes.

The redear's over-all color is dusky olive or blue-green above, lighter below. An identifying mark is the gill cover margined with a broad scarlet band, giving the fish its name. The ear flap is edged with reddish-orange. The pectoral fin is clear and very long; the other fins are dark, often with yellowish rays.

In Florida, where the redear or shellcracker is probably taken by anglers more frequently than other sunfishes, it averages eight to ten inches but quite commonly attains twelve inches and 1½ pounds. There is no official rod-and-reel record, but a specimen weighing 4 pounds 4 ounces was taken by means not stated, in the Chattahoochee River at Gordon, Alabama.

The redear resembles the bluegill in its spawning habits, sporting qualities, and virtue as a panfish. To a lesser extent than the bluegill, the redear is stocked with largemouth bass in farm ponds of the South.

SPOTTED SUNFISH
Lepomis punctatus (Valenciennes)

Another native southern species, the spotted sunfish ranges from South Carolina to Florida and is frequently found in the swifter clear-water streams. This fish is known as the spotted bream and chinquapin perch, but is popularly called the "stumpknocker" in Florida and other Gulf states. This name derives from an old wives' tale concerning a feeding habit of this fish. It is said to haunt old stumps and bankside logs, alert for insects, small toads or frogs approaching the water's edge. When one appears, the fish allegedly surges against the stump, knocking its prey into the water.

Florida fisheries men recognize three varieties of the spotted sunfish: the black-spotted (most common), red-spotted, and blue-spotted. (The true blue-spotted sunfish is a distinct, more northerly species.) Under its spots, the stumpknocker's color is brownish or olive-green, with a yellowish underbody.

The stumpknocker averages about six inches, and sometimes attains eight or nine. It is a popular fish with southern anglers, taking baits and flies, and is reported to be excellent eating.

BLACK CRAPPIE
Pomoxis nigromaculatus (LeSueur)

WHITE CRAPPIE
Pomoxis annularis Rafinesque

The crappies are distinctly different in shape and color from other sunfishes, but so closely resemble each other that some anglers erroneously believe they are merely different color phases of the same species.

They are the largest of the sunfishes, with the exception of the black basses, and are one of the important sport fishes of American fresh waters.

The native range of the crappies extends across southern Canada from the upper St. Lawrence River to Manitoba, and south through the eastern and central United States to Florida and Texas. The black crappie, needing colder and clearer water, is more common northward; the white crappie is more at home in the bayous, lagoons, large lakes and sluggish rivers of the South. Both crappies have been widely introduced into northeastern and far-western waters out of their original range. Some of these plantings are deemed unfortunate, notably in Maine where the crappie competes with trout and landlocked salmon for food.

Many local and regional names have been applied to these species. Calico bass, grass bass, speckled bass, speckled perch, and merely specks are popular aliases for the black crappie; the white is known as white bass, papermouth, tinmouth, bachelor, and newlight, among many others. Strawberry bass is a widely used name for both.

Each fish is distinguished by very large dorsal and anal fins, the anal being about equal to the dorsal, and by a marked depression in the upper outline just above the eyes. The black crappie is a deeper and darker fish than the white. Normally it is dark green to bronze on the forward dorsal surface, this color becoming brassy to light green on the sides and fading to silvery on the belly. Dark irregular blotches, which may be longitudinal or vertical, cover the upper and middle sides, becoming sparse and faint along the region of the anal fin. The white crappie's deep dorsal color does not extend as far down; its sides are pale green-yellow to silvery and are marked with six or seven shadowy vertical bars, fading out rearward to irregular blotches on the caudal peduncle. On both fish, the dorsal, anal, and caudal fins are heavily flecked with grayish green markings. The mouth in each species is large, slanting obliquely upward, and the lower jaw protrudes.

A distinction between the two, often needed for identification, is in the spine count of the forward dorsal. The black crappie has seven spines, rarely eight; the white crappie six, rarely five.

Crappies coming to anglers' landing nets—which should always be used, for the mouth is tender and tears easily from the hook—average eight to twelve inches in most waters, and not uncommonly reach two pounds. Crappies above that weight are rare, but extreme lunkers are recorded. The official sporting records: black crappie, 5 pounds even, 19¼ inches long, Santee-Cooper Reservoir, South Carolina, Paul E. Foust, March 15, 1957; white crappie, 5 pounds 3 ounces, 21 inches long, Enid Dam, Mississippi, Fred L. Bright, July 31, 1957.

The crappies spawn from as early as January in Florida and March in central Texas, to June or July in the North. The males build nests in water that may be ten inches or ten feet deep. Both species are very prolific. Half-pound females have been reported to average 20,000 to 60,000 eggs; large fish have spawned 150,000 and up.

Anglers pursue both crappies with all varieties of baits and artificial lures. Small minnows, spinners, and tiny metal jigs are effective. Successful fishing may depend on locating a school and staying with it. Opinions differ as to the crappies' game qualities. They are generally rated below the bluegill in this respect, but are highly esteemed by thousands of anglers. Ice-fishing is widely practiced in the northern range. The meat of the black crappie is held superior to the white's, probably because the black is more often taken from clear water.

ROCK BASS
Ambloplites rupestris (Rafinesque)

The rock bass is very similar in its features and color to the warmouth, and in its habitat to the smallmouth black bass. It is less broad than the sunfishes, nearly as elongate as the smallmouth, and has a red eye and a projecting lower jaw. Its other names include redeye, redeye bass, and goggle-eye.

Though a dullish fish compared to some of its sunfish kin, it is by no means unhandsome. The deep bronze-green of the back lightens to a sort of brassy or tarnished gold in the sides, and to pale or grayish on the belly. Dark brownish black spots on the scales below the lateral line give the fish an appearance of being striped. Above the lateral line are about four broad, vertical, shadowy bars, less distinct than those of the bluegill and green sunfish. A dark blotch of bluish black is at the tip of the gill cover. The pectoral fins are clear, the others light to dark brownish gray, sometimes with spots on the caudal and soft-rayed dorsal. The over-all color varies in different waters and can change rapidly in the individual fish.

The rock bass is distinguished from its closest kin, the warmouth, by six spines in the anal fin. (The warmouth has three.)

The native range of the rock bass extended from New Brunswick and Quebec across southern Canada to Lake Winnipeg. It included all the Great Lakes, and ran south through the Mississippi and its drainages to the Gulf. The fish is still abundant in much of this territory, and plantings have established it in the East and far West. It is a fish of clear cool lakes, where it frequents rocky outcroppings and reefs, and of clear flowing rivers with deep holes. The rock bass and the smallmouth coexist in many rivers and lakes, and often rock bass are taken accidentally by fishermen seeking the smallmouth.

Good-sized rock bass weigh about 1½ to 2 pounds, but the average in streams is six to eight inches, in lakes up to ten.

Spawning on gravel, sand, or rooted bottoms, the rock bass makes single nests, usually next to a stump, rock, or weed patch. It may appropriate the nests of the black basses and the pumpkinseed. Females deposit 2000 to 11,000 eggs.

Like other sunfishes, the rock bass is prone to overpopulate. Michigan fisheries scientists increased the growth rate and sizes, and improved the condition of rock bass in Booth Lake by poisoning the fish in one area of the lake and thus drastically reducing the population.

Responding avidly to many baits and lures, the rock bass is an easy fish to catch, once a school is located. It is said to be a fine species for the first fishing lessons of children.

As a game fish the rock bass is not in the class of the bluegill, and the same may be said for its gustatory virtue, though it is tasty enough when taken from clear cold water.

WARMOUTH
Chaenobryttus gulosus (Cuvier)

The warmouth—called bigmouth, Indian fish, sun trout, wood bass, mud bass, weed bass, redeye, goggle-eye, and warmouth bass—has a few dubious distinctions. It is the most carnivorous of the sunfishes; more than any of its family it has a fondness for weedy, mud-bottomed, still or sluggish waters, and perhaps because of its chosen habitat, it is inferior as food to any of its kin.

Its range is about that of the rock bass, though originally it was scarce east of the Appalachians. Today it is more abundant west than east, but particularly in the South, where it thrives in the bayous, muddy rivers and big warm lakes.

The warmouth is built and decorated almost exactly like the rock bass, including the large mouth, the protruding lower jaw, and the red eye. The color is similar, too, although generally it is lighter—brassy rather than bronze. The broad dark vertical bars are more numerous and more distinct, and extend downward almost to the belly, giving the fish a mottled appearance. The soft-rayed dorsal and anal fins are usually streaked or spotted. Three or four dark bars radiate from the eye across the cheek and gill cover. The anal spines are three, distinguishing the warmouth from the rock bass. Another feature of the warmouth is a cluster of small teeth on the tongue.

Nests of the warmouth are made singly rather than in colonies, in shallow to fairly deep water. Spawning may occur more than once in a season. Females are quite prolific, some of the larger fish shedding 60,000 eggs. Hybridizing is reported with the bluegill, green sunfish, and pumpkinseed.

Certainly not a game fish of the first rank, the warmouth none the less appeals to thousands of anglers in the South and Midwest. Two-pounders are exceptional, but many of eight to twelve inches provide fair sport on light tackle.

OTHER SUNFISHES

The longear sunfish, *Lepomis megalotis*, is a colorful little fish, blue-bronze above and orange-yellow below, with an extremely long and broad ear flap that is velvety black tipped with bright red, and margined all around in white. It is plentiful in the clear brooks of the Southeast and well up the Mississippi Valley.

More abundant east, from Maine to Florida, is the redbreast sunfish, *Lepomis auritus*. It is called the yellowbreast sunfish, red-bellied sunfish, red perch, robin perch, tobaccobox, and other names which only hint of the beauty of its dark metallic back, orange-red breast, and brilliantly blue-striped cheeks and gill covers. A lake and pond fish more than most of its family, it also thrives in fastwater streams.

One of the smallest of the clan, called the dwarf and pygmy sunfish in some areas, is the orange-spotted sunfish, *Lepomis humilis*. This tiny gem, rarely exceeding four inches (ripe females may be only two and a half inches long), is a midwestern species. It is readily identified by a large black ear flap, encircled in white, and particularly by the red or orange spots of the male.

The Sacramento perch, *Archoplites interruptus*, is the only sunfish native to the far West. Once abundant in central California, it is now very scarce in much of its former range. One of the larger sunfishes, it may attain two pounds but averages less than a pound. It has a dark, metallic blue-black back and upper sides, a bluish to silvery underbody, and irregular brownish longitudinal stripes. The typical sunfish ear flap is lacking, but a dark spot appears at the rear corner of the gill cover. The Sacramento perch is exceptional among sunfishes for not being a nest-builder or a guardian of eggs, and also for its numerous dorsal and anal spines—thirteen and seven respectively.

The flier, *Centrarchus macropterus*, is a sunfish of the Southeast and lower Mississippi Valley. It is small and roundish, seldom exceeding six inches, and is also called the round sunfish. The flier is a greenish fish, with broken rows of dark spots below the lateral line. It has up to thirteen dorsal and eight anal spines.

Still others, absent from most of the country but plentiful here and there, deserve mention. The mud sunfish, *Acanthrarchus pomotis*, is a small species of lowland streams of the Atlantic seaboard from New York to South Carolina. The Roanoke bass, *Ambloplites cavifrons*, is almost identical with the rock bass except for its minute, almost imperceptible cheek scales, but is recognized as a separate species in Virginia. The bantam sunfish, *Lepomis symmetricus*, is closely allied to the green sunfish, unknown in most of the country but a quite common panfish in the lower Mississippi Valley and Texas. The blue-spotted sunfish, *Enneacanthus gloriosus*, is known in a few streams of the Delaware River watershed and sparsely elsewhere in the East. It is another miniature, rarely over three inches, and is fancied for aquaria.

Chapter 16

SMALLMOUTH, LARGEMOUTH, AND SPOTTED BASS

The smallmouth and largemouth bass are commonly called black bass by American anglers, many of whom would rank one or the other at the very top among freshwater game fish. Despite their sensational popularity over a range which today includes every state except

NOTE: Illustration is of adult dobson fly, with hellgrammite—larva of the dobson—under water.

Alaska, plus southern Canada and northern Mexico, they are doubly misnamed. For they are not black (except smallmouth fry in some waters), and they are not bass. They belong to the sunfish family, the Centrarchidae, of which they are the largest members.

The yellow and white bass are true freshwater basses. No matter, though, that the black basses are not. Despite all the inaccuracies of popular nomenclature, the words "smallmouth," "largemouth," "black bass," or just "bass" will continue to hold their single meaning and their special magic for fishermen.

Anglers who rate the bass above anything that swims in fresh water like to quote a famous passage (read "infamous" for trout and salmon adherents). It is repeated here only because some bass men, as truculent as their favorite fish, would deem its omission unforgivable. In his *Book of the Black Bass* Dr. James A. Henshall wrote, "I consider him, *inch for inch* and *pound for pound*, the gamest fish that swims," and thus unwittingly started a row which will continue long after the nations of the world have settled their differences.

SMALLMOUTH BASS
Micropterus dolomieui   Lacépède

LARGEMOUTH BASS
Micropterus salmoides   (Lacépède)

SPOTTED BASS
Micropterus punctulatus   (Rafinesque)

The smallmouth and the largemouth are *the* basses. The spotted or Kentucky bass is a close relative, a smaller but similarly pugnacious breed, not so well known because its range is comparatively narrow and its identification as a separate species somewhat recent. Others in this family, all legitimate species, are the redeye bass, *Micropterus coosae*, of the southeastern states; the Suwannee bass, *M. notius*, now restricted to an area of Columbia County in northern Florida; and the Guadalupe bass, *M. treculi*, of Texas rivers—the Guadalupe, Colorado, and others.

Various subspecies are recognized by some authorities, but are not listed by the American Fisheries Society. Hubbs and Bailey identified in 1940 a local variety of smallmouth, the Neosho bass, *M. dolomieui velox*, in the Neosho River and other tributaries of the Arkansas. The Florida Game and Fresh Water Fish Commission today distinguishes between a smaller "northern largemouth bass," *M. salmoides salmoides*, of extreme northern Florida including the Panhandle, and a larger "Florida largemouth bass," *M. salmoides floridanus*. To the latter subspecies belong the famous Florida lunkers which grow to eighteen or twenty pounds and up.

Similarly, some scientists classify three varieties of spotted bass: the northern, *M. punctulatus punctulatus*; the Alabama, *M. p. henshalli*; and the Wichita, *M. p. wichitae*—which is possibly carrying things a bit too far.

Various local names distinguish the three basses here discussed. The smallmouth is known as bronzeback, redeye, and tiger bass. The largemouth has a host of nicknames: green bass, Oswego bass, straw bass, grass bass, moss bass, linesides, and, in many parts of the South, trout. The less well-known spotted bass has so far acquired no common alias other than Kentucky bass; but give it time.

The scientific name of the largemouth bass had an origin hardly in keeping with ichthyological precision. *Micropterus salmoides* means "salmonlike or troutlike, with a small fin." This fish is remotely removed from any of the salmonids; it has a long dorsal, and indeed no fin anywhere that could be termed small. But when Lacépède, the French naturalist, accorded the fish its name in 1801, the specimen he examined came from the South, where even then this bass was called "trout," and it happened to have a broken fin. Once established, *Micropterus salmoides* had an unshakable priority and has persisted despite its flagrant ineptness.

The smallmouth's specific name *dolomieu* (now *dolomieui*) was chosen by Lacépède in honor of his fellow French scientist, M. Dolomieu.

These basses are much alike; in certain waters jointly inhabited by the smallmouth and largemouth, anglers frequently mistake one for the other. There are positive differences, however. The classic distinction between smallmouth and largemouth has given each species its name. On the smallmouth, the maxillary bone of the upper jaw never extends beyond a point directly under the back of the eye. The large-mouth's maxilla extends noticeably beyond the eye. The spotted bass is like the smallmouth in this respect but is readily identified by other features.

Other marked differences between the smallmouth and large-mouth are noted in the dorsal fin and the scale counts. The dorsals of both fish are in two parts, the anterior portion spiny-rayed, the pos-terior soft-rayed. On the smallmouth the two fin sections are connected by a broad membrane, forming a shallow notch; on the largemouth this membrane is narrow, and the notch so deep that the two segments appear almost as separate fins. The smallmouth has small scales at the bases of the dorsal and anal fins; the largemouth has no scales at these points. Oblique scale rows on the cheek are another distinction: on the smallmouth these rows number 15 to 17, on the largemouth nine to eleven. The largemouth's scales are slightly larger all over, numbering 58 to 65 from gill cover to tail, against 68 to 80 on the smallmouth.

The color and markings of these basses vary widely with environ-ment. Generally, however, the smallmouth has a bronze or brassy over-cast, whereas the largemouth is more definitely dark green on the back, fading to greenish yellow on the sides. Dark vertical bars on the sides usually distinguish the smallmouth. The largemouth has a series of dark blotches extending the entire length of its side and more or less running together, to give the appearance of a broad band. In some waters this band may be indistinct or even absent, and on older fish it becomes obscure; but it is always pronounced on the young of this species.

On both smallmouth and largemouth the lateral line is curved up-ward, paralleling the arch of the back; on the largemouth it is dark and more distinct.

Generally the fins of the smallmouth carry the over-all bronze cast; the largemouth has paler fins, often with a definite light green color in the pectorals. The caudal fin or tail, on all three species, is slightly emarginate or notched, not forked.

The eyes of the smallmouth are distinctly red in some waters. In weedy rivers and lakes the smallmouth may be less bronze and as green as its largemouth relative. Bass colors can change even with a momentary shift of environment. The smallmouth's colors are particularly sensitive to direct light rays and to those reflected off the bottom. Darting out from a dark crypt beneath a bank, it may appear almost black, but a few minutes in clear sunshot water over a sand bottom will transform it into a much lighter-colored fish.

The spotted bass resembles the smallmouth in the length of its maxillary bone and in the broad membrane between the two parts of the dorsal, but lacks the smallmouth's vertical bars. In its over-all color, the spotted bass is perhaps closer to the largemouth, having a similar dark band along the midline. This fish has its distinctions, however. On the lower sides are evenly spaced rows of small dark spots, so close together as to give the appearance of fine dark stripes. The white or pale yellowish color of the belly extends well upward on the sides, and against it the dark spots are distinct, especially on fish taken from clear water. Other identifying marks, to a close observer, are three dark spots: one at the base of the tail, another on the "ear" or hind end of the gill cover, and still another on the tongue. The last is about one-eighth of an inch long in a ten-inch fish.

Though more elongate than their sunfish and crappie cousins, all three basses have deep bodies, and this breadth tends to increase in proportion to length as the fish grows older. An eight-year-old largemouth in southern waters can be a very paunchy individual, nearly half as deep, from dorsal to belly, as it is long. These aldermanic tendencies, however, seem not to affect its agility in feeding or its fighting prowess when hooked.

A minor but distinct feature of all three basses is a set of three to five dark bands radiating backward from the eye across the cheek, and a single band extending forward from the eye to the snout. Sharp teeth are present on the jaws, vomer, and palatine bones.

All of these basses are native only to North America. The smallmouth originally ranged from the St. Lawrence River basin and the Great Lakes to the upper Mississippi and Ohio river systems. The largemouth was known, prior to any transplantings, in southern Canada from Quebec to Manitoba, throughout the entire Great Lakes area and the Mississippi Valley to the Gulf and northeastern Mexico. The spotted bass is native to most of the South from Florida to Texas and northward to Missouri, but east of the Mississippi and north of the Ohio it is rare.

Successful transplantings have widely established the smallmouth, largemouth, or both. In Hawaii they now flourish on the islands of Oahu, Kauai, and Hawaii. Anglers in England, France, and Germany have known both species since the 1890's; in South Africa the large-mouth has long been smashing tackle and multiplying its kind. In Canada, one or the other or both species are now established from Nova Scotia to British Columbia. Transplants of the spotted bass have so far been much less extensive but may well increase; for this is a hardy fish and adaptable to change.

Federal and state conservationists are to be credited for the bass fishing now to be found on the Pacific slopes and in many other areas originally out of the basses' range.

The largemouth is typically a fish of warm sluggish rivers and shallow, weedy, mud-bottomed lakes, and is abundant in bayous and lagoons of the South. It is tolerant of turbidity and roiling to a far greater degree than the smallmouth. Thriving in water temperatures in the eighties and able to survive even at 90° F., it is widely stocked in shallow farm ponds of the South and Midwest. Florida fisheries men say that within their state the largemouth may be found in any sort of water, from the larger lakes to small drainage canals and even roadside ditches. "An athletic fisherman," they observe, "can easily broadjump across some of the finest black-bass canals in the state."

The smallmouth inhabits the clearer and cooler waters of faster-flowing streams and of rocky lakes and bays. Despite such environmental preferences both fishes are frequently found in the same water. The smallmouth, however, apparently dislikes the great largemouth state of Florida, for despite plantings there in 1908, 1910, and 1930, no authentic recoveries of smallmouths have been made.

Both species are shallow-water rather than deepwater fish. The largemouth rarely penetrates below the level of the deepest vegetation, which is perhaps twenty feet. In the Great Lakes even the smallmouth seldom ventures beyond a forty-foot depth, finding water to its liking over sandy shoals and inshore reefs, and along rocky bays and islands.

Though the smallmouth has a fondness for cool currents it is seldom found in brooks or the smaller trout streams. In some larger trout waters of the East, however, the smallmouth is plentiful. The Delaware River system, including several trout-famous tributaries, is smallmouth water. This writer, fly-fishing for trout on the Beaverkill and the Neversink, has frequently taken and released smallmouths averaging nine or ten inches, rarely twelve. These have hit both wet and dry flies in all types of water: fast midstream riffles, rocky pockets, broad pools, and inshore back eddies. Apparently the Beaverkill-Neversink smallmouths go to the main Delaware once they reach a length beyond ten or twelve inches. This river, from Port Jervis to the confluence of the East and West Branches at Hancock, and upstream for several miles on each branch, is famous smallmouth water, yielding many fish of two to three pounds. It is not essentially a trout river, though it is certainly the home of some large rainbows and an occasional big brown, which once were planted in the tributaries and ran down to the main river. Since the damming of the East Branch to form the huge Pepacton Reservoir at Downsville, New York, the smallmouths have grown big in the reservoir, and they now enter its smaller tributaries, doubtless to spawn. These tributaries are among the few eastern trout streams where two- to three-pound smallmouths have been reported.

The smallmouth has been known, rarely, to enter the brackish waters of estuaries along Chesapeake Bay, and the largemouth has a similar history of occasionally appearing in tidal reaches. This apparent phenomenon is common to many strictly freshwater species.

The spotted bass is nearer the smallmouth than the largemouth in its choice of habitat. Commonly it is a river fish, liking cooler streams, though not as cold or as swift as the smallmouth's northern rivers. This fish has a preference for deeper water, and fares well in some southerly lakes, notably in the Ozarks, which have depths beyond those frequented by the largemouth. The two species may live together in such lakes, but at different levels. Fishermen have noticed this, taking the largemouth on surface lures and the spotted bass twenty to thirty feet down.

All three species are alike in their reactions to water temperature. They will hole up in deep or shaded water during the heat of the day, move into open shallows at dusk, and stay there until dawn. Everywhere except in the deep South, autumnal temperatures bring a marked decline in the activity and feeding of bass. Their winter habit in the North has long been thought to be partial or complete hibernation, with little or no feeding, and doubtless this is the fact in many waters of the smallmouth's northerly range. The Michigan Department of Conservation has reported, however, that as long ago as 1946 considerable numbers of smallmouth bass were taken through the ice in Walled Lake. These fish were caught and released by anglers fishing for yellow perch, with minnows as bait, fished close to a peat bottom in 15 to 20 feet of water. The fishermen maintained that the bass took the hook more readily than did the yellow perch they were angling for, and further averred that these bass were more easily taken in winter than in summer.[1]

The basses, particularly the largemouth, attain weights capable of straining any freshwater tackle. "Average" sizes mean little. Most anglers seeking the smallmouth in northern lakes are satisfied with fish of one and a half to three pounds, surprised and delighted with a four-pounder. Fishermen in Florida may consider a four-pound largemouth routine. While a ten-pounder may be unusually good luck, anglers in some Florida waters and elsewhere in the deep South are realistic rather than fanciful in hoping for a fifteen-pound largemouth. The record was a Georgia fish of 22 pounds 4 ounces, 32½ inches long, taken from Montgomery Lake by George W. Perry on June 2, 1932.

The record smallmouth was a southern fish, too—from Dale Hollow Lake on the Kentucky-Tennessee line. It weighed 11 pounds 15 ounces and had a length of 27 inches. D. L. Hayes took this sensational smallmouth on July 9, 1955. Canada's record smallmouth is said to be a fish of 9 pounds 2 ounces, taken from Macauley Lake, Ontario, in 1951.

Bass grow larger in the South, where water temperatures are relatively high during most or all of the year, and feeding is not diminished as it is by the northern winters.

The spotted bass is considerably smaller. Most specimens taken by anglers are probably under twelve inches and weigh less than a

[1] Leland R. Anderson, "A Note on the Capture of Smallmouth Bass by Angling through the Ice," reprinted from *Copeia*, No. 3 (September 12, 1947).

Top: Largemouth Bass, *Micropterus salmoides*; next: Green Sunfish, *Lepomis cyanellus;*
next: Smallmouth Bass, *Micropterus dolomieu;* next: Rock Bass, *Ambloplites rupestris;*
bottom, left: Pumpkinseed Sunfish, *Lepomis gibbosus;* bottom, right: Bluegill Sunfish,
Lepomis macrochirus

pound. There is no official rod-and-reel record. Fish of four pounds and up, reported as spotted bass, may be misidentified.

The growth of bass varies greatly, depending on water temperature, food, range, and other factors. Since growth slows or ceases at temperatures below 50° F., northern growth rates of bass are not comparable to those of southern fish. A Washington report on the average lengths of largemouth bass in that state, as compared with the national average, shows three-year-old fish to be 8.7 inches against the national average of 9.8 inches; five-year-olds in Washington 12.2 inches against 14.9 inches nationally; and eight-year-olds 16.5 inches compared with a national average of 18.9 inches.[2]

By contrast, Florida reports its largemouths as normally attaining ten to twelve inches in one year, fifteen to sixteen inches in two years. In unusually favorable environments, such as the phosphate pits in Florida's Polk County, largemouths are reported to reach four to six pounds in two years.

A lake with too many bass will have a stunted population because of heavy competition for food, and may contain no bass over ten inches long, regardless of age.

Under optimum conditions, the smallmouth, largemouth, and spotted bass attain sexual maturity in the third or fourth year of life, at lengths varying between eight and twelve inches. The life span of bass escaping all predators, including man, is seven to nine years, but exceptional fish have lived to be sixteen years old.

The basses are spring-to-summer spawners. The season begins when the spring sun has warmed the shallows to 60° F. or higher—which may be early March in Florida, July in Ontario. The three species are more or less alike in their spawning habits. The male is the nest-builder and the guardian of the eggs.

Spawning takes place in shallow water, sometimes only eight inches but more often two to four feet deep. The smallmouth and spotted bass prefer gravelly or rocky bottoms; the largemouth nests often in vegetation on mud bottoms, and is rather careless about the

[2] Merrill H. Spence, "Spiny Ray Fishes in Washington," *Washington State Game Bulletin*, Vol. 10, No. 3 (July 1958).

nursery of its young, sometimes making no nest at all but merely clearing a space among waterlily roots. W. F. Carbine (see footnote p. 162) writes of largemouth bass using the nests of rock bass, and vice versa. Apparently such intrusions occurred only after the original owner had finished spawning.[3]

River smallmouths often ascend feeder streams to spawn; the lake-dwelling fish may run up inlet streams, but this is perhaps more exceptional than general.

The male smallmouth is a meticulous nest-builder. Using his tail to fan out all debris over a bottom area perhaps thirty inches in diameter, he creates a saucer-shaped depression with sand and small gravel around the edge, larger stones in the middle. This business may consume two days; when it is finished the male awaits a mate, who is usually not tardy. A rather brief and perfunctory courtship ensues, the male essaying a few advances and the female retreating before both come together within the nest. The female lays her adhesive eggs a few at a time, and the male fertilizes them as they fall upon and stick to the stones. Presently the female is spawned out, at least for the time being. Her eggs do not all ripen at once, and she may return later to deposit more eggs in the same nest, or go to another male. Three females may spawn in the nest of a single male, within a brief period of time. Since a two-pound female may contain 6000 eggs and cast half of them in one nest, three such females may leave nearly 10,000 eggs as the responsibility of the father bass. Once her eggs are laid, the female shows no concern for them—a seemingly remarkable nonchalance in the case of some huge largemouth specimens which may cast over 30,000 eggs before they are fully shed.

The male's parental charge, however, is apparently sacred. For now, until the eggs hatch, he guards them with vigor, fanning the eggs to keep off silt, fungus, and minute predators, and immediately attacking any fish or other intruder that comes near. Though he does not feed during this interval he is particularly vulnerable to fishermen, for he may strike a lure or bait cast into the vicinity of the nest. The sequel is that often he is hooked by the offending plug or bait, leaving

[3] "Observations on the Spawning Habits of Centrarchid Fishes in Deep Lake, Oakland County, Michigan," reprinted from *Transactions of the Fourth North American Wildlife Conference, 1939.*

the unprotected eggs to the mercy of predators. Fortunately, bass are protected in many states by a closed season until their spawning time is over.

Other hazards which often destroy a whole nestful of eggs are a sudden drop in temperature and the scouring and silting of freshets. The rooting of carp sometimes roils the water so thickly as to deplete oxygen to a degree fatal to bass eggs.

Smallmouth-bass eggs hatch in three to five days at higher temperatures, in a week to ten days in colder water. Largemouth incubation averages a little longer; the spotted bass is said to have a shorter hatching time than either the smallmouth or largemouth.

After hatching, the sac fry remain in the nest until the yolk sac is absorbed, a period of six to fifteen days. The male continues his guardianship during this period, but once the fry become free-swimming the parental protection ceases.

Feeding now on minute planktonic organisms, the fry grow rapidly, attaining fingerling size by autumn. As young fish they school, but tend to separate as they grow older and are usually single travelers after reaching a length of ten inches.

Little if any hybridizing seems to occur among the smallmouth, largemouth, and spotted bass despite their similarity of spawning habits and the fact that more than one species may occupy the same water. Possibly the two largemouth species recognized in Florida do crossbreed. The same may be true of the smallmouth and its subspecies, the Neosho bass.

Artificial propagation of bass presents unique problems. The female cannot readily be stripped of her roe, and to strip the male of milt is usually fatal to the fish. Food must be alive or appear to be so. Partly for these reasons, but chiefly because bass seem able to maintain themselves by natural reproduction in lakes and rivers, despite fry mortality and heavy fishing, attempts at hatchery propagation have been discontinued in many states. Wisconsin ended the planting of smallmouth fingerlings in 1954. Prior to that year, investigations showed no correlation between years of stocking and years of bass abundance.

New York and Florida hold similar views on the hatchery propa-

gation of bass. Wisconsin, Maine, and Florida are three of many states
which have removed size limits, hoping thereby to prevent overpopulation of small bass and consequent stunting.

The removal of competing trash fish seems to help bass populations in lakes more than the stocking of bass themselves. The state of
Florida, recognizing that many of its once productive bass waters have
become overpopulated with trash species, recently increased the fishing license fee to residents (but not to tourists) by one dollar, to
provide funds for trash-fish removal.

Bass of two pounds and over have few predators other than man.
Perhaps the bass's worst enemy is a tapeworm which attacks the fish's
reproductive organs and makes it sterile.

The bass is a carnivorous and more particularly a piscivorous fish,
with a high-protein menu that builds the muscle admired by anglers.
A list of its prey includes aquatic and terrestrial insects, crayfish and
other crustaceans, snails, worms, leeches, small fish of many species,
frogs, tadpoles, mice, and moles. Large bass are known to devour
ducklings, snakes, and small muskrats.

Fish, however, compose probably 60 per cent of the diet of all
adult bass. Unquestionably bass prey upon small trout when the opportunity offers, and conservationists are inclined to keep bass out of
streams and lakes managed primarily for their trout populations.

Apparently the bass feeds at all hours, most actively at dusk and
dawn. So greedy a fish is the delight of anglers and the capital gain
of a legion of tackle-makers. Bass are sought by all manner of fishermen, using gear ranging from the cane pole to the $150 fly rod. Fly-
fishing purists seem rather scarce among the bass fraternity, however.
They are mainly trout specialists, and many of them hold the bass to
be only another of the coarse fish. Probably 75 per cent of all bass
coming to anglers' nets are taken by still-fishing with live bait or
worms, and by casting or trolling artificial lures. There is virtually no
end to the fabrications of the bass-lure manufacturers. These gadgets
include surface plugs, underwater plugs, wobbling and popping plugs
—of wood, plastic, and metal, in all colors, *ad infinitum.* This, of course,
is a mere start on the contents of any thoroughgoing bass man's tackle
box. He needs bass bugs too, and spinners and spoons, and frog and

minnow harnesses, and artificial mice and hellgrammites, and pork-rind strips, and maybe a bottle of some secret-formula compound which will excite the olfactory organs of a smallmouth and charm it out of its lair.

For all of this gadgetry, bass fishermen on such famous waters as the Thousand Islands of the St. Lawrence River, Georgian Bay of Lake Huron, and tens of thousands of lesser lakes, ponds, rivers, creeks, sloughs, and bayous, spend (or invest) hundreds of millions of dollars each year. A study of anglers' expenditures at a single lake in Illinois revealed that largemouth bass caught from this lake were worth $9.70 a pound. Such is the commercial value of a fish for which there is no "commercial" fishing in terms of netting and wholesale marketing.

Doubtless the bass is worth the fortune spent upon it, not for its value as food (though the flesh is good eating when taken from clear water), but rather as calculated in medical and psychiatric terms. You may credit the bass for much human good health and relaxation, for the quieting of city-tight nerves and the easing of marital tensions, and for at least a momentary surcease of atomic and related fears.

That the smallmouth, largemouth, and spotted bass are game fish of the first water, no one will deny. They are appealing as sport fish not only because of their "bulldog" strength and tenacity (a term often applied to bass), but because they can be as wary at times as any of the trouts. Anglers know periods when bass will refuse anything offered, and there is considerable evidence that older bass learn to avoid the angler's baits and lures. The largemouth usually swallows a bait quickly, and the sage angling advice is to strike at once. The smallmouth, on the other hand, likes to mouth a minnow or frog or nightcrawler; hence old bass hands counsel against striking a small-mouth until it "turns" the bait or starts moving away with it. With any artificial lure, the bass's strike should of course be returned at once by the angler.

Individual old lunkers in lakes are inclined to take up permanent residence in specially chosen spots—a shoreline cove or the inlet of a tributary or a deep grotto above a dam. River bass, however, some-times have an urge to travel. Recoveries of tagged largemouths in Florida's St. Johns River were made as far as 60 miles upstream and 123 miles downstream from the point of release.

Though each bass has its cult of devotees, comparisons among the three seem futile. The smallmouth and the spotted bass are held by many fishermen to be superior to the largemouth, but that may be because more of them are taken in cool running streams. In the same currents the largemouth will measure up to its kin on all sporting counts.

Whether Henshall's "inch for inch and pound for pound" dictum is more rhetoric than reality is a personal matter. "Inch for inch" is a faulty premise anyway, for a ten-inch smallmouth weighs as much as an eleven-inch wild eastern brook trout. In this writer's appraisal of the two, each hung on a four-ounce fly rod and a No. 12 fly, in the same water, the brook trout shows appreciably more power, drive, stamina, and "bulldog" persistence, if you will, than the bass. And in larger sizes the same ratio applies. That the two may be compared at all is high praise for the bass.

Chapter 17

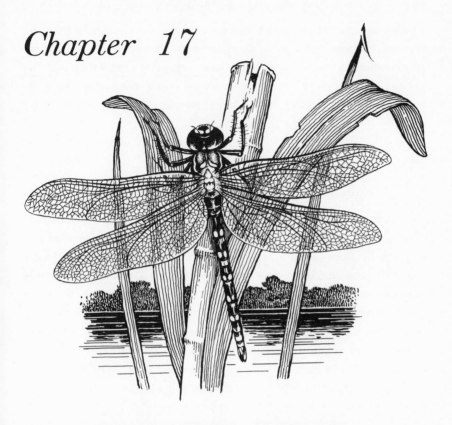

WHITE BASS,
YELLOW BASS,
WHITE PERCH

The white and yellow basses, though not so widely known or so eminent as game fish as the misnamed black bass, are the true fresh-water basses of American and Canadian waters. The anadromous white perch—incorrectly named, for it is not in any sense a perch—is a bass, too.

All three are of the sea bass family, the Serranidae, which in North America numbers sixty species among twenty-four genera. This family's members include the anadromous striped bass and the wholly marine groupers and sea basses; among the latter are the very large jewfish and black sea bass of the Atlantic, and the giant sea bass of the Pacific. In the family Serranidae, only the three fish of this chapter, and the striped bass, are of the genus *Roccus*.

WHITE BASS
Roccus chrysops (Rafinesque)

Locally called the silver bass, black-striped bass, and barfish, because of its bright color and prominent stripes, the white bass is believed by some scientists to be a freshwater derelict of striped bass which became landlocked in long-ago spawning migrations. If this theory is tenable it should apply equally to the similar yellow bass.

The white bass's original range extended from the St. Lawrence River basin across the Great Lakes region to Minnesota and Manitoba, and south to the lower Mississippi drainages. New York has long known this fish in Lake Ontario and Lake Erie waters and in some of the Finger Lakes. Elsewhere in the Atlantic states, however, the white bass is virtually unknown. It has some commercial importance in Lake Erie.

The white bass has been planted in recently man-made reservoirs, and in such waters the species does well, for it is a fish of clear and fairly deep lakes and of the swifter unmuddied reaches of large rivers, where the bottom terrain is clean and unvegetated. At times the river fish congregate in turbulent whitewater stretches below dams and sluiceways. In lakes large schools of the white bass are frequently seen cruising close to the surface far out in open water.

Fresh from its element, the white bass is a beautiful fish, gleaming like bright metal. Its back is a dark brassy green, its broad sides silvery above, tinged with gold below, and often showing a steel-blue overcast. Its distinguishing mark is a series of six to eight dark narrow stripes running horizontally the length of the fish. These are more numerous and more distinct on the upper sides, irregular and faint below the lateral line. The dorsal of the white bass is actually two fins, the forward spiny section distinctly separated from the posterior. The latter is soft-rayed except for a single spine at its forward end. The anal has three anterior spines. The caudal, anal, and rear dorsal show dusky outer margins in most waters. The tail is definitely forked rather than notched, but the fork is not deep. Small scales are present on cheek and gill cover. Body scales are moderately large, numbering 52 to 58 on the lateral line. The upper profile shows a distinct concavity just back of the head. The mouth is well equipped with numerous small sharp teeth, and teeth are present on the base of the tongue. The lower jaw protrudes slightly beyond the upper.

Though young white bass grow rapidly, attaining seven to nine inches in their first year, the species does not reach great sizes. A fish of four pounds is exceptional. Probably most specimens taken by anglers weigh under a pound, with larger fish more common south than north. The official record is a white bass of 5 pounds 2 ounces, taken at Grenada Dam, Mississippi by Eddy Vaughn on July 9, 1960.

Four years seems to be the life span of most white bass, though exceptional individuals live to be nine years old. Females spawn usually at the age of three; males may be sexually mature at two.

Spawning time for the white bass runs from March in the southern end of the range to June in northerly waters. The river fish migrate upstream or into tributaries; the lake-dwellers may enter stream inlets or spawn near shore or on reef shoals.

The white bass makes no nest; the female broadcasts her adhesive eggs indiscriminately, and immediately both parents abandon the eggs and return to deeper water. This lack of parental attention is compensated, however, by the extreme fecundity of this species. Larger females carry more than 500,000 eggs. These hatch in seven to ten days; the fry remain for a short time in the shallows, then move to deeper water. Feeding ravenously on insect larvae and minute crustacea, they grow to four or five inches by autumn.

The food of adult white bass is largely insects, crayfish, and small fishes of many species. In waters inhabited by the gizzard shad this fish is a preferred item. The emerald shiner has a similar role in Lake Erie.

In other waters the white bass consumes astronomical numbers of the tiny crustacea of the genus *Daphnia*, and shows an uncanny ability in following the surface foamlines wherein the *Daphnia* are concentrated. University of Wisconsin scientists Donald C. McNaught and Arthur D. Hasler have reported the white bass's feeding behavior in Lake Mendota, where huge numbers of the *Daphnia* contribute a major food of this fish.[1]

Where foamlines indicating swarms of *Daphnia* are present, schools of white bass invariably move up the foam track in a unique and predictable pattern. *Daphnia* become "airlocked" when a bubble of air lodges within the carapace. These floating crustaceans number about 6500 per square meter of surface; below them the subsurface concentrations are estimated at 8300 per cubic meter. Yearling white bass pick up individual *Daphnia*; older fish make repeated sweeps, "with mouth agape and opercles spread," causing the surface disturbances by which large schools of these fish are frequently spotted by anglers. Vertical migrations of the *Daphnia*—their morning and evening ascents to peak numbers on the surface—are also followed by the white bass. The feeding of these fish at dawn and dusk was shown in this study to be correlated with surface maxima of *Daphnia*. Stomachs of white bass examined after the morning ascent of their food (usually less concentrated than at evening) revealed the intake per fish to be 100 to 2500 *Daphnia*.

Schools of white bass are composed of fish of uniform size, the larger schools being made up of younger fish. The Lake Mendota study showed that the yellow perch, crappie, and northern spottail shiner were common schooling associates of the white bass, but in most schools the bass predominated.

In large lakes, schools of white bass move over great distances. Recoveries of tagged fish in Missouri's Lake of the Ozarks revealed that one individual had traveled forty-three miles, and presumably its schoolmates had covered an approximate distance. Lake Erie white bass, tagged on the Ohio side, have appeared later in Canadian waters across the lake.

Populations of white bass in a given lake are notorious for their fluctuations from abundance to scarcity, and perhaps back to abundance, within a period of a few years. Because these fish are highly

[1] "Surface Schooling and Feeding Behavior of the White Bass in Lake Mendota (Wis.)," reprinted from *Limnology and Oceanography*, Vol. 6, No. 1 (January 1961).

prolific and grow rapidly, populations may outgrow the food supply. Stunting is a first consequence; then a decline in numbers; and eventually perhaps almost complete disappearance. For these reasons fisheries-management men favor a minimum of restrictions upon angling. New York and some other states impose no legal size limit or closed season on the white bass.

With a high reputation as a game and food fish, the white bass is attracting more and more anglers each year. Two factors are important in fishing: first locate a school, then approach it without scaring it away. Schools are usually inshore, surface-feeding, in the morning and evening. At these times, and particularly during the spring spawning migrations, when the fish congregate at the mouths of lake tributaries, they are eager takers of live bait, worms, small spinners, bucktails, white maribous, and even dry flies. During the day, when the schools are in deeper water, trolling or still-fishing, with the bait or lure just off bottom, can be effective.

YELLOW BASS
Roccus mississippiensis (Jordan and Eigenmann)

The yellow bass is a popular game fish in many waters of the South and Southwest. To the north its occurrence is spotty, and it is not known in the Atlantic states. Generally, its range runs down the Mississippi Valley to Louisiana, and includes the lower Tennessee River system to the east and various Mississippi drainages to the west. The rivers and lakes of Iowa, Missouri, Arkansas, Oklahoma, and east Texas have varying populations of the yellow bass.

William T. Helm, of the University of Wisconsin, reports the yellow bass's appearance in certain waters of Wisconsin since the 1930's. Mr. Helm suggests that this somewhat out-of-bounds occurrence may be a northward migration, as has happened with certain birds and mammals, or that the fish were trapped, with other species, in sloughs at periods of low-water levels of the Mississippi River, and stocked in Wisconsin Lakes.[2]

[2] "A 'New' Fish in Wisconsin," reprinted from *Wisconsin Conservation Bulletin*, Vol. 23, No. 7 (July 1958).

Top to bottom: White Perch,
White Bass, Yellow Bass

The yellow bass owes its common name, and various local appellations such as gold bass, streaker, and black-striped bass, to the yellow-brassy color of its upper sides, and its dark stripes. These prominent horizontal bars number seven or eight on each side, most of them above the lateral line. They are broken or interrupted here and there, and because of this feature the yellow bass had formerly

the scientific name of *Morone interrupta*. Taxonomic revision has revealed that *Roccus mississippiensis*, the present name, was an earlier
one. The yellow bass now bears this name, rather than *Morone interrupta*, in accordance with international rules of plant and animal
taxonomy.

In some waters, where the yellow bass's characteristic color is
obscure, it may easily be mistaken for the white bass, for the two are
almost identical in outline. Misidentification is avoided by observing
minor differences. The yellow bass's front and rear dorsals are not
separated, as the white bass's, but joined by a narrow membrane. The
mouth of the yellow bass is slightly smaller and its jaws are approximately even, without the marked protrusion of the white bass's lower
jaw. The yellow bass has no teeth on the base of the tongue. Its scales,
numbering 51 to 55 in a lengthwise row, are slightly larger than those
of the white bass.

Like its white relative, the yellow bass is a springtime spawner,
makes no nest, is very prolific of eggs, and gives no parental attention
to the eggs or young. Growth is slower, and this species does not
attain the size of the white bass. Average yellow bass taken by anglers
weigh perhaps half a pound to a pound. There is no official rod-and-
reel record. Specimens of three pounds are definitely outsize. Usually
such fish are taken from lakes with large expanses of clear unvegetated
water.

Marked changes in lake populations of the yellow bass have been
noted, as with the white bass. The Iowa Conservation Commission
reports that yellow bass were rare in Clear Lake prior to 1930, a time
when white bass were abundant. Within a brief period the yellow
bass far outnumbered the white; later the pendulum swung again the
other way.

The yellow bass is a schooling fish but not markedly a surface
feeder, except in periods of heavy Mayfly hatches. At such times this
fish affords good fly-rod sport. Usually the schools travel at some depth,
feeding on crustaceans and small fish. Most yellow bass in anglers'
creels have been taken by still-fishing or trolling close to the bottom.

As a game fish and as food, the yellow bass is held equal or
even superior to the white bass.

WHITE PERCH
Roccus americanus (Gmelin)

A small anadromous fish, the white perch is native to fresh, brackish, and coastal marine waters along the Atlantic seaboard from the Maritime Provinces to South Carolina, and has landlocked populations in ponds, rivers, and lakes not far from the sea. Through introductions, it thrives in clearwater areas of many inland lakes of the East. It is reported in Cayuga Lake, New York, and in some tributaries of Lake Ontario, through unauthorized stockings of fish thought to be white bass. Via other transplantings the white perch is present in Lake Erie and in the St. Lawrence River as far upstream as Montreal. A springtime abundance of this fish in the lower Hudson River and Long Island waters furnishes sport to thousands of bank fishermen. Great numbers of the white perch in Chesapeake Bay and its drainages support a considerable commercial fishery.

Other names for the white perch, all incorrect, as is its common one, are silver perch, sea perch, gray perch, bluenose perch, and black perch. (How a bass can have spawned so many perches is a puzzle.) One might conclude from this array of localisms that the fish may be almost any color, and such a conclusion would not be far wrong. Generally, however, this fish is dark green on the back, olive or bluish green on the upper sides, and silvery to white below. It lacks the stripes of the white and yellow bass. In some waters it is a very bright and iridescent fish, with a metallic blue sheen upon its gill covers and cheeks. Landlocked white perch are noticeably darker than those in brackish or salt water.

The fins are much like those of the white and yellow bass. The two sections of the dorsal are deeply notched but not separate, being joined by a narrow membrane. A spine is present at the forward end of the ventral fin and the soft-rayed dorsal, and three strong anterior spines are in the anal fin. The tail is slightly forked. The mouth is small but well toothed, and the jaws are of equal length.

White perch of two, three, and four pounds are uncommon to very rare, and the average in anglers' catches is about half a pound. However, the record white perch on sporting tackle weighed 4 pounds

12 ounces. It was taken from Messalonskee Lake, Maine, by Mrs. Earl Small on June 4, 1949.

Depending on latitude, the white perch's spawning time is April to June, in fresh or brackish waters of rivers and in the lakes and ponds where it is landlocked. Females mature when two or three years old, and cast at random 40,000 to 100,000 or more adhesive eggs, which fasten upon rocks and bottom debris. Spawning is spread over ten days to two weeks, during which period a sudden drop in water temperature will destroy all eggs. There is no nest and the spawn is untended by either parent. Eggs hatch in three days, at 58° F., into fry so small as to be almost invisible.

Charles M. Breder, Jr., states that under landlocked conditions white perch reproduce year after year, but each successive generation is usually smaller and less vital than the last. Apparently a recourse to salt water is needed for perpetuation of vigor.[3]

Growth rates of white perch vary widely in different waters, even within the same state. Maine cites six-year-old fish twelve inches long in one pond, fish of the same age only seven inches long in another. Overcrowding and stunting from insufficient food are noted in many eastern lakes. Under such conditions the fish are too small for angling, too large as forage for any but the largest predators; and have become, as New York State conservationists put it, another "problem child" of fisheries management. Legal size and creel limits are believed to aggravate overpopulation and are increasingly being removed.

The white perch of coastal waters is inclined to make permanent residence in brackish estuaries and tidal rivers, seldom venturing seaward and undertaking no long migration upriver. It travels normally in schools which may number a hundred to several thousand, feeding on insects, small crustaceans and fishes. The white perch is accused of eating the fresh-laid spawn of other species and of preying upon the fry of trout and salmon. Despite this reputation, fly-fishermen and other anglers acknowledge the white perch to be a fine little gamester in its own right and a frying-pan morsel with few superiors.

[3] *Field Book of Marine Fishes of the Atlantic Coast* (G. P. Putnam's Sons, New York, 1948).

Chapter 18

YELLOW PERCH, WALLEYE, SAUGER, DARTERS

The perch family, Percidae, is one of seventy-six families of the tremendous order Perciformes, which embraces three to four hundred genera and nearly a thousand species in North American fresh and salt waters, plus others in Europe and Asia.

A large and curious clan, the perch family is represented in the United States, Canada and Mexico by ninety-nine species among only five genera, all of fresh water. Only one of these is universally called a perch, and only four attain sizes of interest to fishermen.

The single perch is of course the yellow perch, the only species of the lonely genus *Perca*. Its familiarity, abundance, and widespread angling appeal give it unquestioned leadership of its family.

Largest of the family is the walleye, called pike perch in some areas—a quite famous game and food fish occasionally reaching twenty pounds. Close kin to the walleye are the smaller sauger and blue pike. The rest, ninety-five species in all, are the tiny, brilliantly colored but little known darters. This group includes two slightly larger species called logperch.

The perches are distinguished from the sunfishes by the possession of two distinct and separate dorsal fins, the first strongly spined, the second soft-rayed.

YELLOW PERCH
Perca flavescens (Mitchill)

In its popularity with anglers of all sorts, the yellow perch is perhaps second only to the bluegill. As a delectable morsel it is generally rated superior to the bluegill and indeed to all other of the so-called panfish.

Many other fishes have wide color variations, but the yellow perch's basic pattern is unique and changes but slightly from one water to another. Its greenish yellow body color, and its six to eight broad, dark, vertical bands extending from the back almost to the whitish belly, identify the yellow perch over all of its range.

In some areas it is called red perch, green perch, ringed perch, striped perch, American perch, and even raccoon perch. Though classed as a warmwater fish, the yellow perch abides in some waters nearly 60 degrees north. Its broad native haunts run from the Lesser Slave Lake in Alberta eastward to New Brunswick and Nova Scotia, thence southward to the Carolinas in the east and Kansas in the west. The Great Lakes system is central in this vast region, and in all of this mid-continent complex of lakes and rivers the yellow perch abounds. It has been introduced into the Rocky Mountain and Pacific states.

This fish has a deeper body, in proportion to its length, than its walleye and sauger cousins, and has a quite conspicuous depression in the upper outline, just back of the eyes. Though it has many small sharp teeth in the jaws, there are no long canine teeth such as the walleye and sauger possess. The ventral fins, and sometimes the anal, are yellow, bright orange, or orange-red, particularly in breeding males. The entire fish is rough to the touch. The dorsal spines, numbering twelve to fourteen, are stiff and sharp; the edges of the ctenoid scales are like coarse sandpaper, and the gills are protected by strong sharp opercle bones.

Other marks of the yellow perch are its notched rather than forked tail, two spiny rays at the forward end of the anal fin, and two or three in the soft dorsal. A distinct dusky blotch is sometimes apparent on the spinous dorsal. The scales number 57 to 62 along the lateral line. Eight to ten rows of scales are on each cheek.

Averaging six to eight inches in small rivers and along shore in large lakes, the yellow perch attains fourteen or fifteen inches, and occasionally a weight of two pounds, in spacious deeper waters. Perch of such size are six or seven years old, and have lived longer than most of their kin. Occasionally in ponds where the population is held in check by fishermen or predators, the perch grow to a pound or so. This writer recalls taking several of about a pound each, on fly tackle, from a three-acre body which in the early 1900's was called Brown's Pond, at Newfoundland, New Jersey. These fish were mostly in a deep hole—ten to twelve feet—just above a dam at the outlet of the pond. They showed little partiality as between worms and small wet flies, were great fun on the fly rod, and superb in the pan. That pond, however, was not heavily fished in those years. If it had a good population of largemouth or smallmouth bass, we were unaware of it. But the big perch were there, and in numbers.

The record yellow perch on sporting tackle was caught about a century ago, in May 1865, in the Delaware River at Bordentown, New Jersey. A Dr. C. C. Abbot landed this lunker, a fish of 4 pounds 3½ ounces. This record is subject to some skepticism on the part of anglers because of its antiquity and the fact that no comparable yellow perch has been taken since.

Primarily a fish of lakes, ponds, and slow-flowing streams, the yellow perch is occasionally found in the still pools and quiet back-waters of some swift salmon and trout rivers of the Northeast. It is a shallow-water species, yet schools of large perch frequent summer-time depths of sixty feet or more in the large bays and inshore areas of the Great Lakes. Its occurrence in brackish waters of the eastern seaboard is recorded but infrequent.

In rivers and even in large lakes, yellow perch show little ten-dency to travel far from the home grounds. Some of the lake fish ascend tributaries a short distance on their spawning runs, but during the rest of the year keep pretty well to their accustomed area, cruising in schools of fifty to two hundred fish, each school seemingly con-stituted by individuals of a common size and age.

Donald Mraz of the U.S. Fish and Wildlife Service reports on a great majority of stay-at-homes and a few exceptional wanderers, in "The Movements of Yellow Perch Marked in Southern Green Bay, Lake Michigan, in 1950."[1] Among the perch tagged and released, 108 were recovered within four months of tagging. Of these, 78 were recaptured within the immediate tagging area. Twenty-one had strayed from a mile to twenty miles; seven had ventured from twenty to forty miles, and just two were recovered beyond forty miles from the point of release.

Prospering in clear water, the yellow perch may die if its habitat becomes excessively turbid or silted. The rooting of carp has un-doubtedly killed thousands of perch. Yet this fish has a quite remark-able resistance to oxygen depletion, and has been known to survive "winterkill" conditions which have been fatal to bluegills and large-mouth bass.

Female yellow perch, sexually mature at the age of two, and males sometimes able to breed as one-year-olds, spawn in the early spring, shortly after the ice breakup. Perch in the Great Lakes and large inland lakes may spawn on the shoreward shoals or over bars, but many undertake mass migrations up the tributary streams.

Neither parent builds a nest; the female drops her eggs haphaz-ardly over gravel, rocks, or roots. The male fish come first to the spawn-ing shoals and linger for a time after the females have gone, but make

[1] Reprinted from *Transactions of the American Fisheries Society*, Vol. 81 (1951).

no attempt to guard the eggs or the hatched fry. The females depart at once after the eggs are shed. The eggs are cast in gelatinous ribbons or streamers, two to seven feet long, which swell considerably after being fertilized. They are highly vulnerable to predators, especially when hung upon submerged vegetation, roots, or rocks, and quite frequently entire masses perish when washed ashore by storms or left stranded by receding water.

The eggs number about 20,000 per average female, and hatch in eight or ten days at normal spawning temperatures. During the fry-to-fingerling stage the young remain in the natal shallows until late summer, then migrate to deeper water.

Adult perch are carnivorous, subsisting chiefly on insects, crustaceans, and small fish. Growth rates depend, of course, upon the available food per fish. The yellow perch can reproduce itself against heavy fishing pressure and is as prone to overpopulate as the bluegill and crappie. In many ponds and small lakes with few natural predators, the population becomes too great for the food supply, and stunted perch are the inevitable result. Seeking to thin out the perches' numbers and increase individual sizes, many states have removed angling restrictions on this fish.

Dr. Edward C. Raney, of Cornell University, writes,[2] "The history of many upland ponds after their [yellow perch] introduction, either as bait fish or otherwise, is a sad story. The perch generally do well for a short time but gradually reduce the native crops of forage fish and then in turn become stunted, often are infested with grub parasites, and are usually worthless. Through competition the native-trout population becomes woefully reduced. . . . While highly regarded by those whose main interest in fishes is gastronomic, most agree that it [the yellow perch] is a deplorable nuisance in our Adirondack ponds and streams." Dr. Raney cites an example of stunting: "A sample of a population of stunted perch from Gilbert Lake, six years old, weighed 1.75 ounces on the average, while those of the same age from Bradley Brook Reservoir weighed almost six times as much."

In a balanced ecology the yellow perch is a valuable fish as food for larger game species; its competition is not serious against such as the walleye and northern pike, and it grows to a size appealing to anglers.

[2] "Perch," published in *New York State Conservationist*.

Preferred still-fishing baits are worms and live or preserved minnows, on No. 6 or 8 hooks. A dobber or float is useful in keeping the bait at the depth of the fish. As a preliminary to still-fishing, trolling with a spinner and worm will often find a school. Wet flies are used mostly at early morning and evening, when the perch are in the shallows and feeding near the surface.

In many lakes of the northern range the yellow perch constitutes the bulk of the ice-fisherman's catch.

This fish has supported a good-sized commercial enterprise in the Great Lakes. In Lake Michigan and its Green Bay arm the annual trap-net and gill-net catch has totaled several million pounds in recent years. Despite the commercial take, the yellow perch is reported on the increase in the Great Lakes.

WALLEYE
Stizostedion vitreum vitreum (Mitchill)

The many who call the walleye the pike perch are using an appropriate name, for it is a perch. Others who call it a walleyed pike, green pike, blue pike, or yellow pike, are making a pike of it—which of course it is not. In this fish's southerly range people who call it a jack salmon are even further from the truth. In French Canada it is called the dory or doré.

The walleye is so named because its large eye is opaque and almost blind-looking. Paul Eschmeyer, investigating the night spawning of walleyes, reports that when a light is trained upon the fish in shoal water, their eyes appear as bright orange-red globes. This reflection facilitates locating the fish in shoals, but they are disturbed by the light and quickly head for deep water.[3]

Another of the "warmwater" fishes, the walleye nevertheless ranges well north—across Canada from Athabaska Lake through the Hudson Bay drainages and east to Labrador. From this northerly sweep the species occurs southward through the Atlantic states to North Carolina. It is abundant in the Great Lakes, particularly Lake Erie, and ranges down the Mississippi Valley to the Tennessee River

[3] *Life History of the Walleye in Michigan* (Michigan Department of Conservation, June 1952).

on the east and northern Arkansas on the west. Here and there in this vast territory are patches of its absence. It was never native to Maine though it was introduced, unsuccessfully, into the Belgrade Lakes in the 1920's.

Throughout its American range the walleye is by choice a denizen of clear lakes and large rivers, and likes hard bottoms of rock, gravel, or sand. Though a fish of moderately deep water, it never plumbs the remoter depths of the whitefish and cisco in the Great Lakes.

The walleye is rather elongate, deepest well forward and tapering gradually to a narrow caudal peduncle. The basic color is green-brownish on the back, lightening to dull brassy on the sides and white on the belly. The sides are mottled obliquely with dark blotches, and may be flecked or barred with numerous irregular greenish-yellow markings. The first dorsal fin, high forward and tapering abruptly, has twelve to fifteen stout spines. The membranes between the last two or three spines are definitely darker than the rest of the fin, giving the appearance of a dark blotch at this point, which is one of the walleye's distinguishing marks. The second dorsal fin is flecked with brownish. The anal fin has two weak spines forward. The caudal is mildly forked, flecked like the soft dorsal, and the point of the lower lobe is tipped with white.

The walleye's mouth is appropriately large for so predatory a fish, and the jaws are equipped with many teeth, including conspicuous canines. Firm sharp opercle bones on the gill cover are capable of cutting an angler's hand. The cheeks are smooth and virtually scale-less. Body scales number 80 to 89 lengthwise.

The walleye is unique among all perches for its ability to attain large size. Though the fish of rivers and small lakes run from one to three pounds, those in the Great Lakes and larger inland bodies are often of ten pounds and occasionally fifteen and over. The sporting record belongs to a 25-pound walleye, 41 inches long, taken in Old Hickory Lake, Tennessee, by Mabry Harper on August 1, 1960.

Spawning of the walleye begins in early spring, sometimes before the breakup of ice. Some of the lake fish favor sites along rocky, windswept and wave-scoured shores, particularly in sheltered water just inside an offshore bar. Others migrate long distances up tributary streams. Paul Eschmeyer reports annual spring migrations of large numbers of walleyes from Lake Michigan and Muskegon Lake up the Muskegon River to the base of Newaygo Dam, forty miles upstream. Walter E. Crowe, also of the Michigan Conservation Department, has estimated from recoveries of tagged fish that walleyes of the 1953–54 spawning runs up the Muskegon River numbered nearly 120,000 individuals each year. Of these, 7000 to 8000 were lifted over the Newaygo Dam and proceeded farther upstream.[4]

Wisconsin scientists Wallace Niemuth, Warren Churchill, and Thomas Wirth write of even longer spawning migrations: as much as 100 miles up the Wolf River from Lake Winnebago.[5]

The walleye spawns on rocky or gravel bottoms but seldom over sand. Apparently this fish needs moving water—river currents or lake shoals with wave action—for its breeding. A common river spawning bed is just below swift rapids.

As with the yellow perch, the males are the first to arrive on the spawning grounds and remain a short time after the females have left. Males and females lurk just off the breeding shoals by day, entering them by night for the act of reproduction.

A single spawning female is usually accompanied by two or more males. The adhesive eggs, numbering 20,000 to half a million or more per female, are shed at random and promptly abandoned. They hatch in one to three weeks.

The young, leaving the shallows soon after hatching, grow normally to five or six inches by fall. Males become sexually mature in two to three years, females in four or five. The average life span is about seven years. Messrs. Niemuth, Churchill, and Wirth, of Wisconsin, report an exceptional female whose first spawning was in 1918, and whose last was in 1929 as a 17½-pound, 18-year-old matron.

Feeding largely upon smaller fishes, the walleyes occupy an important niche in the ecological scheme of predator and prey. Walleye populations undoubtedly are more of a checkrein on the over-multiplication of yellow perch and the sunfishes than are all the anglers combined. They compete seriously with largemouth and smallmouth

[4] "Numerical Abundance and Use of a Spawning Run of Walleyes in the Muskegon River, Michigan," reprinted from *Transactions of the American Fisheries Society*, Vol. 84 (1954).

[5] *The Walleye—Its Life History, Ecology, and Management* (Publication 227, Wisconsin Conservation Department, 1959).

bass, however; introductions of walleyes into bass lakes have caused a decline of the bass.

Walleye populations fluctuate widely, year by year, in a single lake. A good example is reported by J. L. Forney and A. W. Eipper, of Cornell University. In 1957, anglers' catches of walleyes in Oneida Lake, New York, were estimated at 40,000 fish; in 1958 the total had nearly tripled, at 113,000; in 1959 it reached 468,000 fish, weighing about 650,000 pounds.[6] Comparable ups and downs in commercially fished waters result in alternate gluts and scarcities of market walleyes.

Sometimes the natural reproduction of the fish in a single year will be remarkable for its numbers and strength, and this phenomenon is often responsible for a sensational increase in walleye numbers in a given water. The year class of 1943, in the Bay de Noc at the northern end of Green Bay, Michigan, was a striking example. Albert S. Hazzard, formerly of the Institute of Fisheries Research, Ann Arbor, Michigan, reports that the average annual commercial catch in these waters had been 51,000 pounds from 1929 to 1943. By 1947, when the year class of '43 was attaining market sizes, the catch was up to 262,000 pounds; in 1948 it reached 572,000 pounds, and in 1949 it topped one million pounds.[7]

The commercial fishery for walleyes is substantial in several areas, but western Lake Erie dwarfs all others, in some years exceeding four million pounds.

A worthy game fish, with lunkers potential in many easy-to-reach waters, the walleye has a tremendous following among anglers, including thousands of hardy souls who catch the walleye through the winter ice.

A favorite summertime method is trolling to locate a school, marking the site of the first fish with an anchored cork, and then trolling again and again over the hot spot. Casting into a school in shoal water is probably the sportiest walleye fishing, but the opportunity does not often occur. This fish in shallow water fights with considerably more vigor than when dredged up from the depths, for in deep-

---

[6] "Oneida Lake Walleyes," reprinted from *New York State Conservationist*, (February–March 1961).

[7] "The Walleye—Fish of Mystery," reprinted from *Michigan Conservationist*, (July–August 1951).

water trolling the fish is handicapped by the weight needed to keep the lure deep, and by the sharp change of pressure when brought to the surface.

Deep-trolled spoons and live baits probably account for most of the angler-caught walleyes, but streamer and bucktail flies and shallow-running lures are effective when the fish are in the shoals. There is no great amount of fly-fishing for walleyes, and this may seem surprising to trout and salmon men, for a three-pound walleye on a fly rod could surely provide a memorable moment.

SAUGER
Stizostedion canadense (Smith)

The sauger is a smaller and comparatively obscure brother to the walleye, although very much like its famous relative in appearance and habits. Because it is less numerous and does not attain the size of the walleye, it is relatively unimportant as a game fish. It is called sand pike in many places, as well as ground pike, gray pike, spotfin pike, jack, and horsefish.

It has a tremendous native range, running from the Hudson Bay region to the St. Lawrence River, thence southwest to the Tennessee River, and west as far as Montana. It is abundant in Lake Erie, common to occasional elsewhere in the Great Lakes basin and in the Mississippi Valley. A fish of the larger lakes and rivers, the sauger can abide a degree of turbidity that would be intolerable to its walleye kin.

The sauger is marked by rows of dark spots on the first dorsal. It lacks the walleye's black blotch on the rear membranes of this fin and the white tip on the lower lobe of the tail. Its eye has something of the walleye's opacity. The body color differs in being generally less greenish and more brassy, and the sides have large, dark brown, irregularly patterned blotches. The large mouth and canine teeth of the sauger are typical of the genus Stizostedion.

A two-pound sauger is a big one in most waters. Average fish in anglers' catches are under a pound. Rare whoppers are reported, however. The record sauger was an 8-pound 5-ounce specimen, 28

Top to bottom: Walleye,
Yellow Perches, Sauger

inches long, taken at Niobrara, Nebraska, by Mrs. Betty Tepner on October 22, 1961.

Able to breed in the third or fourth year of life, saugers spawn in the early spring, build no nest, and immediately abandon the eggs.

This small edition of the walleye has firm, white, tasty flesh, and has some commercial importance in Lake Erie. A carnivorous fish, it lives on insects, crustaceans, and small fishes. Since it readily takes the usual baits and lures, it is a popular sport fish in some areas.

BLUE PIKE
Stizostedion vitreum glaucum   Hubbs

This third member of the genus *Stizostedion* is in effect a blue or blue-gray walleye. Also called blue walleye and gray pike, it is of course not a pike but as truly a perch as the walleye.

Its range seems to extend vaguely from Lake Ontario westward through the Great Lakes basin, with abundance in Lake Erie, where it is a commercial species.

In such aspects as the fin rays, mouth, teeth, and scales, the blue pike is so close to the walleye that no description is needed. The difference is essentially in the bluish gray body of the blue pike. In size the blue pike seems far inferior. Specimens positively identified have averaged a half pound to a pound.

A haze of confusion surrounds this fish. Jordan and Evermann believed it to be a young color phase of the walleye. Writing of the walleye in *American Food and Game Fishes*,[8] they said: "In the Great Lakes, particularly in Lakes Erie and Ontario, the young of a certain color are known as blue pike, which commercial fishermen believe to be a wholly distinct species from the yellow pike (walleye). So firmly fixed is this belief that they have little patience with naturalists who tell them otherwise." Apparently the commercial fishermen's belief was not only firm but correct, for the blue pike has authoritative listing as a separate species today.

In its feeding and spawning, and the excellence of its flesh, the

[8] Doubleday, Page & Co., New York, 1902.

blue pike is like the walleye. A limited following by anglers, in Lake Ontario and a few other areas, seems the extent of the blue pike's reputation as a game fish.

DARTERS

Smallest members of the perch family, and comprising no less than ninety-five species, the darters are tiny, curious, short-lived, one- to three-inch fishes, many of them very brilliantly colored, and all native only to North America. They have the two distinct dorsals of the perches. Some differ from the genera *Perca* and *Stizostedion* by having rounded tails, others by giving parental care to their eggs and young.

Mostly, the darters lack an air bladder and are bottom-dwellers in fast streams. Some bury themselves in the bottom, with only their snouts and eyes exposed. Suddenly emerging, however, they dart with the speed and direction of a homing bee to whatever mysterious attraction may beckon them. Because of their seclusive nature the darters are known to few but ichthyologists.

A few of the darters compose a rather definite grouping. These have widely separated ventral fins and are scaleless except for a single series of large scales along the midline. On the others, the vast majority, the ventral fins are close together and the body is wholly, or almost wholly, scaled.

All darters are carnivorous, finding their microscopic food chiefly in minute crustacea and insect larvae.

Spawning habits of the darters are but little understood. Most if not all are spring spawners. Some darters bury their eggs in the bottom sand or fine gravel; others may not build nests but guard the eggs; still others shed their eggs at random and leave them unattended.

The range is broad: collectively the darters occur in southern Canada and throughout the United States from the Atlantic seaboard to the Rocky Mountains, and southward to Mexico, but not in the far West.

The Johnny darter, *Etheostoma nigrum* Rafinesque, abundant in

Canada and the United States, is probably the most widely distributed of the perches. In Atlantic coastal streams it occasionally enters brackish water. It is two to three inches long, sandy to greenish in color, with distinct dark markings in the scale pattern forming the letters **V**, **X**, and **W** along the sides. The breast is scaleless. This fish spawns in the spring, the female depositing her eggs under stones, and the male guarding them with its tiny but intense and perhaps often futile courage.

Johnny Darter

The eastern sand darter *Ammocrypta pellucida* (Baird), is one of the few darters with scales only along the midline of the sides. It is a 2½-inch fish, sand-colored and translucent, with rows of almost equally spaced, dark greenish spots along the back and sides. It has the strange habit of burying itself in a sand bottom, with only its eyes and snout protruding into the current.

The swamp darter, *Etheostoma fusiforme* (Girard), is widely distributed in Atlantic coastal waters from southern Maine to the Gulf. It differs from many darters in liking swampy, murky waters.

Largest of the darters is the logperch, *Percina caprodes* (Rafinesque), which grows to five or six inches. It is a northerly fish, from Hudson Bay through the Great Lakes basin and the north central and northeastern United States. Many vertical bars over a gray-green background have given this species the other name of zebra fish. Two species of logperch are recognized. The second, less abundant, is the Roanoke logperch, *Percina rex*.

Chapter 19

BURBOT,
FRESHWATER DRUM,
AND OTHERS

BURBOT
Lota lota (Linnaeus)

The burbot apparently just missed being an eel, yet it belongs to the
cod family, the Gadidae, and is the only freshwater member of that
tribe. In this grouping are the saltiest of marine species—the cod,

pollock, hake, and haddock—and one small member that condescends to be anadromous, the tomcod. But the burbot, despite its family connection, long ago made its home in fresh water and has been there ever since. Though it occasionally enters brackish water in northern estuaries, it manifestly has no inclination to descend to the sea.

In its extensive freshwater habitats (which include Europe and Asia) it is a northern fish, occurring in deep cold lakes and large rivers from Alaska, Yukon, and the Northwest Territories south to the Columbia River watershed. From there it ranges east across Canada and the northern United States to upper New York, New England, the Maritime Provinces, and Labrador. In the Great Lakes and larger inland bodies it is a deepwater fish, competing with the lake trout and whitefish for food and preyed upon by the sea lamprey.

Throughout this range the burbot known to fishermen averages one to five pounds, but it is capable of growing much larger. Ten-pounders are taken from the Great Lakes and elsewhere.

Variously called the ling, freshwater cod, maria, eel pout, lawyer, mud blower, cusk, and gudgeon, the burbot is an elongate fish, heavier forward and eel-like aft. Its body ends in a pointed rear section that is surrounded by the fan-shaped tail. Its colors are somber—dark brown to almost black in more northerly waters, lighter brown to olive in the southerly range—and variously mottled, sometimes showing reddish spots. The underbody is white. A pronounced light-colored lateral line runs the length of the fish. The embedded scales are so small as to be almost invisible. The dorsal fin is double, the forward fin being very short and narrowly separated from the extremely long posterior dorsal, which has 70 to 75 rays and extends nearly to the tail. The anal fin is almost as long as the posterior dorsal, and directly below it. The ventral fins are as far forward as the pectorals. All fins are soft-rayed. This fin arrangement would precisely duplicate the eel's except for the narrow break in the dorsal and the notched separations of the tail from the dorsal and anal.

Other distinguishing marks of the burbot are its flat, pointed head, a single stout barbel under the chin, and two shorter barbels above, one at each nostril.

Spawning in late fall or winter, the burbot may ascend tributaries for its breeding or choose spawning grounds in lake shoals or

Top to bottom: Burbot,
Freshwater Drum

big-river shallows. Females are ripe in their third year and are prolific
of eggs. Among burbots studied by Candian fish culturists[1] at Lake
Simcoe, Ontario, a 16½-inch female contained 45,600 eggs; an eight-
year-old fish 28 inches long carried well over a million.

The burbot is not reported to be a nest-builder, and apparently
there is no parental guarding of the eggs during the long incubation
period.

A carnivorous fish, equipped with broad bands of fine teeth in

[1] H. R. McCrimmon and O. E. Devitt, "Winter Studies on the Burbot of Lake
Simcoe, Ontario," *The Canadian Fish Culturist*, Issue 16, (August 1954).

each jaw, the burbot is a great predator upon smaller fishes, as the Lake Simcoe studies confirmed. The stomach of one large burbot examined during these investigations contained 101 small yellow perch; another had 135 emerald shiners; still another had swallowed three pumpkinseed sunfish, an eight-inch sucker, and an eight-inch smallmouth bass. Other foods of the burbot are insects, crayfish, and plankton.

The burbot has enthusiastic followers among anglers in some areas, but in much of its range it is despised as a trash fish and a predator upon more valuable species.

The flesh is palatable to some, distasteful to others. The large liver yields an oil similar to that of the cod, and the burbot is commercially processed for this purpose.

FRESHWATER DRUM
Aplodinotus grunniens   Rafinesque

Though vastly different fishes, the burbot and the freshwater drum have a common distinction: each is the only freshwater member of an otherwise solidly marine family. In the freshwater drum's case the family is the Sciaenidae, embracing thirty-three Atlantic and Pacific species, among them the various southern drums, the channel bass (red drum), the weakfish, the northern and southern kingfish, several croakers, and others.

Primarily a warmwater species reaching its greatest abundance in the South, the freshwater drum nevertheless includes in its wide range lakes and large rivers as far north as a line from the St. Lawrence basin to Manitoba and Montana. From this upper limit it occurs southward to Texas, Mexico, and Central America. It has its populations in the Great Lakes but is rare in Lake Superior, and attains peak numbers in the Mississippi and lower Missouri river systems.

It is known around the Great Lakes as the sheepshead, croaker, crocus, white perch, and gray perch; farther south people call it the thunderpumper; in Louisiana and Texas it is the gaspergou. Such names as "drum," "croaker," and "thunderpumper" derive from the fish's drumming, croaking, or grunting utterances, typical of many species among its marine relatives. The sound has been attributed to the grinding of the drum's millstonelike throat teeth but actually is caused by the forcing of air from one segment of the air bladder to another.

Shaped like the marine drums, the freshwater species has an arched back and an almost straight lower line from head to tail. The back is grayish to dusky green; the sides gray-silvery, often with a rose to yellow iridescence; the belly white, the pectoral fins pale, the other fins dull gray-brown. Each ventral fin has a long filament on its forward edge. The snout overhangs the lower jaw slightly; the eyes are large, near the top of the head. The dorsal fin is in two parts: a short spiny-rayed forward part, high in front and tapering downward to a notch, behind which is the long, soft-rayed second section of the fin, reaching nearly to the tail. The tail is slightly rounded or fan-shaped. The short anal fin has two spines ahead of the soft rays. The scales are large, numbering 50 to 56 in a lengthwise row.

One of the larger freshwater fishes, this drum has been reported to reach 50 to 60 pounds. Skeletal remains of the fish found in ancient Indian campsites indicate that the species once attained a weight of 200 pounds. So huge a drum far exceeds today's top specimens. However, the Iowa Conservation Commission reports a 50-pounder from Spirit Lake, and states that drums of 20 pounds are not uncommon. Fish of this size may be twenty to twenty-five years old. The average taken by anglers, always far under the top weights, is about one to five pounds.

Moving into sandy or gravelly shallows to spawn in May or June, the female freshwater drum broadcasts numerous eggs. No nest is made, and no care of the eggs or young is provided by the adults.

The drum is chiefly a bottom-feeder, finding its nourishment in mollusks and crustaceans, and occasionally moving upward for minnows or insects. Its strong throat teeth are admirably suited to crushing mussel shells. Crayfish, worms, and minnows are baits favored by most fishermen.

One- to three-pound drums are considered good on the table; large specimens are inclined to be tough. A considerable commercial fishery exists in western Lake Erie and along the Mississippi-Missouri river system.

MOSQUITOFISH
Gambusia affinis (Baird and Girard)[2]

This tiny creature—the female does not exceed 2½ inches and the male reaches a maximum of 1½—is little known though it has contributed hugely to human health and comfort. Its chief food is mosquitoes, or more properly their larvae, including the species that cause malaria and yellow fever, and in satisfying this appetite it is highly efficient. Harnessed to this end by man, the tiny mosquitofish has reduced the mosquito population of many a swamp.

Of the family Poeciliidae, the mosquitofish is one of six Gambusias, all of which, except itself, are freshwater species. Affinis occurs in fresh, salt, and brackish water. It lives wherever a mosquito will breed, except in the far North. It thrives in sluggish and standing water, clear or vegetated or muddy, deep or shallow; in ditches, cisterns, potholes, and rain barrels. It has been known to live, keeping close to the surface, in a municipal septic tank containing sewage.

The original range of the mosquitofish ran from the mouth of the Rio Grande River eastward along the Gulf coast to approximately the Louisiana-Mississippi line, and up the Mississippi River and its tributaries as far north as central Illinois. A more easterly subspecies, previously called Gambusia affinis holbrooki, is known in marshes and lagoons along the Atlantic seaboard from Delaware to Florida. Today both of these fish are classified as the single species, G. affinis.

This little fish's value in mosquito control was first recognized by David Starr Jordan in 1905, when at the request of the city of Honolulu, Hawaii, he procured from Texas three different genera: the Gulf killifish, Fundulus grandis; the sailfin molly, Molliensis latipinna; and Gambusia affinis affinis, as our hero was then called. The last proved most effective and has since been widely used in man's campaigns against the mosquito around the world.[3]

From stocks grown in Carbondale, Illinois, in the 1920's, a shipment of mosquitofish went to Italy, and thence spread throughout

[2] Much of this section is drawn from an excellent paper, The Mosquitofish, by Lola T. Dees (Fish and Wildlife Service, U.S. Department of the Interior, September 1961).

[3] Louis A. Krumholz, "Northward Acclimatization of the Western Mosquitofish." A doctoral thesis, University of Michigan; reprinted from Copeia (June 30, 1944).

Europe and Asia. Today *affinis* has been acclimatized in southern Canada, in almost all southern European countries, in Germany and Austria, in Russia as far north as Moscow, in the Near East and Far East, in Hawaii, the West Indies, and Argentina. Selective breeding for greater ability to withstand cold may well extend this fish's range.

In its color the mosquitofish is dusky green or olive to silvery, darkest on the head and forward sides, lightest on the belly. Its scales are large and each is outlined in dark pigment. The tail is rounded; the single short dorsal is posterior, originating behind the anal. The dorsal and caudal fins have two to four rows of dark spots.

The mosquitofish has still another distinction: it is ovoviviparous, the female producing eggs which hatch within her body. The gonopodium or sexual organ of the male is produced by a fusion and lengthening of the third, fourth, and fifth rays of the anal fin. With this instrument he deposits sperm in the female's genital tract. The fertilized eggs hatch in twenty-one to twenty-eight days; several hours later the female expels the live young as fully formed, free-swimming, tiny fish about a third of an inch long. In their new and microscopic life they immediately begin to seek any of the minute, threadlike mosquito larvae which may be present in their environment.

Some females mature in their first summer, others in the second, and they die during the summer of their maturity.

Throughout its short life the mosquitofish performs its benefactions if it eludes such predators as birds, frogs, fish, and watersnakes. Cold winters destroy it too, though new strains are reported to have survived under thick ice.

Gambusia affinis is easily bred in aquaria but is not ideal for this purpose. The males fight among themselves, often with fatal results, and attack other species; the females may eat their young if their natural diet of larvae is lacking.

BROOK STICKLEBACK
Eucalia inconstans (Kirtland)

The sticklebacks are small, slender, scaleless fishes, inhabiting the fresh and salt waters of North America. They are characterized by strong dorsal and pelvic spines, and of interest chiefly because of the male's extraordinary nest-building and pugnacious breeding behavior.

The five-spined or brook stickleback is the one strictly freshwater species of the family Gasterosteidae, which includes four others, bearing various numbers of spines from two to nine. Of these, one is wholly marine; three inhabit both fresh and salt water.

A tiny fish, not exceeding three inches, the brook stickleback has a tremendous range, occurring in clear weedy streams, ponds, and small bog lakes across the United States and Canada, as far north as Hudson Bay and as far south as Virginia.

The brook stickleback is usually brownish above, pale green to white below, with translucent pale green fins. Its five dorsal spines are widely spaced, with no membranes between them. The fifth spine is immediately ahead of the nine-rayed soft dorsal fin. The tail is fan-shaped with an almost square outer edge; the anal fin, with a sharp spine as its first ray, is directly under the dorsal. Each pelvic or ventral fin is equipped with a spine.

At spawning time, in late spring or early summer, the male brook stickleback builds a tiny cylindrical or spherical nest of sticks and vegetable detritus, binding these materials together with silklike threads formed from a secretion of the fish's kidneys. Once finished, ‣this structure resembles an oriole's nest on a small scale. The male now invites one or more females inside for the business of reproduction. The eggs usually number less than a hundred per female.

During the ten- to twelve-day period of incubation the male, now vivid in color but with almost jet-black fins, becomes a tight little essence of fury. Within the immediate area of the nest he will unhesitatingly attack, with all spines erect, any intruding fish five times his size.

Naturalist Konrad Z. Lorenz, describing this phenomenon,[4] says the basic principle of the male stickleback's fighting is "my home is my castle." Away from his nest his aggressiveness vanishes, but at the nest itself he will recklessly ram the strongest opponent, or even a human hand dipped into an aquarium tank. When two male sticklebacks meet in battle the one nearest his nest is the certain victor.

[4] *King Solomon's Ring* (Thomas Y. Crowell, New York, 1952).

Sometimes, chasing his opponent off in the flush of triumph, the victor pursues the vanquished too close to the latter's nest, whereupon the fugitive now becomes the aggressor and the previous aggressor rapidly loses his courage away from his own nest. Such combats may ebb and flow in the course of several sorties away from and toward each nest, until a point of equilibrium is reached.

At all times the brook stickleback is a voracious feeder upon water insects and tiny crustacea, and may devour large numbers of game-fish fry. Probably because of its spines, it is not important as forage or bait for game species. It is an interesting aquarium fish but requires live food.

BROOK SILVERSIDE
Labidesthes sicculus (Cope)

In the family Atherinidae the brook silverside is the only species of its genus but is related to eight other silversides and to similar small fishes of different genera, variously inhabiting Atlantic, Pacific, and fresh waters.

This is a beautiful two- to three-inch miniature, slender and semi-transparent, pale green with a violet iridescence about the gill covers, and a pronounced silvery lateral line. The double dorsal fin, forked tail, and extremely long anal fin are pale emerald edged with white; the other fins are glassy and transparent. The eyes are very large, occupying virtually the entire sides of the head.

Despite its name, the brook silverside is not exclusively a denizen of brooks, but occurs as well in large rivers, ponds, and lakes from the upper St. Lawrence basin to Georgian Bay in Lake Huron, southward through the Mississippi Valley to the Gulf, and eastward to the Atlantic states.

It is a springtime spawner, choosing its breeding sites among aquatic vegetation in shallow water. In lakes it travels in huge schools, usually frequenting the shoreward shallows but sometimes venturing far out in open water. When alarmed by a marauding pike or other predator these schools literally take flight, shattering the surface in all

Top to bottom: Banded Killifish,
Sticklebacks (female in nest)

directions in their efforts to escape. For these tactics the fish is called "skipjack" in some quarters.

Insects and plankton are the principal foods of the brook silverside. In turn, it feeds many game fishes, as natural forage or from an angler's hook.

BANDED KILLIFISH
Fundulus diaphanus (LeSueur)

The banded killifish belongs to the family Cyprinodontidae and claims as its kin twenty-one other freshwater and marine killifishes, many topminnows and pupfish, and a close cousin, the mummichog. The banded member is exclusively a freshwater species, occupying shallow weedy bays of lakes, and coves of rivers from the Maritime Provinces and New England to Lake Michigan, southward in the Mississippi Valley to Iowa and Missouri, and east to South Carolina.

The killifishes are often confused with the small minnows, but are identifiable by the placement and shape of their fins. The killifish's dorsal is well back of the middle and has a rounded outer edge. The caudal is definitely rounded, whereas in the small minnows and shiners it is always forked. The so-called topminnows are not of the order Cypriniformes, the true minnows, but belong to the order Cyprinodontiformes which embraces all killifishes.

The banded killifish is alternately blackish to greenish-yellow on the top and upper sides; in some waters it may be rose-violet along the middle, and is generally white below. Its sides are crossed vertically by a series of twelve to fifteen dark bands. The fins are a pale greenish gray. The dorsal fin may be barred horizontally, and the upper scales are well defined in dark outlines.

This little species, three to five inches long, spawns in midsummer in weedy shallows, attempts no nest-building, and does not protect its eggs or young. It feeds on the usual fare of such smallish fishes: water insects and their larvae, minute plankton organisms, and aquatic vegetation. Rarely straying beyond the shoreward shallows, the banded killifish is of limited value as food for game species, but can be an effective bait.

MOTTLED SCULPIN
Cottus bairdi Girard

The genus *Cottus* includes eighteen freshwater sculpins and two which inhabit both fresh and salt water. Among the genera of the family Cottidae are sixty-four marine sculpins of Atlantic and Pacific waters. Some of the Pacific sculpins grow to be over two feet long.

The freshwater sculpins are small fishes native to clear cold lakes and streams, ranging across the northern United States and southern Canada. Hiding usually under stones, they are seldom seen except when dislodged by an occasional wading trout fisherman.

Averaging three to four inches in length, the mottled sculpin is without scales but possessed of a short spine on the gill cover and numerous small tubercles or spiny processes about the head. The over-all color is brownish, mottled or irregularly spotted with darker brown or black. The head is large, the body thick at the shoulder and narrowing toward the tail. The pectoral fins are large and winglike; the dorsal is in two parts, the hind section very long, almost reaching the tail. The tail is rounded and shows a distinct black vertical bar at its base. The pectoral, dorsal, and caudal fins are yellowish, barred in brown or gray. The skin of the mottled sculpin is slimy but less so than that of its relative the slimy sculpin, *Cottus cognatus* Richardson.

The mottled and slimy sculpins spawn in the spring, depositing clusters of eggs under stones. The male guards the eggs until hatched.

Both of these species have some value as natural food for the brook trout, landlocked salmon, and lake trout, since they inhabit many of the same waters. They have been accused of eating trout eggs, but this charge seems unconfirmed. As Maine conservationists point out, trout eggs available to the sculpin would not be covered and hence doomed to destruction in any event.

PIRATE PERCH
Aphredoderus sayanus (Gilliams)

The specific name of this little fish tells its odd story. If you "say anus" you have said about all that needs to be told, for the anus of pirate perch adults is situated in the region of the throat.

The pirate perch is not a perch at all. It has no close relative, in fact, being the only member of the family Aphredoderidae and of the genus *Aphredoderus*. The so-called "trout perch," which likewise is not a perch, is of the same order as the pirate perch, but of a different family—the Percopsidae.

A small, somber-hued fish, reaching four to five inches, the pirate perch lives in weedy overflow ponds of the Mississippi Valley and elsewhere. It is reported from Michigan to Florida, and is apparently more abundant south than north. Its spawning habits seem but little known.

Chapter 20

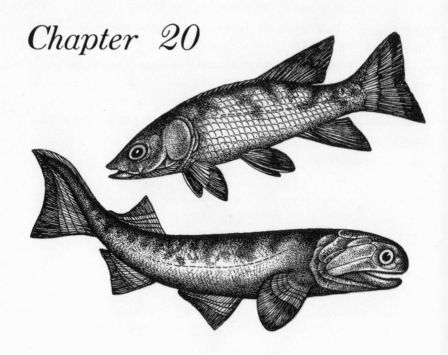

STURGEONS, PADDLEFISH, GARS, BOWFIN

These are old, old fishes, ancient beyond human reckoning, survivors of the lower Mesozoic murk, their ancestors in the limbo of the dinosaur and pterodactyl and coelecanth. They swim today in the coastal seas and inland waters as they swam many millions of years ago. Fossils in the rocks of Europe, Asia, and North America attest their antiquity, but the sturgeons, paddlefish, gars, and bowfin which today

NOTE: Illustrated are reconstructions of two extinct ray fishes, the forerunners of today's primitive ganoid fishes.

lend a kind of museum-piece interest to North American waters are anything but fossilized. The gars and bowfin are among the most predacious of all freshwater fishes; the sturgeons and paddlefish, though less thoroughly carnivorous, are the embodiment of living strength, as anglers who have taken them know. All of them, indeed, have survived because they are durable. They constitute a vestige of holdovers from ancient families which once numbered many more, and doubtless weaker, species.

STURGEONS

The sturgeons of North American waters include seven species among two genera, in the order Acipenseriformes and the family Acipenseridae. None is wholly marine, though the white and green sturgeons are anadromous in Pacific coastal rivers, and the Atlantic and shortnose sturgeons ascend eastern rivers to spawn. The lake sturgeon, shovelnose sturgeon, and pallid sturgeon are exclusively freshwater dwellers. No sturgeon is found in the tropics or the Southern Hemisphere. Eurasian species, commercially fished for caviar before this virtue of the sturgeon was appreciated in America, include the huge beluga sturgeon, *Acipenser huro*, known to reach sixteen feet and 2200 pounds, and the small but valuable sterlet sturgeon, *A. ruthenus*. The roe of the latter makes an exceptionally fine grade of caviar; prior to World War I it was reserved almost exclusively for the Russian Imperial Court.[1]

By comparison with most of the freshwater fishes and many marine species the sturgeons are a curious breed, looking like the prehistoric monsters which essentially they are. They are almost without body scales but possess five (rarely seven) lengthwise rows of bony humps or shields: a dorsal row plus a lateral and ventral series on each side. On young sturgeons each of these bony shields is equipped with a keel-like ridge and a spine, but this extra armor tends to become blunted and may disappear entirely as the fish ages.

The head, on all species except the shortnose sturgeon, tapers narrowly to a thin snout and shows a marked concavity in the upper

[1] Lola T. Dees, *Sturgeons* (U.S. Fish and Wildlife Service, September 1961).

profile. The mouth, toothless except in the larval young, is situated underneath, well behind the snout and just back of four lower barbels which act as sensory organs in detecting food. The sturgeon is a bottom feeder; as it cruises along the barbels make contact with a crustacean, mollusk, or other morsel, and immediately the large thick-lipped protrusile mouth lowers itself to suck in its prey.

At the other end of the sturgeon the heterocercal tail, with the vertebral column extending into the upper lobe, is typical of many primitive fishes, including the paddlefish and the sharks. On all species of sturgeon the upper caudal lobe is longer than the lower. The single dorsal fin is far to the rear, the anal even more posterior, the ventrals slightly ahead of the anal, and the huge pectorals far forward.

Colors of the sturgeons differ from one species to another, but no outward difference between the sexes of a single species is perceptible except in the case of a ripe female swollen with roe.

Sharklike, also, is the sturgeon's cartilaginous skeleton. In place of a backbone, the sturgeon possesses a white tubular column called the notochord. An efficient air bladder governs the specific gravity of the fish, helping it cruise without effort in shallows or at depths beyond a hundred feet.

Three species—the white, Atlantic, and lake sturgeons—attain sizes which distinguish them as the largest of our freshwater fishes. They require many years to reach sexual maturity and are capable of living 50 to 150 years. It is possible that the sturgeon you hooked and lost today will be taken eventually by your grandson.

The sturgeons are spring or summer spawners, ceasing to feed at spawning time. The anadromous species may deposit their eggs just above tidewater or after long migrations upstream. The adhesive eggs, numbering as many as four million from a single large female, stick to the bottom stones or vegetation in large clusters, and hatch in a week or so into larvae less than half an inch long. No nest is built and no care of the eggs or young is provided by the adults. Several males may attend a single female; the commotion of spawning is sometimes visible and audible a long way off as the big fish roll and splash and erupt from the surface. The young of anadromous species live in the parent stream or its estuary for one to three years before migrating to sea.

One thinks of the sturgeon as a kind of philosopher among fishes, as if its ancient lineage had bred, over the thousands of centuries, a curious old wisdom and a quiet acceptance of change. The sturgeon has seen more years when it first spawns than many fishes see in a lifetime. After its initial act of reproduction it descends to the coastal estuary or the sea or the lake, and may stay there three years before returning upriver to spawn again. In its feeding it is deliberate, thorough, and omnivorous, sucking up all manner of animal and vegetable food from the bottom terrain. Though the normal diet is insect larvae, crustaceans, mollusks, and small fish, one huge captured white sturgeon had a tomcat in its stomach; another had a half bushel of onions which presumably had come from a cannery or warehouse upstream.

Despite the sturgeon's great size and long tenure of this planet, it is a strange fish to many people. Quite unobserved, these giants course upstream on their spring spawning runs and later return to the sea. An eight-foot Atlantic sturgeon, enmeshed in a herring net and brought ashore in a Canadian bay a few years ago, was unidentified by its captor and by most of the local people who came to see and photograph it.

In the years of their great abundance sturgeons were taken by the thousands in the nets of commercial fishermen. Considered a net-damaging nuisance, they were thrown on the banks to rot or carted away as food for hogs. Not until the mid-nineteenth century was the sturgeon justly appraised for the excellence of its meat, the value of its roe for caviar, and the incidental worth of its air bladder as a raw material for isinglass. Despite Russia's traditional pre-eminence in caviar, the United States was a foremost source of supply in the late 1800's, exporting this delicacy to many European countries.

Thereafter the sturgeon's decline paralleled that of the salmon and the shad. Overfishing, industrial pollution of rivers, and the isolation of spawning beds by dams wrote another dreary chapter in the familiar history of man's despoilment of his resource. The sturgeon fishery in the Delaware River alone totaled five million pounds in 1890; the ten-year average for the entire United States (1949–58), as reported by Lola T. Dees of the U.S. Fish and Wildlife Service, was down to 657,700 pounds.

Man has now contrived his protections for this vanishing fish, possibly too late. Angling for sturgeons, by rod and line in the summer and by spearing through the ice, is increasing, and is regulated in many waters by strict limits on numbers and size. Existing wild stocks must be preserved if the sturgeon is to be saved, for artificial propagation of this fish is impracticable.

WHITE STURGEON
Acipenser transmontanus Richardson

The white sturgeon, known also as Pacific sturgeon, Oregon sturgeon, Columbia River sturgeon, and Sacramento sturgeon, is not white but light gray in its youth, dark gray in its maturity. Native to major rivers of the Pacific slopes from middle California to Alaska, it is the largest fish cruising the fresh waters of the United States and Canada. Along such rivers as the Columbia, Snake, and Fraser, stories of huge white sturgeon strain one's credence, yet there is little reason to doubt that the white sturgeon is capable of attaining well over a thousand pounds. Possibly the largest specimen was a fish of approximately 1800 pounds, reported in the *British Columbian* of New Westminster, British Columbia, issue of October 14, 1897, as having been taken some years previously at Mission, British Columbia, on the Fraser River.

Sporting records, though far below such figures, are sensational enough. The largest white sturgeon entered to date in the *Field & Stream* contest weighed 360 pounds and was 9 feet 3 inches long. This fish was taken by Willard Cravens on sporting tackle, in the Snake River, Idaho, on April 24, 1956. Larger white sturgeon on sporting gear are reported, however, including one of 394 pounds, taken by Glen Howard of Boise, Idaho, in the spring of 1953. Doubtless several in the 400- to 500-pound bracket have been hooked and lost. "Average" sizes of white sturgeon landed by rod-and-reel methods are impossible to compute. Relatively few anglers seek the fish. The famous white-sturgeon waters, such as Idaho's Snake River, provide fishing for steelhead and chinook salmon with far more promise of success. A vacationing angler who devotes his time exclusively to the sturgeon may give up two weeks without a sign of a strike.

Many baits are used; perhaps the most favored is the lamprey or a whole smelt. The seemingly placid and almost bovine white sturgeon, peacefully grazing the bottom of a deep pool and by chance sucking in the smelt bait, may seem at first unaware that the fatal steel is inside the smelt, for his contemplative habits are unaccustomed to being thus outraged. Once he feels the hook, however, he may surge to the surface or buck back and forth like a steer before taking off on a straight run that will neither stop nor slow down until the angler's line is all off the reel and the weakest link of the terminal gear is severed by the unbrakable power of the fish.

Such a sturgeon may be 50 to 100 years old and still fairly active, considering its age and the imaginable condition of its arteries (though no evidence exists of arteriosclerosis among sturgeons). White sturgeon are estimated to live as long as 150 years in extreme cases. Huge specimens occasionally reported from headwaters far above dams may well have migrated thither and become landlocked long before the dams were built. Age determination of sturgeons is accomplished by a microscopic reading of the light and dark bands in a cross section of the first bony ray of the pectoral fin.

Female white sturgeons become sexually mature at thirteen to sixteen years, males slightly earlier. After an unknown time in Pacific coastal waters they ascend such rivers as the Columbia, Willamette, Umpqua, Rogue, and Fraser, to spawn. The heavy adhesive eggs are deposited in May, June, or later if the migration is a long one. A female eight or nine feet long and fifty years old may spawn three to four million eggs, equivalent to more than 100 pounds of caviar.

The white sturgeon has 11 to 14 dorsal shields, 36 to 50 lateral shields, and 9 to 12 ventral shields. The snout, rather sharp in young fish, becomes blunter in adults.

"California Sturgeon Tagging Studies,"[2] reporting on 62 returns from 994 white sturgeon tagged in San Pablo Bay in the fall of 1954, says one fish was recaptured on August 25, 1955, at the mouth of the Columbia River, 660 miles from the point of release. The returns, however, did not reveal a migratory pattern in this area. White sturgeon at sea evidently cruise for long distances along the coast but are inclined to stay close to shore.

The decline in the white-sturgeon commercial fishery is evident in the simple statistics. In the early 1890's the Columbia River catch

[2] Harold K. Chadwick, in *California Fish and Game*, October 1959.

exceeded five million pounds; today it is less than one-twentieth of that figure, and the fishery can be considered negligible. All the western states have tight angling restrictions, allowing only two or three fish a year in various waters and imposing both minimum and maximum length limits. Sturgeons above 72 inches are generally protected, for females of such size are potential spawners of a million or more fry.

GREEN STURGEON
Acipenser medirostris   Ayres

The smaller and less important of the two Pacific species, the green sturgeon has approximately the range of the white, but is rare south of San Francisco and not abundant north of Puget Sound. Al-

White Sturgeon

Top to bottom: Paddlefish, two Atlantic Sturgeon,
Shortnose Sturgeon, Lake Sturgeon

though it is considered anadromous, it spends most of its time in salt or brackish water. Little is known of its breeding habits, but probably it enters fresh water only a short way to spawn, or indeed may deposit its eggs in brackish tidewaters.

The green sturgeon is so called because of its olive-green basic color, over which are three longitudinal greenish stripes, one on the belly and one on each side above the row of ventral shields. Its dorsal shields number 9 to 11, the lateral 26 to 30, and the ventral 7 to 10. The snout is longer, proportionally, than that of the white sturgeon.

Though reported to reach seven feet and 350 pounds in rare instances, the green sturgeon probably averages well under 100 pounds. It is infrequently taken by anglers. Since its flesh is inferior, it has little or no commercial importance.

The green sturgeon's travels at sea approximate those of the white, as shown by the California tagging studies (footnote 2). Three specimens among twenty-five tagged in San Pablo Bay were later recovered 550 to 660 miles away—two in the mouth of the Columbia River and one in Winchester Bay, Oregon.

ATLANTIC STURGEON
Acipenser oxyrhynchus   Mitchill

Sometimes called the common sturgeon and sea sturgeon, the anadromous Atlantic species is the largest fish entering rivers of the eastern seaboard. Judging by recently taken specimens, which rarely have exceeded 350 pounds, the Atlantic sturgeon is undoubtedly second to the white sturgeon in size, but on the basis of earlier records it seems equal to the white. Canadian scientist Vadim D. Vladykov cites one of 14 feet and 811 pounds, from New Brunswick, in 1924.[3] Comparisons of the two species are perhaps meaningless, for certainly each has the capacity for great age and tremendous growth.

The Atlantic sturgeon's natural range extends from the Gulf of St. Lawrence to the Carolinas, with rare occurrence in Florida. The European sturgeon, Acipenser sturio, is close kin to the Atlantic; indeed, the two are considered identical by some scientists.

[3] "Sturgeons," Fishes of Quebec, Album No. 5, Department of Fisheries, Quebec.

This sturgeon's color is blue-black to dark olive from the top down to the lateral row of shields, gray below this line, and whitish on the belly. The middle of each shield in the dorsal and lateral rows is white. The shields number 10 to 14 in the dorsal series, 27 to 29 in the lateral, 8 to 11 in the ventral. Young specimens have a rather long and sharp snout which becomes blunter with age.

Males of this species are sexually mature at about the age of ten, at which time they may weigh seventy pounds. Females are relatively older and heavier when first ready to spawn. Entering rivers in the spring, at the time of the shad runs, the Atlantic sturgeon may not spawn until summer. Preferred sites are moving currents over gravel bottoms, at a depth of ten or twelve feet, rarely in brackish water, generally just above the reach of the tide, and sometimes much farther upstream. Large Atlantic sturgeon females spawn more than three million eggs. Small, heavy, and adhesive, they hatch in a week or two.

Tagging has revealed that the Atlantic sturgeon is a long-distance voyager with few equals among anadromous fishes. Dr. Vladykov reports that an individual tagged at Kamouraska, Quebec, on the St. Lawrence River, in 1945, was recaptured eight years later at Hermitage Bay, Newfoundland, probably 700 miles from the point of tagging. Another, tagged at the same spot, was retaken a year later near Halifax. This journey, probably involving a passage through the Cabot Strait at the north end of Cape Breton Island, was even longer, totaling some 900 miles. (See footnote 3.)

Angling for the Atlantic sturgeon has never been a widely practiced sport, and there is no official record of the largest fish on sporting tackle. Commercial fishermen, however, have caught this species in tremendous numbers. Intensive fishing, plus harbor pollution and up-river dams, have depleted Atlantic sturgeon populations almost to the vanishing point. William Penn was only one among thousands of early (and later) colonists in Pennsylvania and New Jersey to be impressed by the enormous size and great numbers of sturgeon in the lower Delaware River. The major sturgeon fishery in the Delaware did not begin until the 1850's, more than a hundred years after William Penn's death; less than seventy-five years after that it was ended except as a sporadic enterprise of a few hopeful netters. Today the Atlantic sturgeon is still taken in some numbers in Chesapeake Bay; elsewhere on the U.S. eastern seaboard it is a scarce fish indeed.

SHORTNOSE STURGEON
Acipenser brevirostrum   LeSueur

The shortnose is another Atlantic coast species which enters rivers to spawn. It is much smaller than the Atlantic sturgeon, averaging two to three feet. Its range is approximately from Cap Cod to Florida. It is more numerous south than north, though not abundant anywhere.

This lesser eastern sturgeon has a short, broad snout, olive-brown color, and separated rather than overlapping shields in the dorsal row. The dorsal shields number 8 to 11, the lateral 22 to 33, the ventral 6 to 9.

Little is known of this fish's spawning habits, but they are assumed to be similar to the Atlantic sturgeon's. The shortnose is of little interest to anglers and is unimportant commercially.

LAKE STURGEON
Acipenser fulvescens   Rafinesque

The lake sturgeon is strictly a freshwater fish, rarely showing up in tidal estuaries. Possibly it was a marine creature at some long-ago time. Even if it were another of the glacial relics in northern lakes today, which almost certainly it is not, to appraise its history on a mere 10,000 years is to affront its ancient lineage.

A giant among inland fishes, the lake sturgeon is capable of attaining eight feet and 300 pounds. Specimens taken by anglers and commercial fishermen, however, rarely exceed 100 pounds and most are much smaller.

The lake sturgeon's northerly range extends from Saskatchewan to Quebec and Lake Champlain. Southward it covers the Great Lakes and the Mississippi Valley to the Ohio and Missouri rivers. Once abundant in the Great Lakes, it is now greatly depleted in numbers, especially on the American side. There are still fair populations in Lake Champlain and the St. Lawrence river system.

In eastern Canada the lake sturgeon is called the rock sturgeon and, by the French, the camus. Elsewhere it has such names as red sturgeon, black sturgeon, rubbernose, Ohio sturgeon, and stone sturgeon. It is a fish not only of lakes, as its name implies, but of large rivers.

Differences between young and adult lake sturgeons are notable. The young have a suction disk on the snout, enabling them to rest by clinging to vegetation and stones. Before they have reached two feet in length they have dark spots on the snout and body, and rough shields bearing hooked spines. As adults they lose the suction cup and the spots, and the shields become flattened and spineless. Their color is a dark olive-brown along the back and sides, creamy white on the belly. The dorsal and lateral shields are the same color as the skin at these areas. Shield counts: dorsal series, 11 to 16; lateral, 30 to 39; ventral, 8 to 11. A muscular, gizzardlike stomach is doubtless useful in grinding up mollusks and crustaceans.

This species lives to venerable ages. The oldest recorded lake sturgeon was a fish of 152 years, caught in Lake of the Woods in 1953. Sexual maturity is reached at ages of fifteen to twenty-five, when the fish is about four feet long and weighs 25 to 30 pounds. The springtime spawning is in swift-flowing tributaries or over clean gravel bottoms of lake shoals. Several males wait upon a single female and the breeding is an active business for a while, featured by great splashings and rollings. Vladykov reports 650,000 eggs from a 40-pound female, and about three million from a 200-pounder. It is believed that spawning is not an annual rite with the lake sturgeon; there is evidence that females spawn every five or six years, males every other year.

Age-length-weight relationships are so variable as to be almost meaningless. Wisconsin scientists submit the following figures for lake sturgeon in the Lake Winnebago area:[4]

AGE (years)	MEAN LENGTH (inches)	MEAN WEIGHT (pounds)	WEIGHT RANGE (pounds)
10	35.7	9	5 to 18
15	44.5	18.9	7 to 38
20	49.8	29	15 to 42
30	60.6	54.9	28 to 99

[4] Robert T. Probst and Edwin L. Cooper, "Age, Growth and Production of the Lake Sturgeon in the Lake Winnebago Region, Wisconsin," reprinted from *Transactions of the American Fisheries Society,* Vol. 84 (1954).

The lake sturgeon is normally a more chunky fish than the Atlantic species, but these tabulations show that it may be fat or it may be lean. No difference is noted in the growth of males and females, but females live longer and thus attain greater sizes.

Sea lampreys in the Great Lakes prey upon the lake sturgeon, but the lampreys' invasion was too late to do widespread damage to A. *fulvescens*, for this great fish had long since been depleted throughout the Great Lakes. Its history reveals, as usual, that man has been its chief predator. John E. Williams, writing of the lake sturgeon,[5] says that prior to 1870 this fish had no use except as fertilizer. Hundreds of thousands taken by commercial fishermen were piled on shore and burned, to reduce their numbers and thus protect nets. By 1880, however, several sturgeon industries were in full stride, smoking the flesh and making caviar from the eggs, isinglass from the air bladders, and leather from the skins. Dr. Williams reports that the fishery in 1885, in Michigan waters of the Great Lakes, totaled 1.5 million pounds. By 1928 it had virtually evaporated to less than 2000 pounds. Similar declines are noted elsewhere.

In Canada there are still lake-sturgeon fisheries, particularly in Quebec, Ontario, and Manitoba. These are the sources of exports of caviar, and fresh and frozen sturgeon meat, to the United States.

Despite its declining numbers, the lake sturgeon is drawing more and more angling interest in Michigan, Wisconsin, and elsewhere, particularly on the part of the ice-fishermen, who spear the fish with the aid of wooden decoys. Michigan, having closed all sport and commercial fishing for the lake sturgeon in 1929, opened a winter spearing season in 1948, restricting the take to two sturgeon per angler per year, of 36 inches minimum size.

Wisconsin conservationists Probst and Cooper (see footnote 4) report that winter spearing of lake sturgeon in the Lake Winnebago area yielded 2838 fish weighing about 100,000 pounds, in the open season of February 1953. These sturgeon measured from 30 to 79 inches. Wisconsin increased the minimum length to 40 inches the following year, and now has an angler's "creel" limit of one lake sturgeon a year.

[5] *Michigan Conservation*, November–December 1951.

SHOVELNOSE STURGEON
Scaphirhynchus platorynchus (Rafinesque)

PALLID STURGEON
Scaphirhynchus albus (Forbes and Richardson)

These two minor freshwater species are of a different genus but could never be mistaken for anything but sturgeon.

The shovelnose, called hackleback, switchtail, and sand sturgeon, ranges through the Mississippi-Missouri river system, from Montana to the Gulf of Mexico. Throughout this range it is nowhere abundant, and is particularly scarce in northern waters. Apparently it is absent from the Great Lakes.

It is a small, very elongate, yellowish brown sturgeon, averaging four or five pounds. Features of the shovelnose are its broad, depressed, shovel-shaped snout, an extremely long and slender caudal peduncle which is armored all around with shields, and a long filament extending from the upper lobe of the tail. The last, accounting for the name "switchtail," may be absent from older specimens.

Though its flesh is excellent and its roe superior for caviar, the shovelnose is too small a sturgeon, and too scarce, to have any status as a sporting or commercial fish.

The pallid sturgeon, called rock sturgeon in some areas, is a bluish gray fish, larger than the shovelnose but small as sturgeons go, rarely more than four feet and fifteen pounds. Virtually absent to the northward, its range includes the more southerly Mississippi-Missouri drainages inhabited by the shovelnose.

Resembling the shovelnose in many respects, the pallid sturgeon can be identified by its color and other features. The snout is longer and sharper, the belly without scales (the shovelnose has small hard scales in this area), and the two inner barbels are only half as long as the outer.

PADDLEFISH
Polyodon spathula (Walbaum)

The paddlefish is another of the primitive fishes, a survivor of a very ancient life form, virtually unchanged in many millions of years. It is distantly related to the sturgeons, belonging to the same order, the Acipenseriformes, but to a different family, the Polyodontidae. In this family it is the only known species inhabiting waters of the United States.

A creature of mud-bottomed lakes and large rivers, the paddlefish has a broad geographical range: roughly the Mississippi-Missouri river system and the major drainages thereof, south to Louisiana and Texas, and west to Montana. In the upper Ohio-Allegheny river system it has been reported from Chautauqua Lake, New York.

The paddlefish derives its correct name (and such erroneous localisms as spoonbill cat and shovelnose cat) from the most curious of its many strange features. The snout is greatly extended into a broad, thin, flat, spatula-like protrusion, somewhat flexible, and about half as long as the fish's body from mouth to tail. Since the paddlefish often swims with its mouth open, feeding on plankton, the snout may have a stabilizing function and help to guide into the fish's mouth a stream from which plankton is strained. Bearing touch receptors and probably taste structures, the snout also may help in the selection of food.

The skin is smooth and scaleless except on the upper caudal lobe. The skeleton is largely cartilaginous; the vertebral column, as in the sturgeons, is a white, flexible, tubelike notochord. A grotesquely large flap on the gill cover, terminating in a long point, extends rearward to about the middle of the body. The tail is heterocercal, the vertebral column reaching out to the point of the upper lobe. The single large dorsal fin is situated far back, and the equally large anal is even more posterior. The over-all color varies from bluish gray or dull gray in some waters to olive-brown in others. The long opercular flap may be covered with dark spots.

A thickset fish, heavy in proportion to its body length, the paddlefish is capable of attaining huge size. Jordan and Evermann reported a specimen of six feet total length, four feet in greatest circumference, and 150 pounds in weight, from Lake Tippecanoe, Indiana, in the last century. The Iowa Conservation Commission records a 200-pounder from Lake Okoboji "many years ago." Paddlefish of such sizes are not reported today, but specimens of 30 to 60 pounds are common, and 90-pounders are not rare.[6]

[6] A Chinese species of paddlefish, inhabiting the Yangtze River, is said (probably with great exaggeration) to reach 20 feet.

Though the age of the paddlefish may be determined by microscopic observation of a small cross section of the jawbone, data on ages are not precise. The fish is believed to be very long-lived, and slow to reach maturity.

Until recently, virtually nothing was known of the spawning of the paddlefish. A midwestern industrialist with an ichthyological interest sponsored a long-standing offer of $1000 for a paddlefish specimen under two inches long. The prize was never claimed. This miasma of ignorance was eventually dispersed by Charles A. Purkett, Jr., of the Missouri Conservation Department, when he investigated paddlefish spawning on the Osage River fifty miles upstream from the Lake of the Ozarks, in 1960.[7] On April 20 of that year, after a freshet, Mr. Purkett observed what he believed to be paddlefish-spawning activity over a large gravel bar in rapid water opposite the mouth of Weaubleau Creek, an Osage tributary.

Verification of spawning came four days later, after a drop of seven feet in the water level, when eggs and newly hatched larval fry were found on the exposed gravel bar. Purkett reports that the eggs are non-adhesive when shed but acquire a sticky coating immediately after fertilization by the males. Adhesion to pebbles and rocks was so strong that some eggs were broken in the attempt to remove them. Once free from the eggs, the fry apparently descended at once to the headwaters of the Lake of the Ozarks, for post-spawning seining failed to capture any small paddlefish in the spawning area.

From his observations Mr. Purkett deduces that paddlefish require clean gravel bars and flowing water for their breeding. Since these are not present in the Lake of the Ozarks, the upstream spawning migration becomes necessary. Incidentally, a proposed reservoir and its dam, at Warsaw, Missouri, will block off the Osage River spawning run unless the dam is fitted with lifts to accommodate the paddlefish.

Since the paddlefish is a plankton eater, sifting out unwanted foods by a filtering system on the gill arches, it does not take baits. It has been caught in large numbers by "snagging"—casting one or more large hooks into schools or spawning congregations and dragging the rig across bottom until a paddlefish is hooked. This method, illegal in

[7] Charles A. Purkett, Jr., "Reproduction and Early Development of the Paddlefish," reprinted from *Transactions of the American Fisheries Society*, Vol. 90, No. 2 (April 1961).

some waters, has accounted for 100 tons or more of paddlefish annually in the Osage River, and is practiced elsewhere. Most states which allow snagging restrict it to short open seasons and severely limited catches per angler.

Commercially, the paddlefish has value for its flesh, and its roe can be made into a good grade of caviar. A considerable commercial fishery was operated on the Mississippi and major tributaries in the early 1900's, but has greatly declined because of overfishing, dams, and pollution.

GARS

Vestigial tough survivors of an ancient and once numerous family, the American gars today number five species composing a single genus. They are of the order Semionotiformes and the family Lepisosteidae.

The gars are essentially freshwater fishes, not anadromous though they sometimes enter salt water. All are featured by a long, cylindrical body, a large, beaklike, heavily toothed mouth, a single, posterior dorsal, rounded tail, and hard, interlocking, diamond-shaped ganoid scales. The gar's air bladder enables the fish to inhale air at the surface; thus it can thrive in turbid water where other fish would die for lack of oxygen.

Chiefly a warmwater fish, the gar is most abundant in the bayous, lakes, and sluggish rivers of the southern states and of Mexico, Central America, and the West Indies. Two species, however, occur in the Great Lakes and at least one in the inland waters of Ontario.

Seemingly sluggish by nature and appearing sometimes to doze near the surface, the gar can explode into swift and violent action when attacking its prey. Lesser gars are chiefly piscivorous; the food of the great alligator gar includes fishes, small animals, birds, reptiles, worms, mollusks, crustaceans. The gar's reputation is balanced between good and bad. Since its food may be dead or alive it is both a great scavenger and a help in controlling overpopulations of gizzard shad and other trash fish. On the other hand it is a predator upon game fishes and, to some extent, upon waterfowl.

Spawning of the gars occurs in March or April in the South, in May or June in the northerly range. The female sheds her adhesive

Top to bottom: Alligator Gar, Spotted Gar,
Longnose Gar, male and female Bowfins

eggs over bottom vegetation in weedy shallows. Gars are not reported to build nests or to guard the eggs or young.

The gar's meat is not sufficiently esteemed to give the fish much commercial importance. The eggs of some species are believed to be poisonous; in any case gar eggs are definitely not the material of caviar. The armorlike scales are sometimes fashioned into ornaments and other trinkets.

ALLIGATOR GAR
Lepisosteus spatula Lacépède

This is the largest of the gars and, according to dim legends in the deep South, may at one time have been the largest fish in American fresh waters. Unauthenticated and doubtless exaggerated tales of alligator gars fifteen to twenty feet long may be heard here and there in the bayou country. In any event, the alligator gar is a huge fish in its maximum sizes. Specimens of five or six feet are not uncommon in the lower Mississippi and its drainages. A Louisiana fish measured 9 feet 8½ inches and weighed 302 pounds. The sporting-tackle record belongs to an alligator gar of 279 pounds, 7 feet 9 inches long, taken in Texas from the Rio Grande River by Bill Valverde on December 2, 1951.

Despite the alligator gar's great size and ferocity, there is no verified instance of one attacking a man in the water. More or less commonly, however, fishermen have been bitten after the gar has been boated.

This species derives its name from its huge size and from the fact that its head is broad and triangular, somewhat like that of an alligator, and distinguished by two rows of big teeth on each side of the upper jaw.

The alligator gar ranges throughout the large sluggish rivers and the bayous, lakes, and even the small drainage ditches of the southern states and northern Mexico. It was previously known in the Mississippi as far north as Quincy, Illinois; today it is seldom reported above St. Louis and is probably absent from the Missouri River. Sometimes it swims into the salt waters of the Gulf at the Mississippi's mouth, particularly in areas where refuse is dumped.

The color is brownish or olive-gray on top, fading to lighter below. Spots are present on the fins of the young, but are usually absent from larger specimens.

Anglers take the alligator gar with a baited hook only by letting the fish swallow the bait, for the mouth is too tough to be pierced. Other methods are spearing, and snaring with a small fish tied in the middle of a wire noose.

LONGNOSE GAR
Lepisosteus osseus (Linnaeus)

The longnose is second in size to the alligator gar, attaining three to four feet in the North and occasionally above five feet in the South. The record specimen on sporting gear was a fish of 50 pounds 5 ounces, just a quarter inch over six feet, taken by Townsend Miller in the Trinity River, Texas, on July 30, 1954.

L. osseus is known from the lower Great Lakes, Lake Nipissing, Ontario, and the St. Lawrence River southward through the Mississippi basin. Along the Gulf coast it occurs from northwestern Florida to Texas. It seldom enters salt water.

Called gar pike and bony gar, the longnose is distinguished by an attenuated pair of jaws constituting a beak fifteen to twenty times as long as it is wide. Both jaws are strongly toothed. This gar is more highly colored than the alligator gar; in northern waters particularly its back is dark green, the sides lighter green to silvery, and the dorsal, anal, and caudal fins yellowish with dark spots.

The longnose is taken by anglers on live baits and artificial lures, but is scarcely edible and is considered a nuisance by commercial fishermen.

SPOTTED GAR
Lepisosteus oculatus (Winchell)

The spotted gar occurs rather sparsely in the shallow weedy bays of Lake Erie, more abundantly southward through the Mississippi system to the Gulf, and westward up the Missouri River.

It is a small gar, averaging about two feet in the North, somewhat larger southward. It is named for the large dark spots on the dorsal, anal, and caudal fins, the top of the head and both jaws. The beak is appreciably shorter than that of the longnose gar. The color is olive-green on the back, grayish green on the sides, pale gray along the belly.

SHORTNOSE GAR
Lepisosteus platostomus   Rafinesque

FLORIDA GAR
Lepisosteus platyrhincus   DeKay

The shortnose gar is abundant in the muddy rivers and occasionally in lakes of the Mississippi-Missouri system, and is sometimes reported from the salt waters of the Gulf. It closely resembles the longnose gar in color, but the spots on the dorsal, anal, and caudal fins are few or perhaps absent, and the beak is much broader and shorter.

The Florida gar has a restricted range in the Atlantic coastal streams of Florida and Georgia, but is quite abundant in this confined habitat. It may be spotted, vaguely striped, or without markings.

The shortnose and Florida gars are among the small species, rarely attaining a length of three feet. Both are taken by anglers, sometimes purposely but mostly when fishing for other species. They are seldom eaten, and have no commercial value.

BOWFIN
Amia calva   Linnaeus

The bowfin, another holdover from the ancient past, is unique in being the one surviving species, in American waters, not only of its genus, Amia, but of its family, Amiidae, and of its order Amiiformes.

This fish is virtually cylindrical in shape, but stout and thickset throughout, weighing perhaps five times the poundage of a gar of equal length. The bowfin is not notably a large fish, however, reaching about two feet at the maximum, at which length it may weigh twelve pounds, but averaging perhaps two to five pounds in most waters.

The bowfin is characterized by a large head and mouth, strong sharp teeth, a single very long dorsal fin with 47 to 51 close-cropped soft rays, and a broad rounded tail. The body is fully scaled, having 66 to 68 in a lengthwise row, but the head, gill covers, and cheeks are smooth-plated and scaleless. The color is dull brownish green along the back and upper sides, lighter green on the lower flanks and white on the underbody. Numerous dark, vertical to diagonal bars cover the bowfin's sides from the dorsal surface almost to the belly. The caudal fin is similarly barred, and the dorsal may have vague diagonal stripes. A distinguishing mark is a prominent black spot at the base of the caudal; in breeding males this spot is ringed with yellow or orange. Short barbels point forward from the area of the nostrils. A hard bony plate in the angle of the lower jaws is called the gular plate and is a feature of the bowfin possessed by no other freshwater fish. Like the gars, the bowfin has an air bladder which enables it to breathe air at the surface.

The range of the bowfin runs from the St. Lawrence River, Lake Champlain, and the inland lakes of Ontario to the Great Lakes (except Lake Superior) and southward through the Mississippi Valley to the Gulf. On the Atlantic slope, east of the Appalachians and north of the Carolinas, the bowfin is rare or absent. Throughout its range it is known by an odd variety of names: lawyer, lake lawyer, grindle, dogfish, mudfish, choupique, and speckled cat.

The bowfin prefers warmer sluggish rivers and the shallow weedy waters of bays, inlets, and lagoons. It spawns from April to June, the male contriving a round nest on sand or gravel bottoms or in vegetated patches of shoal water, where it may fertilize the eggs of several females. Eggs thus deposited in the nest of a single male may number 30,000 or more. The male guards them during the week or more of incubation, and herds the hatched fry until they can shift for themselves.

Strictly carnivorous, and a solitary, non-schooling predator, the bowfin competes with game fishes, particularly the largemouth bass and walleye, and eats the young of many game species. Lagler and Hubbs (1940), examining the stomach contents of 131 bowfins, found that game fishes composed 59.7 per cent of the food intake, forage fish 16.6 per cent, and the rest largely crayfish and frogs.[8] Like all predators, the bowfin can be valuable at times in checking overpopulations of trash fish.

Readily taking various live baits and artificial lures, and a strong fighter when hooked, the bowfin is admired by many anglers. The flesh is inferior, and among commercial fishermen the fish has little reputation except as an annoyance.

[8] Reported by Karl F. Lagler and William C. Latta, in *Michigan Fish Predators*, Michigan Department of Conservation, Lansing, February 1954.

Chapter 21

AMERICAN EEL AND THE LAMPREYS

AMERICAN EEL
Anguilla rostrata (LeSueur)

The American eel is a true fish, with articulated jaws and paired fins, and a unique creature in many respects. In our waters it is the only freshwater member of the order Anguilliformes, and is the single species of the family Anguillidae and the genus *Anguilla*. It is migratory in the fresh waters of the Atlantic side only, never occurring

295

in Pacific rivers. A close relative in Europe, of the same genus and similar migratory habits, is the European eel, *Anguilla vulgaris*.

Other eels—the morays, conger eels, snake eels, mustard eels, and spiny eels—are exclusively marine, numbering some forty-five species in American salt waters. Of these, all but six are native to the Atlantic. None of the eels is remotely related to the lampreys.

The freshwater eel has been familiar for centuries to naturalists and fishermen, and in Europe highly esteemed as food since the days of the Roman Empire. Yet virtually nothing was known of the eel's sex life until comparatively recent times, and the first definite clues to its remarkable migrations were not uncovered until early in the present century.

The Greeks, despite the advanced state of their thinking, had some comfortable and rather naïve notions about reproduction. Jupiter was generally credited as the sire of any offspring of uncertain paternity. In the case of the eel, however, Aristotle denied Jupiter this distinction since the mother, too, was not identified. In his *History of Animals* Aristotle held that eels were sexless, and arose from *ges entera*, "the entrails of the sea." Some three centuries later Pliny the Elder suggested that eels reproduced their kind by rubbing against rocks, and that the fragments thus loosened eventually became mature eels.

The first glimmer of truth shone faintly in 1777 when Carlo Mundini, a professor of anatomy at the University of Bologna, identified a pair of ovaries in a female eel. The male eel, historically the smaller and more obscure parent, maintained his sexual anonymity for nearly a century more, being identified in 1874 by a Polish biologist, Simone de Syrski.

Nothing was known of the eel's spawning migration until about 1900, when a Danish fisheries officer, E. Johannes Schmidt, found a tiny leptocephalus—the larval form of the eel—in the North Atlantic between Iceland and Scotland. In 1904 Schmidt was commissioned to study the origins and migratory habits of the eel, and his researches are credited as the basis of the current knowledge.[1]

The American eel is unique among our fishes in being catadromous (from the Greek *kata*, "down," and *dromos*, "running"). Its spawn-

[1] Lorus and Margery Milne, *Paths Across the Earth* (Harper & Row, New York, 1958).

American Eels

ing migration is the reverse of that of the salmon, shad, and other anadromous fishes. The mature eel returns from fresh water to its native ocean to spawn, and dies after spawning in the depths of the sea. Its progeny then migrate from the ocean to fresh water.

The inland range of the American eel includes virtually all fresh waters tributary to the Atlantic, from Labrador to Panama. Entering rivers from the sea, the male eel rarely moves much above tidewater and may spend years in brackish estuaries. The female, however, often migrates hundreds of miles upstream, surmounting dams, negotiating tunnels, aqueducts, and underground streams, sometimes traveling over flooded or even dew-wet fields, and turning up eventually in a pond or lake with no apparent access to any sea-connected river.

The eel is known up the Mississippi as far north as Minnesota; it ascends the Missouri River to Kansas and Nebraska, the Ohio to western Pennsylvania. Its presence in the Great Lakes above Niagara Falls may be attributed to the Welland Ship Canal. Landlocked in many lakes, the eel is able to live in a permanent freshwater habitat, but cannot breed there. In the landlocked state eel populations will disappear unless periodically replenished by fresh introductions.

For the mature American eel must spawn in salt water—in that area of the Atlantic Ocean known as the Sargasso Sea, lying between Bermuda and the Bahamas, in latitudes 20° to 32° N., and longitudes 60° to 78° W. The European eel has a spawning ocean area running eastward to 52° W., its westerly edge slightly overlapping the American eel's spawning waters. In this region all American and European eels are born, and to it all except the permanently landlocked return, after years in fresh water, to spawn for the first and only time, and then to die.

Details of the eels' spawning are as yet not fully known. The eggs are believed to be shed deep down in the sea, during the winter or early spring, and to number from 10 million to 20 million for a large female. The eggs drift in the sea until hatching into the larval forms called leptocephali ("thin heads"). The newly hatched leptocephalus is a curious pale transparent creature, flat and leaflike in shape, half an inch long, with a definitely-formed head in which are tiny black eyes and jaws armed with sharp teeth. Drifting and swimming now in multitudes, gradually rising surfaceward, glinting perhaps like a myriad flakes of metal in the sunlit sea, and guided ever coastward by an apparently errorless impulse, the leptocephali reach American shores in the following winter or early spring, about a year after hatching.[2]

[2] The European leptocephali, on their longer migration northeastward, are helped by the Gulf Stream, but need more than two years to reach their coasts. Some accompany the American leptos for a short distance, then diverge toward their parental shores.

Having attained a length of nearly three inches, the leptos now inexplicably shrink to perhaps two inches, and lose their teeth, in the transformation to "glass eels." In this second stage they are still whitish and transparent but have achieved in miniature the eel shape, the gill covers, the paired pectoral fins, and the long combined fin which is dorsal, caudal and anal, all in one. As they enter fresh water they acquire a dark, grayish pigmentation, and are known as elvers. Now the females begin that other and equally extraordinary upstream migration which may persist beyond a thousand miles.

The catadromous eel, as contrasted to the anadromous salmon and shad, achieves virtually all its growth in fresh water. After eight to twelve years upriver, or in her ultimately chosen lake or pond,

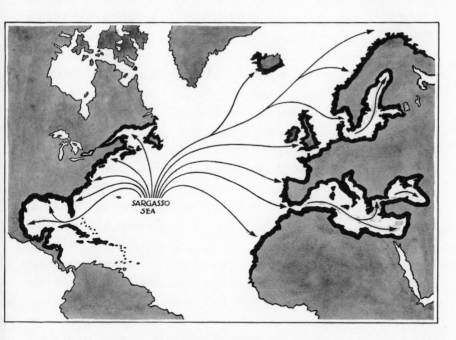

Eel Migration

The common American (*Rostrata*) and European (*Vulgaris*) freshwater eels spawn in the Sargasso Sea near Bermuda. The female larvae of *Rostrata* enter rivers along the coast of America; those of *Vulgaris* cross the Atlantic and enter the rivers of Europe and Africa.

the female has attained a length of two to three feet, rarely four feet and seven pounds. She has acquired the colors all fishermen know: olive-brownish or greenish on top, fading to yellow-green on the sides and white on the belly. The mouth is large and strongly toothed, and the lower jaw projects. The long combined dorsal-caudal-anal fin has about 100 soft rays. The scales are very small and deeply embedded. The well-known mucous coating is believed to enable the eel to live for some time out of water. The American eel has 103 to 110 vertebrae in the spinal column, differing from the European's 110 to 119.

In her far-inland haunt, the female eel eventually knows the onset of the reproductive impulse and the attendant urge to head back to sea. Now on the verge of her maturity she turns a very dark blackish brown. As the females migrate toward the ocean, traveling mostly at night, they are joined in the lower reaches of the river by the smaller and earlier-maturing males, twelve to sixteen inches long, which have spent their briefer freshwater lives not far from the sea.

Little is known of the route back to the native Sargasso. Probably it is deep rather than surfaceward, for a pre-spawning enlargement of the eyes is known to occur, at least in the European eel, and one function of this transformation may be to provide dim-light vision. V. D. Vladykov states, "So far not one American eel has been observed in the final stage of development, that is to say with large eyes."[3] In the ocean journey to the spawning waters perhaps succeeding generations follow the same course from each river mouth. These are still speculative quantities; in any event this voyage is one from which there is no return.

The last of the mature eels are believed to be out of Atlantic-coast rivers by the end of November. Presumably they reach the Sargasso by mid-winter. In fresh water they have been omnivorous feeders, seizing upon any living or dead animal matter; but now on this ultimate journey they forsake all food. The seaward males have turned dark also; the gonads virtually fill their body cavities, and doubtless they are as exhausted as any Atlantic salmon upon reaching the spawning grounds. They breed and die, and shortly the little leaf-like leptocephali begin the new cycle.

[3] "Eels," *Fishes of Quebec*, Album No. 6, Department of Fisheries, Quebec.

Few studies have been made of the maximum life span of the American eel. In Europe, where the eel is far more popular as a food fish, aquarium specimens have lived twenty-five years. Probably such ages are achieved by landlocked females which never spawn. Possibly the oldest eel of record was a Swedish specimen reported by Dr. V. D. Vladykov. This eel was caught in 1863 at the age of three, and kept in captivity until 1948. Many successive owners inherited it before it died at eighty-eight in the Museum of Hälsingborg.

Wherever it abides in numbers the eel is easily caught on worms and other baits by anglers who appreciate its high virtue as food. Popular squeamishness, however, has kept the eel from its deserved niche as a food fish, and the commercial fishery is not extensive. Here and there individual entrepreneurs operate eel traps and profit thereby from the local and tourist trade. In the Province of Quebec the eel fishery has been quite substantial, running in recent years around 700,000 pounds annually, via traps, seines and set lines. Much of this catch is frozen and exported; also, as reported by Vladykov, about 100,000 pounds of live eels are shipped annually from Quebec to the United States, particularly for Italian consumption during the Christmas–New Year season.

The eel is despised and feared by commercial shad fisherman in some rivers as a serious predator upon shad caught in gill nets. Elsewhere it is considered destructive of young salmon and trout.

LAMPREYS

Though eel-like in appearance and popularly called lamprey eels or lamper eels, the lampreys have not the slightest kinship to the true eels. They are among the most primitive of all higher animal forms, more ancient than the sturgeons, belonging to the class Agnatha, or jawless fishes, the order Petromyzontiformes, and the family Petromyzontidae. Their nearest but still very distant relatives in American waters are the hagfishes, sometimes called slime eels, which are of a different order and exclusively marine.

The American lampreys include fourteen species, ten of which are strictly freshwater dwellers, most of them small, non-parasitic and harmless. Of the four marine species, three are anadromous in Pacific rivers, one in Atlantic drainages. The last is the so-called sea lamprey, whose devastation of the lake trout and whitefish in the Great Lakes has brought the entire tribe of lampreys into national focus in recent years.

The lampreys are distinguished from the eels and fishes by various easily discernible features. They have no jaws; the mouth is a circular suction disk, which in the parasitic species is exceptionally large and fitted with strong teeth and a rasplike tongue. Where a fish has a gill cover a lamprey has seven circular porelike openings in a straight line on each side, immediately back of the head. The lamprey has a smooth slippery skin in place of scales, and several series of minute sensory pores in place of a lateral line. Dorsal and caudal fins are present, but the paired fins (pectoral and ventral) are absent. The anal fin is lacking or is represented by a rudimentary fold.

Once in their lives all lampreys, whether freshwater or marine, ascend streams to spawn, and all die after spawning.

SEA LAMPREY
Petromyzon marinus Linnaeus

Originally the sea lamprey was a wholly marine species, reaching its maturity in the Atlantic Ocean from Labrador to Chesapeake Bay, rarely to Florida, and entering Atlantic rivers in the spring to spawn and die. Long ago it entered Lake Ontario and several of the inland lakes of New York. In these lakes it became landlocked, spawning and dying in the tributary streams.

The Welland Ship Canal, completed in 1829, provided navigation from Lake Ontario around Niagara Falls to Lake Erie, but apparently no sea lamprey utilized this passage for nearly a century. The canal was deepened in the years 1913–18; on November 8, 1921, the first known sea lamprey in Lake Erie was taken by a Canadian commercial fisherman. The species appeared not to thrive in Lake Erie's warmer waters, but by the 1930's it had reached Lake Michigan and Lake Huron, and had begun to multiply in earnest. Here the late trout and whitefish were abundant enough to become the lamprey's favorite prey, and the colder and deeper waters and gravel-bottomed spawning tributaries proved ideal for growth and survival. The invasion of Lake Superior, though delayed by navigation locks at the head of the St. Marys River, followed in due course. Specimens were taken off Whitefish Point, Michigan, and near Isle Royale, in 1946.[4]

What followed is a chapter in the history of American fisheries as tragic as the decline of the salmon. Norman S. Baldwin, executive secretary of the Great Lakes Fishery Commission, reports it in a few statistics. In the 1930's the commercial lake-trout catch from lakes Huron, Michigan, and Superior averaged 14,800,000 pounds a year. In 1961 these three lakes yielded less than half a million pounds, mostly from Lake Superior.[5]

As of today, because of sea lamprey predation, the lake trout is commercially extinct in lakes Michigan and Huron. The economic loss incident to the decline of the sports fishery cannot be calculated, but certainly amounts to many millions of dollars. Having virtually killed off the lake trout, the lamprey turned to whitefish and ciscoes, and has made serious inroads upon these species.

The sea lamprey preys upon its freshwater victims and upon cod, haddock, salmon, and many others at sea, by attaching its suction mouth to the fish, rasping a hole with its teeth and tongue, and sucking out the blood and body fluids of the host. Moreover, lamphedrin, a substance in the lamprey's saliva, prevents clotting of the victim's blood. This feeding ceases only when the host dies or the attacker becomes surfeited or, rarely, when the lamprey is shaken off. Sometimes two or more lampreys attach themselves to a single fish. If the fish escapes it may die from the wound and loss of blood; if it survives, its wound makes it vulnerable to parasites and infections, and the three-quarter-inch scar may render it unmarketable. During the sea lamprey's parasitic stage—a period of twelve to twenty months in the Great Lakes—it may kill thirty to forty pounds of fish. The parasitic period may be longer at sea, with a proportionally greater kill of fish.

The sea lamprey's identifying marks are its color, its size and, chiefly, its month. Adults are slate-blue to brownish, irregularly spotted on the sides, grayish below. Largest of the lampreys, they

[4] Lola T. Dees, Sea Lamprey (U.S. Fish and Wildlife Service, March 1961).
[5] "Closing in on a Silent Killer," reprinted from New York State Conservationist (December–January 1962–63).

Lake Trout with Lampreys

attain a length of two to two and a half feet, rarely three. The mouth, with a diameter exceeding that of the body, is lined with circular rows of teeth, many of them bicuspid, the larger teeth in the inner rows surrounding the filelike tongue. There are two dorsal fins, well separated in anadromous lampreys, closer together in the landlocked. The angular caudal is separated by a notch from the second dorsal.

After entering a lake cove or saltwater estuary in late winter, the lamprey's sexual equipment grows while its digestive system shrinks and degenerates. Now it ceases to feed and lives upon its stored fat.

As the water warms to about 50° F., it enters a tributary to spawn on a gravel bottom in flowing water. Both male and female construct a nest by picking up small stones with their suction-cup mouths and depositing them in an arc at the downstream end of the space thus cleared. Large female landlocked lampreys may lay 100,000 eggs; sea-run females are said to spawn more than 200,000. Shortly after spawning, both male and female die.

The larvae hatch in two or three weeks and remain in the nest perhaps three weeks more. They then emerge, drift downstream to still water, and burrow into a mud bottom. Here they remain for five to seven years, occasionally ten or eleven years, blind and harmless, with only their mouths exposed at the upper end of their almost vertical burrows. Feeding on the microscopic life of the stream as it drifts by, the ammocoete, as the lamprey is called at this stage, attains a growth of five to seven inches. When its inner processes decree that it is ready for transformation into its parasitic adulthood, it develops eyes and the toothed suction mouth, and emerges from its burrow, usually in early spring, to descend to the lake or the ocean and begin its predatory career.

A thoroughgoing and costly campaign to control the Great Lakes sea lamprey is in progress. Cooperative research sponsored by seven Great Lakes states, the Province of Ontario, and the federal governments of the United States and Canada was begun in 1947, under the direction of Vernon Applegate, a U.S. government fisheries scientist. Control efforts were focused upon preventing adult lampreys from entering streams to spawn.

Mechanical weirs were tried first, but proved expensive in proportion to their effectiveness and vulnerable to destruction by floods. They were largely supplanted by electric weirs. These blocked upstream traffic by producing an electrical field in the water and guiding all upstream migrants into traps. Lampreys so caught were destroyed.

Although the weirs succeeded in capturing many mature lampreys on their way upstream to spawn, they had no effect on larvae already upstream, some of which may remain in their burrows ten or eleven years.

The focus of attack then shifted to the larvae and to a selective poison as the weapon. The Great Lakes Fishery Commission was established, in 1954, to survey the distribution of lamprey larvae and to direct chemical and electric-weir operations and lake-trout rehabilitation. This work is supported by an appropriation of about $1,300,000 annually, 69 per cent from the United States and 31 per cent from Canada.

Mr. Baldwin reports that by 1957 the Commission was operating 108 electric barriers. Some six thousand chemicals were tested at the Hammond Bay, Michigan, laboratory of the U.S. Fish and Wildlife Service. Among them, a fluorinated nitrophenol was found lethal to lamprey larvae at two parts per million parts of water, but harmless to fish at concentrations below seven parts per million. As of October 1962, chemically treated streams numbered 150. Many more are scheduled for treatment. Meanwhile, some electric weirs are being retained to help interpret changes in lamprey populations.

Though the poison kills lampreys of all year-classes up to twelve years, some larvae survive the treatment in protected locations where back eddies prevent the poison from reaching them. Also, new larval populations are constantly being discovered in streams hitherto untreated.

The anti-lamprey campaign is a huge, painstaking, and often discouraging job, but hopeful signs are beginning to show. Catches of lampreys at all electric-barrier sites decreased significantly between 1957 and 1963. Incidence of lamprey wounds on lake trout have shown a comparable decline, and the average size of captured lake trout has increased. Also, in 1963, some mature female lake trout showed up in the biological samples—an event not witnessed for a number of years in Lake Superior. Mr. Baldwin points out that up to the fall of 1961 the incidence of lake-trout wounds had followed a distinct pattern: high in the fall, winter, and spring; low in the summer, after mature lampreys had entered tributaries to spawn and die; then increasing rapidly in September as the new age group migrated to the lake to renew the attack. A marked change occurred in this pattern in 1961. Scarring remained relatively low in all areas, showing a 95-per cent decrease in some. This trend continues, as of the close of 1963.

Even, however, if the sea lamprey can be controlled in the Great Lakes, there remains the problem of restoring the lake trout to anything approaching former numbers. So far, the lake-trout comeback lags. Natural reproduction has fallen so low that repopulation must depend upon hatchery fish for some time to come.

As of late 1962, some 70,000 brood lake trout were available in various state and federal hatcheries. Since 1958, planted fingerlings have numbered several millions, with high survival indicated. These, however, are but a small fraction of natural lake-trout reproductions in the pre-lamprey era.

Some hope is based on selective breeding. A hybrid called "splake"—a cross between the eastern brook trout and the lake trout (both chars), and a further backcross between the splake and the lake trout are being bred and stocked. These fish will grow as large as a lake trout, and mature earlier. The splake female at three years is mature and weighs three and a half pounds; the lake trout female is usually not mature until seven years old.

Oddly, the sea lamprey has annually run up the rivers of Maine, New York, and other eastern states for centuries past without causing a small fraction of the havoc it has perpetrated in the Great Lakes. It enters the Hudson River and its tributaries; in the Delaware it spawns as high as the Beaverkill and Willowemoc. It has been land-locked for ages in Lake Champlain and in New York's Cayuga and Seneca Lakes. In none of these are there reports of serious depletion of lake trout, though considerable scarring has been noted in Seneca.

An exceptional report of lamprey predations comes from John R. Greeley of the New York State Conservation Department. Lampreys formerly spawned well up the East Branch of the Delaware River, but since the Pepacton Reservoir was completed they can no longer ascend above its dam. However, lampreys grown to adulthood from previous spawnings upstream have descended to the reservoir and attacked large brown trout. Some have run out of Pepacton via the long tunnel to the Rondout Reservoir, and have there fastened upon other large browns. So far, there is no record of fatal attacks, and little apprehension is voiced.

In these waters the threat, if any, is against the sport fishery. In the Great Lakes the accent has been on the commercial fishery. Ultimate victory over the Great Lakes lamprey may take several decades. Meanwhile, the high cost of the campaign, and the question of an adequate return on the investment, cannot be ignored. Dr. John E.

Bardach of the School of Natural Resources, University of Michigan, has been and continues to be close to the anti-lamprey work. In a letter to this writer, in October 1963, Dr. Bardach pointed out that the old-timers in the commercial lake-trout fishery have dropped out and there is no incentive for the younger generation to take their place. In this situation the continued spending of millions of dollars to restore a commercial fishery may well be unwarranted. On the other hand, an investment to build a sport fishery to meet the recreational demands of the future, in an area of vastly increasing population, could yield a substantial return. Dr. Bardach sees such economic considerations as receiving too little recognition in the often emotional thinking about the lake trout–lamprey problem. "The predator's case," he emphasizes, "depends entirely on what value we place on the animals it lives on."

PACIFIC LAMPREY
Lampetra tridentata (Gairdner)

This is another marine species, anadromous in rivers from southern California to Alaska. Ascending far up the Columbia and other rivers, it has been landlocked in some high lakes. Smaller than its eastern counterpart, the Pacific lamprey averages about twelve inches, is dark brown to almost black, and is favored as a bait for the white sturgeon. Its parasitic life is chiefly confined to salt water, where it preys upon salmon, steelheads, and various marine fishes.

SILVER LAMPREY
Ichthyomyzon unicuspis Hubbs and Trautman

The silver lamprey is strictly a freshwater species, a parasite upon fishes as the sea lamprey is, but causing only minor damage because of its smaller size and relative scarcity. It is present in all the Great Lakes, though rare in Lake Ontario, and is reported from the St. Lawrence drainages, including Lake Champlain. Westward, the silver lamprey occurs in Lake of the Woods and well down the Mississippi system of lakes and rivers.

The common name of this lamprey derives from its silvery blue color; the scientific name stems from its inner row of unicuspid teeth. It is further distinguished from the sea lamprey by its single, long dorsal fin. The caudal is broad and oval, rather than angular, and is rather widely separated from the dorsal. As with other parasitic lampreys, the mouth has a greater diameter than the body.

The silver lamprey seldom exceeds a foot and averages less. The spawning female casts about 10,000 eggs; thereafter the cycles of the ammocoetes and adults approximate those of the sea lamprey, although the parasitic period is believed not to exceed a year.

AMERICAN BROOK LAMPREY
Lampetra lamottei (LeSueur)

NORTHERN BROOK LAMPREY
Ichthyomyzon fossor   Reighard and Cummins

These are small, non-parasitic and thus harmless lampreys, exclusively of fresh waters, inhabiting the clearer and swifter brooks and creeks of the eastern and midwestern United States and southern Canada.

The northern brook lamprey is the smallest of the tribe, averaging about five inches. It is sharply bicolored, the dark gray-brown of the back and sides ending abruptly at the silver-white belly. The American brook lamprey may be six or seven inches long, and its color fades gradually from blue-gray or brownish above to pale gray below. Both have small mouths with weak teeth arranged in clusters rather than in the radiating circles typical of the parasitic lampreys.

The northern brook female spawns about 1000 eggs, the American brook up to 3000. Both are worthy of note perhaps only because they illustrate an extraordinary difference between the harmless and the destructive lampreys. When the non-parasitic species emerge from their burrows as adults, in the fall, they have well-developed reproductive organs but their digestive tracts are degenerate and nonfunctioning. They spend the winter completely without food, spawn in the spring, and then die.

BIBLIOGRAPHY

American Fisheries Society, McLean, Va. *A List of Common and Scientific Names of Fishes from the United States and Canada*, 2nd Ed., 1960.

ANDERSON, LELAND R. "A Note on the Capture of Smallmouth Bass by Angling through the Ice," reprinted from *Copeia*, Michigan Department of Conservation, September 12, 1947.

ANDREWS, C. W., and LEAR, E. *The Biology of the Arctic Char in Northern Labrador*, Fisheries Research Board of Canada Biological Station, St. John's, Newfoundland.

BALDWIN, NORMAN S. "Closing in on a Silent Killer," reprinted from *New York State Conservationist*, December–January 1962–63.

BANCROFT, HUBERT H. *History of Alaska, 1730–1888*, Antiquarian Press, New York, 1958.

BREDER, CHARLES M., JR. *Field Book of Marine Fishes of the Atlantic Coast*, G. P. Putnam's Sons, New York, 1948.

BREZOSKY, PETER E. *Observations on the Golden Trout*, Salvelinus aureolus, *in Tewksbury Pond, Grafton, New Hampshire*. New Hampshire Fish and Game Department, Concord.

BROWN, C. J. D., and MOFFETT, J. W. "Observations on the Number of Eggs and Feeding Habits of the Cisco in Swains Lake, Jackson County, Michigan," reprinted from *Copeia*, October 8, 1942.

BROWN, JOHN T. *A Report on Fisheries Investigations and the Selective Treatment of Lake Talquin in 1961*, Florida Game and Fresh Water Fish Commission, April 1962.

CARBINE, W. F. "Observations on the Spawning Habits of Centrarchid Fishes in Deep Lake, Oakland County, Michigan," reprinted from *Transactions of the Fourth North American Wildlife Conference*, 1939.

———. *The Pike—A Prized and Spurned Fish*, Michigan Department of Conservation, April 1947.

CHADWICK, HAROLD K. "California Sturgeon Tagging Studies," from *California Fish and Game*, October 1959.

CHENEY, A. N. "Shad of the Hudson River," from *First Annual Report of the Commissioners of Fisheries, Game and Forests*, State of New York, 1896.

COOLEY, RICHARD A. *Politics and Conservation*, Harper & Row, New York, 1963.

CROWE, WALTER E. "Numerical Abundance and Use of a Spawning Run of Walleyes in the Muskegon River, Michigan," reprinted from *Transactions of the American Fisheries Society*, Vol. 84 (1954).

DAVIS, BARNET H. et. al. *First Annual Report of the Commissioners of Fisheries, Game and Forest*, State of New York, 1896.

DAVIS, JAMES T., and POSEY, LLOYD E., JR. *Length at Maturity of Channel Catfish in Louisiana*, Louisiana Wildlife and Fisheries Commission, Baton Rouge, 1958.

DEES, LOLA T. *The Mosquitofish*, Fish and Wildlife Service, U.S. Department of the Interior, September 1961.

————. *Sea Lamprey*, Fish and Wildlife Service, U.S. Department of the Interior, March 1961.

————. *Sturgeons*, Fish and Wildlife Service, U.S. Department of the Interior, September 1961.

DONALDSON, LAUREN R., and ALLEN, GEORGE H. "Return of Silver Salmon to Point of Release," reprinted from *Transactions of the American Fisheries Society*, Vol. 87 (1957).

DRUCKER, PHILIP. *Indians of the Northwest Coast*, McGraw-Hill Book Co., New York, 1955.

DUFRESNE, FRANK. *Alaska's Animals and Fishes*, A. S. Barnes & Co., New York, 1946.

ESCHMEYER, PAUL H.; DALY, RUSSELL; and ERKKILA, LEO F. "The Movements of Tagged Lake Trout in Lake Superior, 1950–1952," reprinted from *Transactions of the American Fisheries Society*, Vol. 82 (1952).

————. *Life History of the Walleye in Michigan*, Michigan Department of Conservation, June 1, 1952.

EVERHART, W. HARRY. *Fishes of Maine*, Maine Department of Inland Fisheries and Game, Augusta, 1961.

FORNEY, J. L., and EIPPER, A. W. "Oneida Lake Walleyes," reprinted from *New York State Conservationist*, February–March 1961.

GREELEY, JOHN R. *Survivals of Planted Atlantic Salmon in Lake George*, New York State Conservation Department; published by American Fisheries Society, September 22, 1953.

HACKER, VERNON A. "Biology and Management of Lake Trout in Green Lake, Wisconsin," reprinted from *Transactions of the American Fisheries Society*, Vol. 86 (1956).

HAIG-BROWN, RODERICK L. "Canada's Pacific Salmon," reprinted from *Canadian Geographical Journal* by the Department of Fisheries of Canada, Ottawa, 1956.

HARLAN, JAMES R., and SPEAKER, EVERETT B. *Iowa Fish and Fishing*, State of Iowa, 1956.

HAZZARD, ALBERT S. "The Walleye—Fish of Mystery," reprinted from *Michigan Conservationist*, July–August 1951.

HELM, WILLIAM T. "A 'New' Fish in Wisconsin," from *Wisconsin Conservation Bulletin*, July 1958.

HENSHALL, JAMES A. *Culture of the Montana Grayling*, U.S. Fisheries Station, Bozeman, Mont., 1907.

HOURSTON, ALAN S. *The Food and Growth of the Maskinonge in Canadian Waters*, Fisheries Research Board of Canada, 1952.

JONES, J. W. *The Salmon*, Harper & Row, New York, 1959.

JORDAN, DAVID STARR, and EVERMANN, BARTON WARREN. *American Food and Game Fishes*, Doubleday, Page & Co., New York, 1902.

KRUMHOLZ, LOUIS A. "Northward Acclimatization of the Western Mosquitofish," University of Michigan; reprinted from *Copeia*, June 30, 1944.

LAGLER, KARL F., and LATTA, WILLIAM C. *Michigan Fish Predators*, Michigan Department of Conservation, Lansing, February 1954.

LAMONTE, FRANCESCA. *North American Game Fishes*, Doubleday & Co., Inc., Garden City, N.Y., 1958.

LANGLOIS, T. H. "Observations on Bait Culture," *Ohio Conservation Bulletin*, 1941.

LEONARD, JUSTIN W. "Feeding Habits of the Montana Grayling in Ford Lake, Michigan," Michigan Department of Conservation; reprinted from *Transactions of the American Fisheries Society*, Vol. 68 (1938).

LORENZ, KONRAD Z. *King Solomon's Ring*, Thomas Y. Crowell Co., New York, 1952.

McCAMMON, GEORGE W. "A Tagging Experiment with Channel Catfish in the Lower Colorado River," reprinted from *California Fish and Game*, October 1956.

McCRIMMON, H. R., and DEVITT, O. E. "Winter Studies of the Burbot of Lake Simcoe, Ontario," from *Canadian Fish Culturist*, Issue 16, August 1954.

McNAUGHT, DONALD C. and HASLER, ARTHUR D. "Surface Schooling and Feeding Behavior of the White Bass in Lake Mendota (Wisconsin)," reprinted from *Limnology and Oceanography*, January 1961.

MIGDALSKI, EDWARD C. *Angler's Guide to the Fresh Water Sport Fishes of North America*, The Ronald Press Co., New York, 1962.

MILLER, ROBERT RUSH. *Preliminary List of Rare, Restricted, and/or Threatened North American Freshwater Fishes*, Museum of Zoology, University of Michigan, May 1963.

314

MILNE, LORUS J. and MARGERY. *Paths Across the Earth*, Harper & Row, New York, 1958.

MRAZ, DONALD. "The Movements of Yellow Perch Marked in Southern Green Bay, Lake Michigan, in 1950," reprinted from *Transactions of the American Fisheries Society*, Vol. 81 (1951).

NEWELL, ARTHUR E. *The Life History and Ecology of the Sunapee Trout*, New Hampshire Fish and Game Department, Concord, 1958.

NIEMUTH, WALLACE; CHURCHILL, WARREN; and WIRTH, THOMAS. *The Walleye—Its Life History, Ecology, and Management*, Wisconsin Conservation Department, 1959.

NOBBS, PERCY E. *Things Known and Knowable about the Atlantic Salmon*, Atlantic Salmon Association, Montreal, July 1949.

OEHMCKE, ARTHUR A. et. al. *The Wisconsin Muskellunge—Its Life History, Ecology, and Management*, Wisconsin Conservation Department, Madison, 1958.

Pacific Fisherman, Seattle, January 25, 1963.

POWER, G. "The Evolution of Freshwater Races of the Atlantic Salmon," reprinted from *Arctic*, Vol. 11, No. 2.

PRITT, T. E. *The Book of the Grayling*, Goodall and Suddick, London, 1888.

PROBST, ROBERT T. and COOPER, EDWIN L. "Age, Growth and Production of the Lake Sturgeon in the Lake Winnebago Region, Wisconsin," reprinted from *Transactions of the American Fisheries Society*, Vol. 84 (1954).

PURKETT, CHARLES E., JR. "Reproduction and Early Development of the Paddlefish," reprinted from *Transactions of the American Fisheries Society*, Vol. 90, No. 2, April 1961.

RANEY, EDWARD C. "Perch," reprinted from *New York State Conservationist*.

ROECKER, ROBERT M. "*Osmerus Mordax*—the Smelt," reprinted from *New York State Conservationist*, April–May 1961.

RUCKER, W. E. "Pacific Salmon for Atlantic Waters?" from *Canadian Fish Culturist*, Issue 16, August 1954.

RUPP, ROBERT S. "American Smelt," from *Fishes of Maine*, Maine Department of Inland Fisheries and Game, Augusta, 1961.

SCOTT, W. B. *Freshwater Fishes of Eastern Canada*, 2nd Ed., University of Toronto Press, Toronto, 1955.

SHAPOVALOV, LEO, and TAFT, ALAN C. *The Life Histories of the Steelhead Rainbow Trout and Silver Salmon*, California Department of Fish and Game, 1954.

SMEDLEY, HAROLD H. *Trout of Michigan*, privately printed, 1938.

SPENCE, MERRILL H. "Spiny Ray Fishes in Washington," from *Washington State Game Bulletin*, July 1958.

TALBOT, GERALD B. *The American Shad*, U.S. Fish and Wildlife Service, February 1961.

U.S. Fish and Wildlife Service. *Intertidal Spawning of Pink Salmon*.

VAN OOSTEN, JOHN. *The Smelt*, Michigan Department of Conservation, March 1953.

VLADYKOV, VADIM D. "Trout," *Fishes of Quebec*, Album No. 1, Department of Fisheries, Quebec.

————. "Atlantic Salmon," *Fishes of Quebec*, Album No. 2, Department of Fisheries, Quebec.

————. "Sturgeons," *Fishes of Quebec*, Album No. 5, Department of Fisheries, Quebec.

————. "Eels," *Fishes of Quebec*, Album No. 6, Department of Fisheries, Quebec.

————. *Les Formes Locales de la Truite Rouge du Québec*, Département des Pécheries, Province de Québec, 1957.

————. *Movements of Quebec Shad as Demonstrated by Tagging*, Department of Fisheries, Quebec, 1950.

WARFEL, HERBERT E. *Biological Survey of the Connecticut Watershed*, New Hampshire Fish and Game Department, Concord, 1939.

WARNER, KENDALL. "Migrations of Landlocked Salmon in the Fish River Lakes, Maine," reprinted from *Journal of Wildlife Management*, Vol. 23, No. 1, January 1959.

Washington State Department of Fisheries. *Pacific Northwest Marine Fishes*, 1961.

WATERS, CHARLES A. *A Study of the Life History and Taxonomic Position of the Blueback Trout*, a thesis, University of Maine, Orono.

WEISS, GILBERT. *Leatherbacks*, Missouri Conservation Department, Jefferson City.

WILLIAMS, JOHN E. "The Lake Sturgeon," from *Michigan Conservation*, November–December 1951.

WOODING, F. H. "Canada's Atlantic Salmon," reprinted from *Canadian Geographical Journal* by the Department of Fisheries of Canada, Ottawa, 1956.

WULFF, LEE. *The Atlantic Salmon*, A. S. Barnes & Co., New York, 1958.

ZEUNER, F. E. *A History of Domesticated Animals*, Harper & Row, New York, 1963.

INDEX

Abbott, Dr. C. C., 246
Acipenser, 273-288
Æolian, 116
Age of fish, determination by otoliths, 51-52
Alabama Agricultural Research Station, 211
Alabama hog sucker, 177
Alabama shad, 141
Alevin, 70
Alewife, 35, 39, 42, 84, 131, 137, 139-140
Allen, George H., 102
Alligator gar, 288, 289, 290-291
Alosa, 131-141
Alpine trout, 48
Ameiurus pricei, 193n
American eels, 295-301; elvers, 299; "glass eels," 299; landlocked, 298, 301; leptocephali, 298, 300; life span of, 301; spawning migration, 296-300
American Fisheries Society, ix, 46, 50, 54, 59, 61, 87, 94, 112, 121, 128, 141, 150, 179, 223
American perch, 245
American pike, 159
American shad, 131-136, 138
American smelt, 142-148
Amia calva Linnaeus, 292-294
Ammocoete, 305
Anguilla, 295-301
Appert, Nicolas, 106
Applegate, Vernon, 305
Arctic char, ix, 20, 46, 47-53, 54, 59, 61, 62
Arctic grayling, 112-118, 145; odor of, 111, 115-116, 145
Arctic smelt, 149-150
Arctic trout, 48
Aristotle, 296
Atlantic salmon, 11, 15, 48, 53, 64-85, 94, 101, 103, 104, 107, 120, 128, 147, 215, 300, 303; alevin, 70; "black," 73; "bright," 65; commercial fishing for, 80, 107; decline of, 80-81, 303; deterioration of after spawning, 67;

fertilization of eggs by brown trout, 11; fly-fishing for, 77-80, 85; grilse, 65, 66, 71, 72, 75, 78, 94; habitat of, 68-69; homing, 74-75, 101, 103, 104; kelt, 73; landlocked, 58, 81-85, 87, 89, 147, 215; "lost" fish, 74; maiden fish, 65, 72; mended kelt, 73; ouananiche, 82; reading rings on scales of, 73; Sebago salmon, 82; "slinks," 68, 73; spawning habits, 67-68; "spent," 73; stages of development, 70-72; survival of progeny, 76-77; upstream migration, 64-67
Atlantic Salmon Association, 75n, 81
Atlantic sturgeon, 274, 275, 279, 280-281
Aurora trout, 49

Bachelor, 216
Baldwin, Norman S., 303, 306
Bantam sunfish, 220
Bardach, Dr. John E., 307-308
Barfish, 236
Barnaby Rudge, 45
Barnes, Dame Juliana, 7
Bass, 6, 58, 138, 163, 179, 186, 208, 211, 215, 216, 217, 221-243, 246, 247, 251-252, 262, 293; artificial propogation of, 231-232; black, 208, 215, 222, 235; differences between, 223-225; growth of, 229; largemouth, 138, 208, 211, 221-234, 246, 247, 251-252, 293; range of, 225-226; sea, 235-236; smallmouth, 208, 221-234, 246, 251-252; smallmouth black, 58, 217; spawning habits, 229-231; spotted, 221-234; white, 216, 235-239, 240, 241; white perch, 235-236, 240, 242-243, 262; yellow, 235-236, 239-241
Beluga sturgeon, 273
Beluga whale, 52, 109
Bering, Vitus, 106
Bigmouth, 218
Bigmouth buffalofish, 169, 170, 173, 175-177

317